# Current Northeast Paleoethnobotany

# Current Northeast Paleoethnobotany

*Edited by*
*John P. Hart*

New York State Museum Bulletin No. 494

1999

The University of the State of New York
The State Education Department

© The New York State Education Department, Albany, New York 12230
Published 1999

Printed in the United States of America

Copies may be ordered from:
    Publication Sales
    New York State Museum
    Albany, New York 12230
    Phone: (518) 449-1404

Library of Congress Catalog Card Number: 98-61784

ISSN: 1-55557-164-6
ISBN: 0278-3355

This book is printed on acid-free paper.
Cover illustration by Patricia Kernan.

# CONTENTS

# LIST OF FIGURES

FIGURES

# LIST OF TABLES

## TABLES

# PREFACE

This volume evolved from a symposium presented in the New York Natural History Conference IV, which was held at the New York State Museum in April of 1996. I was asked by the conference chair to organize a symposium that would draw the interest of archaeologists who might otherwise not think of coming to a conference focused on natural history. My initial intent was to have a short symposium with five or six presentations on paleoethnobotanical research in the Northeast. Several months later, after a handful of telephone calls, some e-mail messages, and a call for papers on the Internet, I was pleased to have tentative commitments from over 20 individuals, including palynologists, archaeobotanists, and archaeologists. My short symposium had turned into a day-long affair. During the months leading up to the conference, I responded to over 50 requests for information about the symposium from as far away as California and England.

What all of this told me is that there is a lot of active paleoethnobotanical research going on the Northeast, and, just as importantly, it also told me that there is a great deal of interest in the results of that research. The Northeast has been almost invisible as paleoethnobotany has grown to be an important discipline in Eastern Woodlands archaeology. This volume is presented as an attempt to raise the visibility of paleoethnobotanical research being carried out in the Northeast. As such, although most of the chapters are concerned in one way or another with prehistoric agriculture, there is no single paleoethnobotanical theme guiding the volume's content.

Not all of the symposium participants were able to contribute chapters to the volume, but a number of individuals active in Northeast paleoethnobotanical research that did not participate in the symposium were able to contribute chapters. Original contributors to the symposium, Nancy Asch Sidell, Heather Almquist-Jacobson and David Sanger, Connie Cox Bodner, Elizabeth Chilton, David George and Robert Dewar, John Hart, Frances King, and Tonya Largy and associates provided updated versions of their symposium papers. David Bernstein, Jeffrey Bendremer, and Daniel Cassedy and Paul Webb contributed papers originally written for other purposes. Gary Crawford, who had a previous publication commitment for his presentation at the symposium, courageously agreed to write a summary chapter for the volume. I thank all of the contributors for helping to make this volume a reality. I also thank all of the peer reviewers for providing timely and well-considered comments on the chapters.

*J.P.H.*

# CHAPTER 1

# INTRODUCTION

John P. Hart

This volume presents the results of current paleoethnobotanical research in northeastern North America, defined here as New England, New York, and Pennsylvania (Figure 1.1). Paleoethnobotany encompasses all aspects of the investigation of prehistoric human-plant relationships from the identification and dating of plant remains to modeling the evolution of prehistoric plant communities and agriculture (Gremillion 1997a; Pearsall 1989; Popper and Hastorf 1988). As such, it incorporates but also transcends archaeobotany, which involves the recovery and identification of plant remains (e.g., macrofossils, pollen, and phytoliths) from archaeological sites (Gremillion 1997a; Popper and Hastorf 1988).

## CURRENT NORTHEAST PALEOETHNOBOTANY IN CONTEXT

Although the discipline of paleoethnobotany is only recently defined, research on prehistoric human-plant interactions has a long history in the Eastern Woodlands of North America. Until relatively recently, this research has focused primarily on the adoption of maize *(Zea mays)* and other tropical domesticates, including beans *(Phaseolus vulgaris)* and squash *(Cucurbita pepo)*. Historically, maize particularly was thought to have been a primary catalyst in the development of complex culture-historical taxa like Adena, Hopewell, and Mississippian in the riverine interior and Iroquois in the Northeast (Hart 1999a). Although there was early interest in pre-maize agricultural systems in the Eastern Woodlands (Gilmore 1931; Jones 1936), it was not until the 1960s and early 1970s (Asch et al. 1972; Struever 1962; Struever and Vickery 1973) that concerted efforts were made to document and model these systems. It was only in the 1980s that the existence of pre-maize agricultural systems consisting of indigenous crops were widely accepted (Asch and Asch 1985; Cowan

1985; Ford 1985a; Smith 1987; Watson 1985). Today, the Eastern Woodlands are identified by many paleoethnobotanists as an independent center of agricultural origins (Fritz 1990; Smith 1992, 1995; cf. MacNeish 1992).

Largely because of interest in pre-maize agricultural systems and their relationships to the adoption of maize and maize agriculture's subsequent developments, paleoethnobotany has become a highly visible discipline in Eastern Woodlands archaeology. Collections of papers on Eastern Woodlands paleoethnobotany are published regularly (Green 1994; Gremillion 1997b; Keegan 1987; Scarry 1993; Smith 1992; Woods 1992). Eastern Woodlands paleoethnobotany is included regularly in volumes concerned with prehistoric agriculture on larger geographical scales (Cowan and Watson 1992; Ford 1985b; Harris and Hillman 1989; Johannessen and Hastorf 1994; Price and Gebauer 1995). It is unusual for an annual volume of *American*

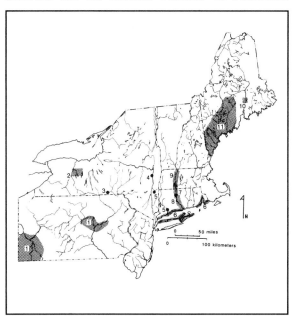

**Figure 1.1** Location of studies presented in this volume. (1.) King; (2.) Bodner; (3.) Hart; (4.) Largy et al.; (5.) Cassedy and Webb; (6.) Bernstein; (7.) George and Dewar; (8.) Bendremer; (9.) Chilton; (10.) Almquist-Jacobson and Sanger; (11.) Asch Sidell.

*Antiquity, Midcontinental Journal of Archaeology, or Southeastern Archaeology* not to contain at least one article dealing with paleoethnobotany of the Eastern Woodlands. Enough Eastern Woodlands paleoethnobotanical data were produced during the 1970s and 1980s for major reviews and syntheses to be published in the early 1990s (Fritz 1990; Smith 1992, 1995). Finally, the results of paleoethnobotanical research are regularly integrated into synthetic research on the prehistory of specific regions and time periods in the Eastern Woodlands (Cobb and Nassaney 1995; Hart 1993).

Despite the broad coverage of the studies presented in this literature, there has been a major gap–the Northeast is woefully under represented. For example, in Keegan's 1987 edited volume, *Emergent Horticultural Economies of the Eastern Woodlands*, only one of the 16 chapters is concerned with the Northeast (McBride and Dewar 1987); the others are concerned with the Midwest and Southeast. In Scarry's 1993 edited volume, *Foraging and Farming in the Eastern Woodlands*, all of the 16 chapters deal with the Midwest and Southeast; the Northeast is excluded. Most recently in Gremillion's 1997 edited volume, *People, Plants and Landscapes: Studies in Paleoethnobotany*, none of the seven chapters presenting Eastern Woodlands case studies is concerned with the Northeast.

One reason for this under representation is that the primary driving force behind the growth of paleoethnobotany in the Eastern Woodlands, the use of indigenous crops, only recently has begun to be recognized in the Northeast (Gardner 1993; Hart and Asch Sidell 1996, 1997; King 1992; Petersen and Asch Sidell 1996). None of the early pioneers in the "Flotation Revolution" (Chapman and Watson 1993) was actively involved in northeastern archaeology as defined in this volume, and as a result, the Northeast has contributed relatively little to our understanding of pre-maize prehistoric human-plant interaction variability in the Eastern Woodlands. This lack of contribution also can be traced to a persistent presumption that climatic and soil conditions in at least some portions of the Northeast are not favorable for the preservation of macrobotanical remains and thus for paleoethnobotanical research. This perception has

only recently begun to change with the use of flotation recovery on a large scale (Bendremer et al. 1991; Crawford et al. 1997; Hart and Asch Sidell 1996, 1997; Heckenberger et al. 1992; McBride and Dewar 1987; Petersen and Asch Sidell 1996; Scarry 1990).

Despite some early mentions by Ritchie (1969; Ritchie and Funk 1973) of the possibility of indigenous crop use in the Northeast, until recently, the region has lacked long-term, focused paleoethnobotanical research efforts. Much of the effort in paleoethnobotanical research in the Northeast has centered on the introduction of maize and its effects or lack thereof on prehistoric subsistence-settlement and sociopolitical systems (Bendremer and Dewar 1994; Ceci 1979-80; Crawford et al. 1997; McBride and Dewar 1987). Only recently has the presence of indigenous gourds *(Cucurbita pepo)* in Mid-Holocene (8,000-4,000 B.P.) contexts been demonstrated in the Northeast with AMS dates of 5,695 B.P. in Maine (Petersen and Asch Sidell 1996) and 5,400 B.P. in Pennsylvania (Hart and Asch Sidell 1997). The presence of that potentially early crop in the mid-latitude riverine interior by at least 7,000 B.P. (Asch 1994; Smith 1992) was established in the 1980s (Asch and Asch 1985). Domesticated indigenous *C. pepo* has only just been identified as present in the Northeast before 950 B.P. with an AMS date of 2,625 B.P. in north central Pennsylvania (Hart and Asch Sidell 1997). It has been reported at numerous sites in the riverine interior by at least 4,500 B.P. (Smith 1995) since the 1980s (King 1985).

Recently the seed-bearing indigenous crops little barley *(Hordeum pusillum)* (Gardner 1992; Hart and Asch Sidell 1996; King 1992) and domesticated or possibly domesticated chenopod *(Chenopodium berlandieri)* (Gardner 1993; Hart and Asch Sidell 1996) have been recovered from early late prehistoric (1,150-650 B.P.) sites in Pennsylvania. Although domesticated taxa indigenous to the Northeast have yet to be identified, humans have interacted with seed-bearing annuals in the region since the ninth and tenth centuries B.P., as demonstrated by the recovery of wild *Chenopodium* at the Shawnee-Minisink site in northeastern Pennsylvania (McNett 1985) and later sites in New England dating to the fourth and fifth centuries B.P. (McBride 1978; Pfeiffer 1984). Finally, the timing of the first archaeological visibility of maize in the Northeast has been pushed back with direct AMS dates as early as 1,570 B.P. in southern Ontario (Crawford et al. 1997) and a consistent association with radiocarbon dates on associated wood charcoal beginning around 1,200 to 1,100 B.P. in the West Branch of the Susquehanna River basin in north-central Pennsylvania (Hart and Asch Sidell 1996).

## CHAPTER SUMMARIES

It is against this backdrop that the current volume is offered. The papers collected here present a cross section of current paleoethnobotanical research in the Northeast. They include regional syntheses of research results over the last several decades and case studies that examine specific taxa, archaeobotanical collections from specific archaeological sites, and prehistoric landscape and vegetation evolution. The volume is organized (Figure 1.1) to provide the reader with a sense of the diversity of paleoethnobotanical research being carried out in the Northeast and of similarities and differences of that research within and between various subregions.

King begins the volume with a review of recent paleoethnobotanical studies in Pennsylvania that provides a bridge between the riverine interior and the Northeast. King stresses that Pennsylvania provides both geographical and environmental transitions between the two regions, which must be taken into account to understand relationships between developments in the riverine interior and Northeast. Bodner places historic Seneca sunflower (*Helianthus annuus*) use in a broader context of sunflower evolution in the Eastern Woodlands. She argues against transplanting agricultural evolution models from the riverine interior to the Northeast, where unlike the riverine interior, all agricultural crops were presumably domesticated elsewhere. Hart presents the results of recent AMS dating of maize and beans from the Roundtop site in the upper Susquehanna River basin of New York. The results indicate that beans do not occur at the site

until the seventh-century B.P. contradicting Ritchie's (1969, 1973) assertion for ninth-century B.P. maize-beans-squash agriculture at the site. Hart stresses that site descriptions in the literature are interpretations, not observations, which need to be carefully scrutinized before they are used in synthetic research. Largy and associates provide results of the first archaeobotanical research done on an historic (350 B.P.) Mahikan site. The botanical contents of one pit feature at the Goldkrest site in the mid-Hudson valley were dominated by buttercup (*Ranunculus* sp.) achenes, which may have been used for medicinal purposes to fight European diseases. Cassedy and Webb provide a series of AMS dates on maize from potentially early contexts at three sites in southeastern New York and southwestern Connecticut. Dates from one of these sites as well as previously published dates from other sites lead Cassedy and Webb to assert that the Northeast can be included in Smith's (1992:111) empirical generalization that an expansion of maize-based agriculture occurred around 1,100 B.P. over large portions of the Eastern Woodlands.

The next four chapters present recent paleoethnobotanical research in Southern New England. Bernstein reviews archaeobotanical data generated over the last several decades from sites located on the coasts of Long Island and Block Island sounds. He argues that maize was a late addition that had little impact on broad-spectrum subsistence systems, which had been in place for the four or five millennia before European contact. George and Dewar present recent morphological analysis of *Chenopodium* seeds recovered from the seventh to sixth centuries B.P. Burnham-Shepard site in the Connecticut River valley. The presence of both thin- and thick-testa seeds suggests exploitation of two *Chenopodium* populations. The thin-testa seeds may represent a population under initial phases of selection for domestication, a fully domesticated population, or a weedy conspecific population. A final determination awaits resolution of taxonomy and analysis of additional collections.

In their chapters, Bendremer and Chilton both explore Late Woodland (ca. 1,000-500 B.P.) subsistence-settlement based on research centered in the Connecticut River basin, paying particular attention to the question of the importance of maize agriculture. Bendremer argues that the adoption of maize around 950 B.P. had varied effects on populations across Southern New England. Distinct subregional systems with different degrees of dependence on maize agriculture were evident at the time of European contact. Chilton argues that use of dichotomous models (e.g., coastal vs. interior, staple vs. supplement) of maize agriculture during the Late Woodland obscures finer-scale intraregional variability. She calls for more precise use of terms to describe maize agriculture and more explicit hypothesis-testing methods for investigating maize agriculture's impact on Late Woodland populations in Southern New England.

The next two chapters present results of recent paleoethnobotanical research in Maine. Almquist-Jacobson and Sanger provide a detailed paleogeographical study in the Milford drainage basin of the Penobscot River valley. They show how a number of lines of evidence, including sediments, macrofossils, pollen, and radiocarbon dates, can be used to model Holocene landscape and vegetational evolution as an aid to understanding prehistoric settlement patterns. Asch Sidell summarizes recent archaeobotanical research in Maine from 10 archaeological sites ranging in age from 10,500 to 200 B.P. She demonstrates the potential of archaeobotanical research to modify some traditionally held assumptions about prehistoric plant use in northern New England. The recovery of *Cucurbita pepo* gourd rind fragments AMS-dated to 5,695 B.P. and maize from late prehistoric sites in Maine dating to the Little Ice age indicate a much longer and more complex history of agricultural evolution in the north than was previously thought possible. In the final chapter, Crawford places the volume in a broader context of research, drawing on the work he and his colleagues have been doing in eastern Canada.

## FUTURE DIRECTIONS FOR PALEOETHNOBOTANY IN THE NORTHEAST

As the chapters in this volume demonstrate, this is an exciting time in Northeast paleoethnobotany. While still lagging behind the Midwest and Southeast in empirical understandings of prehistoric plant-human interactions, there is now a strong foundation on which to build similar levels of understanding in the Northeast over the next several years. In his summary chapter, Crawford addresses some issues facing Northeast paleoethnobotany. The following paragraphs represent my own thoughts on a few of these issues.

As already discussed, evidence is now coming to light that human populations in the Northeast adopted crops indigenous to the riverine interior. Research is now needed to gain better understandings of the temporal and spatial distributions of these crops to enable development of more informed models of agricultural evolution in the Northeast. Undoubtedly, Mid-Holocene *C. pepo* gourd is present at more than two sites, and early Late Holocene (4,000-2,000 B.P.) domesticated *C. pepo* is present at more than one site in the Northeast. The distribution of sunflower in the Northeast suggests varied functions as discussed by Bodner. While little barley and riverine-interior-like domesticated or possibly domesticated *Chenopodium* have now been found at several early Late Prehistoric sites in the Susquehanna River basin, we do not understand their full temporal and spatial distributions in the Northeast. Given the recentness of these discoveries, we cannot assume that they and sunflower are the only crops indigenous to the riverine interior adopted in the Northeast. As King suggests, a reexamination of knotweed (*Polygonum erectum*) and other seeds in Northeast collections could result in the identification of additional crops.

Understanding the adoption of riverine-interior crops in the Northeast is only part of the picture. We also need to determine through sustained, directed archaeobotanical studies if any plants indigenous to the Northeast were domesticated. While some researchers in the Northeast downplay this possibility, there is evidence for human interaction with seed-bearing annual plants like *Chenopodium* in the Northeast beginning with some of the earliest occupations. Sustained interactions between human and plant populations have the potential to result in one of several modes of domestication (Rindos 1984; Smith 1992). George and Dewar's analysis of *Chenopodium* from the Burnham-Shepard site is certainly suggestive and should lead to additional research on *Chenopodium* and other potential crops in the Northeast. Paleoethnobotanical research must concretely demonstrate a lack of indigenous crops before the Northeast is considered only an area of secondary agricultural origins.

As demonstrated by a number of chapters in this volume, issues of the adoption of tropical domesticates is far from settled in the Northeast, both in terms of the timing of their entry and subsequent impact on subsistence systems. Although it has now been demonstrated that some varieties of squash were domesticated in the Eastern Woodlands (*Cucurbita pepo* spp. *ovifera*; e.g., acorn, crookneck, fordhook, ornamental gourds), other squashes were domesticated in Mexico (*Cucurbita pepo* spp. *pepo*; e.g., pumpkins, marrows) (Decker 1988; Decker-Walters 1993). While it is thought that *Cucurbita pepo* spp. *pepo* was adopted in the riverine interior around 950 B.P. (Yarnell 1993), there is no way at present to know when it was adopted in the Northeast.

As reviewed by Hart, the timing of the first archaeologically visible beans in the Northeast is now questionable. Based largely on Ritchie's (1969, 1973) publications on Roundtop, the presence of beans in the Northeast by the ninth century B.P. has been widely accepted. AMS dating of the Roundtop beans places them no earlier than the mid-seventh century B.P. The lack of earlier AMS dates on beans in the Northeast raises serious doubts that the first archaeologically visible beans in the Northeast are contemporaneous with those in the riverine interior.

The timing of maize's entry into the Northeast as defined in this volume is also uncertain. As reviewed by Cassedy and Webb, current earliest dates indicate its presence before 1,000 B.P. in Southern New England and New York and around 1200 B.P. in north-central Pennsylvania. However, the potential for earlier maize in the

Northeast is suggested by AMS dates in southern Ontario as early as 1570 B.P. (Crawford et al. 1997). As demonstrated in Ontario (Crawford et al. 1997), the riverine interior (Chapman and Crites 1987; Riley et al. 1994), and New York (Cassedy and Webb, this volume) recovering maize from early contexts at open-air sites requires extensive flotation and intensive archaeobotanical analysis. We cannot assume that the current earliest dates for maize in the Northeast reflect the timing of its adoption until its absence at earlier sites is firmly demonstrated (Hart 1999a).

As discussed and presented in numerous publications concerned with paleoethnobotanical research elsewhere in the Eastern Woodlands, standard methods of recovery, analysis, and reporting have been developed for botanical remains from prehistoric archaeological sites (Johannessen 1984; Wymer 1992; also see Hastorf and Popper 1988; Pearsall 1989). These methods, standardizing for preservation and recovery rates, enable quantitative comparison of samples between sites and among components of single sites. As suggested by Crawford, these methods and reporting conventions, along with large-scale flotation and identification procedures, must be more widely adopted in the Northeast.

## CONCLUSION

In order to make important contributions to our understanding of the puzzle of prehistoric plant-human interactions in the Eastern Woodlands, Northeast paleoethnobotany faces several challenges. The first is clarifying and assembling the various puzzle pieces of human-plant interactions, including the adoption of riverine-interior crops, the possibility of domestication in the Northeast, the adoption of tropical domesticates, and the evolution of agricultural complexes. The second major challenge is realizing that there are probably many puzzles, each of which may have a different combination of pieces, and that do not necessarily correspond to traditional culture-historical taxa and time period boundaries (Hart 1999b). If Northeast paleoethnobotanical research continues to build on the recent advances presented in this volume, there is little doubt that it will make important contributions to our knowledge of prehistoric human-plant interaction variability in the Eastern Woodlands during the coming years.

## ACKNOWLEDGEMENTS

I thank David Bernstein, Gary Crawford, Robert Dewar, and David George for reading and commenting on an earlier draft of this chapter.

## REFERENCES CITED

Asch, D. L. 1994. Aboriginal Specialty-Plant Cultivation in Eastern North America: Illinois Prehistory and A Post-Contact Perspective. In *Agricultural Origins and Development in the Midcontinent*, edited by W. Green, pp. 25-86. Report 19, Office of the State Archaeologist, The University of Iowa, Iowa City.

Asch, D. L., and N. B. Asch. 1985. Prehistoric Plant Cultivation in West Central Illinois. In *Prehistoric Food Production in North America*, edited by R. I. Ford, pp. 149-204. Anthropological Papers No. 75. Museum of Anthropology, University of Michigan, Ann Arbor.

Asch, N. B., R. I. Ford, and D. L. Asch. 1972. *Paleoethnobotany of the Koster Site: The Archaic Horizons*. Report of Investigations No. 24. Illinois State Museum, Springfield.

Bendremer, J. C. M., and R. E. Dewar. 1994. The Advent of Prehistoric Maize in New England. In *Corn and Culture in the Prehistoric New World*, edited by S. Johannessen and C. A. Hastorf, pp. 369-393.Westview Press, Boulder.

Bendremer, J., E. Kellogg, and T. B. Largy. 1991. A Grass-Lined Storage Pit and Early Maize Horticulture in Central Connecticut. *North American Archaeologist* 12:325-349.

Ceci, L. 1979-80. Maize Cultivation in Coastal New York: The Archaeological, Agronomical, and Documentary Evidence. *North American Archaeologist* 1:45-73.

Chapman, J., and G. Crites. 1987. Evidence for Early Maize (*Zea mays*) from the Icehouse Bottom Site, Tennessee. *American Antiquity* 52:352-354.

Chapman, J., and P. J. Watson. 1993. The Archaic Period and the Flotation Revolution. In *Foraging and Farming in the Eastern Woodlands*, edited by C. M. Scarry, pp. 27-38. University Press of Florida, Gainesville.

Cobb, C. R., and M. S. Nassaney. 1995. Interaction and Integration in the Late Woodland Southeast. In *Native American Interactions: Multiscalar Analysis and Interpretations in the Eastern Woodlands*, edited by M. S. Nassaney, and K. E. Sassaman, pp. 205-226. University of Tennessee Press, Knoxville.

Cowan, C. W. 1985. Understanding the Evolution of Plant Husbandry in Eastern North America: Lessons from Botany, Ethnography, and Archaeology. In *Prehistoric Food Production in North America*, edited by R. I. Ford, pp. 205-244. Anthropological Papers No. 75. Museum of Anthropology, University of Michigan, Ann Arbor.

Cowan, C. W., and P. J. Watson (editors). 1992. *The Origins of Agriculture: An International Perspective*. Smithsonian Institution Press, Washington, D.C.

Crawford, G. W., D. G. Smith, and V. E. Bowyer. 1997. Dating the Entry of Corn (*Zea mays*) into the Lower Great Lakes. *American Antiquity* 62:112-119.

Decker, D. S. 1988. Origin(s), Evolution, and Systematics of *Cucurbita pepo* (Cucurbitaceae). *Economic Botany* 42:4-15.

Decker-Walters, D. S. 1993. New Methods for Studying the Origins of New World Domesticates: The Squash Example. In *Foraging and Farming in the Eastern Woodlands*, edited by C. M. Scarry, pp. 91-97. University Press of Florida, Gainesville.

Ford, R. I. 1985a. Patterns of Prehistoric Food Production in North America. In *Prehistoric Food Production in North America*, edited by R. I. Ford, pp. 341-364. Anthropological Papers No. 75. Museum of Anthropology, University of Michigan, Ann Arbor.

Ford, R. I. (editor). 1985b. *Prehistoric Food Production in North America*. Anthropological Papers No. 75. Museum of Anthropology, University of Michigan, Ann Arbor.

Fritz, G. J. 1990. Multiple Pathways to Farming in Precontact Eastern North America. *Journal of World Prehistory* 4:387-435.

Gardner, P. 1992. Identification of Some Plant Remains from the Binghamton Mall Site, New York (ca. A.D. 100-A.D. 1400). In *Under the Asphalt: The Archaeology of the Binghamton Mall Project, Volume I: Report Narrative*, by L. Wurst and N. M. Versaggi, pp. 669-676. Prepared for The City of Binghamton Urban Renewal Agency by The Public Archaeology Facility, Binghamton University, Binghamton, New York.

————. 1993. Carbonized Plant Remains from 36Ti58, ca. A.D. 900-1300, Tioga County, Pennsylvania. In *Archaeological Data Recovery: Site 36Ti58*, edited by P. Miller. Archaeological and Historical Consultants, Inc., Centre Hall, Pennsylvania.

Gilmore, M. R. 1931. Vegetal Remains of the Ozark Bluff-Dweller Culture. *Papers of the Michigan Academy of Science, Arts, and Letters* 14:83-105.

Green, W. (editor). 1994. *Agricultural Origins and Development in the Midcontinent*. Report 19, Office of the State Archaeologist, The University of Iowa, Iowa City.

Gremillion, K. J. 1997a. Introduction. In *People, Plants, and Landscapes: Studies in Paleoethnobotany*, edited by K. J. Gremillion, pp. 1-12. University of Alabama Press, Tuscaloosa.

Gremillion, K. J. (editor). 1997b. *People, Plants, and Landscapes: Studies in Paleoethnobotany*. University of Alabama Press, Tuscaloosa.

Harris, D. R., and G. Hillman (editors). 1989. *Foraging and Farming: The Evolution of Plant Exploitation*. Unwin Hyman, London.

Hart, J. P. 1993. Monongahela Subsistence-Settlement Change: The Late Prehistoric Period in the Lower Upper Ohio River Valley. *Journal of World Prehistory* 7:71-120.

————. 1999a. Maize Agriculture Evolution in the Eastern Woodlands of North America: A Darwinian Perspective. *Journal of Archaeological Method and Theory* 6: in press.

————. 1999b. Another Look at "Clemson's Island." *Northeast Anthropology* 57: in press.

Hart, J. P., and N. Asch Sidell. 1996. Prehistoric Agricultural Systems in the West Branch of the Susquehanna River Basin, A.D. 800 to A.D. 1350. *Northeast Anthropology* 52:1-30.

————. 1997. Additional Evidence for Early Cucurbit Use in the Northern Eastern Woodlands East of the Allegheny Front. *American Antiquity* 62:523-537.

Hastorf, C. A., and V. S. Popper (editors). 1988. *Current Paleoethnobotany: Analytical Methods and Cultural Interpretations of Archaeological Plant Remains*. University of Chicago Press, Chicago.

Heckenberger, M. J., J. B. Petersen, and N. Asch Sidell. 1992. Early Evidence of Maize Agriculture in the Connecticut River Valley of Vermont. *Archaeology of Eastern North America* 20:125-149.

Johannessen, S. 1984. Paleoethnobotany. In *American Bottom Archaeology*, edited by C. J. Bareis and J. W. Porter, pp. 197-214. University of Illinois Press, Urbana.

Johannessen, S., and C. A. Hastorf (editors). 1994. *Corn and Culture in the Prehistoric New World*. Westview Press, Boulder.

Jones, V. H. 1936. The Vegetal Remains of Newt Kash Hollow Shelter. In *Rock Shelters in Menifee County, Kentucky*, edited by W. S. Webb and W. D. Funkhouser. University of Kentucky Reports in Archaeology and Anthropology 3(4):147-167.

Keegan, W. F. (editor). 1987. *Emergent Horticultural Economies of the Eastern Woodlands.* Center for Archaeological Investigations, Occasional Papers No. 7. Southern Illinois University at Carbondale.

King, F. B. 1985. Early Cultivated Cucurbits in Eastern North America. In *Prehistoric Food Production in North America,* edited by R. I. Ford, pp. 73-98. Anthropological Papers No. 75. Museum of Anthropology, University of Michigan, Ann Arbor.

—————. 1992. Floral Remains. In *The Prehistory of the Catawissa Bridge Replacement Site (36CO9), Columbia County, Pennsylvania,* by T. C. East, J. A. Adovasio, W. C. Johnson, and D. R. Pedler. Prepared for the Cultural Resource Management Program, Department of Anthropology, University of Pittsburgh.

MacNeish, R. S. 1992. *The Origins of Agriculture and Settled Life.* The University of Oklahoma Press, Norman.

McBride, K. A. 1978. Archaic Subsistence in the Lower Connecticut River Valley: Evidence from Woodchuck Knoll. *Man in the Northeast* 15/16:124-131.

McBride, K. A., and R. E. Dewar. 1987. Agriculture and Cultural Evolution: Causes and Effects in the Lower Connecticut River Valley. In *Emergent Horticultural Economies of the Eastern Woodlands,* edited by W. F. Keegan, pp. 305-328. Center for Archaeological Investigations, Occasional Papers No. 7. Southern Illinois University at Carbondale.

McNett, C. W. (editor). 1985. *Shawnee Minisink: A Stratified Paleoindian-Archaic Site in the Upper Delaware Valley of Pennsylvania.* Academic Press, Orlando.

Pearsall, D. M. 1989. *Paleoethnobotany: A Handbook of Procedures.* Academic Press, New York.

Petersen J. B., and N. Asch Sidell. 1996. Mid-Holocene Evidence of *Cucurbita* sp. from Central Maine. *American Antiquity* 61:685-698.

Pfeiffer, J. E. 1984. The Late and Terminal Archaic Periods of Connecticut Prehistory. *Archaeological Society of Connecticut Bulletin* 47:73-88.

Popper, V. S., and C. A. Hastorf. 1988. Introduction. In *Current Paleoethnobotany: Analytical Methods and Cultural Interpretations of Archaeological Plant Remains,* edited by C. A. Hastorf and V. S. Popper, pp. 1-16. University of Chicago Press, Chicago.

Price, T. D., and A. B. Gebauer (editors). 1995. *Last Hunters First Farmers.* School of American Research Press, Santa Fe, New Mexico.

Riley, T. J., G. R. Walz, C. J. Bareis, A. C. Fortier, and K. E. Parker. 1994. Accelerator Mass Spectrometry (AMS) Dates Confirm Early *Zea mays* in the Mississippi River Valley. *American Antiquity* 59:490-498.

Rindos, D. 1984. *The Origins of Agriculture: An Evolutionary Perspective.* Academic Press, New York.

Ritchie, W. A. 1969. *The Archaeology of New York State.* Revised edition. Natural History Press, Garden City.

—————. 1973. The Roundtop Site (Apl.1). In *Aboriginal Settlement Patterns in the Northeast,* by W. A. Ritchie and R. E. Funk, pp. 179-194. Memoir 20, New York Museum and Science Service. The University of the State of New York, Albany.

Ritchie, W. A., and R. E. Funk. 1973 *Aboriginal Settlement Patterns in the Northeast.* Memoir 20, New York Museum and Science Service. The University of the State of New York, Albany.

Scarry, C. M. 1990. Plant Remains: 1985-1987 Seasons. In *Excavations at the Boland Site 1984-1987: A Preliminary Report,* by S. Prezzano and V. P. Steponaitis, pp. 143-460. Research Report 9, Research Laboratories of Anthropology, University of North Carolina, Chapel Hill.

Scarry, C. Margaret (editor). 1993. *Foraging and Farming in the Eastern Woodlands.* University Press of Florida, Gainesville.

Smith, B. D. 1987. The Independent Domestication of Indigenous Seed-Bearing Plants in Eastern North America. In *Emergent Horticultural Economies of the Eastern Woodlands*, edited by W. F. Keegan, pp. 3-47. Center for Archaeological Investigations, Occasional Papers No. 7. Southern Illinois University at Carbondale.

—————. 1992. *Rivers of Change: Essays on Early Agriculture in Eastern North America.* Smithsonian Institution Press, Washington, D.C.

—————. 1995. Seed Plant Domestication in Eastern North America. In *Last Hunters First Farmers*, edited by T. D. Price and A. B. Gebauer, pp. 193-214. School of American Research Press, Santa Fe, New Mexico.

Struever, S. 1962. Implications of Vegetal Remains from an Illinois Hopewell Site. *American Antiquity* 27:584-587.

Struever, S., and K. D. Vickery. 1973. The Beginnings of Cultivation in the Midwest-Riverine Area of the United States. *American Anthropologist* 75:1197-1220.

Watson, P. J. 1985. The Impact of Early Horticulture in the Upland Drainages of the Midwest and Midsouth. In *Prehistoric Food Production in North America*, edited by R. I. Ford, pp. 99-148. Anthropological Papers No. 75. Museum of Anthropology, University of Michigan, Ann Arbor.

Woods, W. I. (editor). 1992. *Late Prehistoric Agriculture: Observations from the Midwest.* Studies in Illinois Archaeology No. 8, Illinois Historic Preservation Agency. Springfield.

Wymer, D. 1992. Trends and Disparities: The Woodland Paleoethnobotanical Record of the Mid-Ohio Valley. In *Cultural Variability in Context: Woodland Settlements of the Mid-Ohio Valley*, edited by M.F. Seeman, pp. 65-76. The Kent State University Press, Kent.

Yarnell, R. A. 1993. The Importance of Native Crops during the Late Archaic and Woodland Periods. In *Foraging and Farming in the Eastern Woodlands*, edited by C. M. Scarry, pp. 13-26. University Press of Florida, Gainesville.

# CHAPTER 2

# CHANGING EVIDENCE FOR PREHISTORIC PLANT USE IN PENNSYLVANIA

Frances B. King

## INTRODUCTION

At a time when prehistoric plant use over much of North America is well-documented and thoroughly discussed and interpreted, the Northeast remains one region that still requires additional research in order to address important subsistence questions and to test models that have been derived from other regions. It is becoming increasing obvious, however, that Native Americans of the Northeast were relying on native and introduced cultigens earlier in time, and to a greater extent, than was believed to be the case prior to the advent of flotation recovery techniques. This newfound evidence is largely due to the increased use of flotation and other methods developed in the Midwest and only relatively recently finding their way into general usage in other regions.

Understanding the history of aboriginal plant use in Pennsylvania is crucial to understanding the relationship between plant use in New England and the Middle Atlantic Region and that in the midcontinent. Geographically, Pennsylvania stretches from Ohio on the west, to New York on the north and almost to the Atlantic Ocean on the east. With Lake Erie to the northwest, Pennsylvania lies across any eastern route to New England, although not those going north around the western end of the lake. Although aboriginal people moving north or northeast into New England may have taken either a water route across one of the Great Lakes or a northerly route through Canada, many undoubtedly crossed the upper Ohio and Susquehanna river drainages in the area that is now Pennsylvania.

Geographically, this area has strong and varied topography dominated by various north-south trending ridges associated with the Appalachian Mountains. These features could have acted as funnels or barriers to prehistoric

human movement just as they did to historic exploration and development. Likewise, the drainage systems formed transportation routes that facilitated movement to both the north and west. In many locations, the headwaters of the Susquehanna drainage system of central Pennsylvania and southern New York State lie within a few kilometers of those of the upper Ohio system.

The climate of Pennsylvania is transitional between the Midwest and New England, and the rugged topography of many parts of the state creates a wide variety of microenvironments. The climate of most of the western and northern parts of the state is continental, with cold winters and relatively hot summers. Of 117 recording stations scattered fairly evenly over the state, fewer than 10 percent have a mean frost-free season of fewer than 150 days, and none has a growing season of fewer than 120 days (Dailey 1975), the period that Richard Yarnell (1964) suggested was minimal for Indian agriculture, particularly the cultivation of maize (*Zea mays*). The coldest part of the state is the north-central section, some distance from the moderating influences of either Lake Erie or the Atlantic Ocean.

Because the topography of Pennsylvania is so extremely varied, however, some locations away from official recording stations, particularly in stream valleys and basins, undoubtedly do have growing seasons as short or shorter than 120 days. Many of these locations may have been otherwise desirable for prehistoric human habitation and, in these cases, some care must have been taken in the location of fields for frost-sensitive crops such as maize or squash (*Cucurbita pepo*). Length of the frost-free season is a minor problem in Pennsylvania, however, when compared to many parts of New England, or to the northern Midwest, where site selection or manipulation, careful selection of short-season cultivars or species, and careful timing were important aspects of agriculture.

The prehistoric Native American use of topographic location to avoid late spring and early autumn frosts has been used, for example, in interpreting the location of late prehistoric Monongahela sites in southwestern Pennsylvania. These, like some late Iroquois sites farther north, were located in palisaded, upland, or hilltop locations, and it has been suggested by William Johnson and others (1989) that the locations were chosen to avoid areas with short growing seasons caused by cold air drainage. Alternatively, Richard George (1983) has presented evidence that suggests such sites were primarily defensive in nature.

The use of climate in interpreting late prehistoric behavior is complicated by the fact that the climate has changed significantly over the last 2,000 years (Bernabo 1981; Gajewski 1988; Gajewski et al. 1987). The period from about A.D. 1000 to A.D. 1200 was relatively warm; this was the period recognized in Europe as the Medieval Warm period. In addition to being warm, it was also relatively dry because of enhanced westerly air flow. Because this warm period persisted until at least A.D. 1200 before starting to gradually cool, changes in other human settlement or subsistence occurring before about A.D. 1250 would have been anticipating climatic cooling rather than responding to it. After A.D. 1250, the climate cooled until about A.D. 1700, when the estimated average temperature reached a point approximately 1°C cooler than it had been during the early Monongahela period. The frost-free period would also have been shortened, increasing the need to find suitable agricultural soils in protected locations. There was undoubtedly increased competition for such locations, and Hart (1990, 1993) has suggested that Monongahela subsistence-settlement change is best explained as a result of the complex interaction of a number of social and environmental factors potentially including population increases, warfare, and climatic change. He has noted that the effects of environmental and social risks on agricultural subsistence and settlement systems are opposed to one another.

Increased environmental risk tends to decrease agricultural reliability and, as a result, reduces agricultural intensity and forces increased mobility. On the other hand, increased social risk limits mobility and encourages greater agricultural productivity.

## PLANT DOMESTICATION AND CULTIVATION

The most intriguing part of prehistoric plant use is the introduction or domestication of crop plants and the development of agricultural systems. Although the use of indigenous cultigens during the period A.D. 200 to 800 is well-documented for the Midwest and Southeast, the history of plant use in the Northeast, including Pennsylvania, is still relatively poorly understood.

The record for Ohio, however, is quite good. In a summary of research that she has done on numerous sites in the mid-Ohio valley, Wymer (1992, 1993) reported that the taxa represented in archaeobotanical records for Middle and early Late Woodland, a period lasting from about 100 B.C. to A.D. 800, are similar to those from sites in the lower Illinois and central Mississippi River valleys (D. L. Asch and N. B. Asch 1985; N. B. Asch and D. L. Asch 1985a, 1985b, 1986; Johannessen 1984). Cultivated plants include squash and the oily-seeded and starchy-seeded members of the Eastern Agricultural Complex. The oily-seeded members of this complex include sunflower (*Helianthus annuus*) and sumpweed (*Iva annua* var. *macrocarpa*), while the starchy-seeded types include chenopod (*Chenopodium berlandieri* var. *jonesianum*), maygrass (*Phalaris caroliniana*), erect knotweed (*Polygonum erectum*), and little barley (*Hordeum pusillum*).

Wymer has found that the early Late Woodland in Ohio was a time of increasing diversification with apparent use of a greater variety of wild plants coupled with intensification of certain resources, particularly nuts, squash/gourd, and small starchy seeds, especially maygrass (Wymer 1993:150), than was characteristic of the Middle Woodland. Among the sites studied by Wymer, maize first appears in small amounts at the Childers site in the early Late Woodland, about

A.D. 425, although it was present at the not-too-distant Edwin Harness some 200 years earlier. In comparison, the late Late Woodland sites of the mid-Ohio valley, A.D. 800-1000, have a much greater amount of maize, a lower density and diversity of nutshell, replacement of sumpweed by sunflower as a high-oil seed crop, and increasing dominance of the starchy-seeded types by chenopod (Wymer 1992, 1993). Wymer has suggested that, while the early Late Woodland record suggests diversification in the face of resource stress, perhaps caused by human population growth, the Late Woodland pattern suggests increased agricultural specialization with an emphasis on maize and the elimination of less desirable or less efficient resources.

Work by Gail Wagner (1987, 1989) shows that subsequently, after about A.D. 1000, the Fort Ancient populations of the mid-Ohio valley apparently relied very heavily on maize agriculture, and on the cultivation of squash, beans (*Phaseolus vulgaris*), sunflower, and tobacco (*Nicotiana rustica*), along with the utilization of some wild resources. Wagner found maize to be ubiquitous in Fort Ancient sites, while the Eastern Agricultural Complex was generally absent, except for small quantities of possibly domesticated chenopod (Wagner 1987). Wagner has also found that sumac (*Rhus* sp.) and purslane (*Portulacca oleracea*) may be ubiquitous within sites and that there can be masses of seeds of maize, beans, sumac, or purslane.

Thus, the plant resources used by Fort Ancient are distinctly different from those used by the Middle Woodland or earlier Late Woodland peoples in the same area. Interestingly, this change is not found to the west and south of the Fort Ancient area. For example, sumpweed and other members of the Eastern Agricultural Complex continued to be used in the lower Illinois River valley and adjacent portions of the Midwest during this period (N. B. Asch and D. L. Asch 1985a). Botanical data and isotopic analysis of skeletal material both indicate that maize played a much larger dietary role in the Fort Ancient societies of the mid-Ohio valley than in the Midwest (Broida 1983, 1984; Wagner 1987, 1989; Wymer 1987; 1992).

## THE PENNSYLAVANIA RECORD

Given the data from the Midwest and Ohio regions, the major questions for Pennsylvania and the Northeast then become: (1) How far east and north did this heavy dependence on maize exist? (2) To what extent were beans, squash, tobacco, and members of the Eastern Agricultural Complex used? (3) What was the importance of wild foods in the diet?

The archaeobotanical record of Pennsylvania is poor compared to states farther west such as Ohio or Illinois, but perhaps good compared to some other parts of the Northeast. There have been relatively few major site excavations, especially in the years since flotation recovery of plant remains has become standard. Because most archaeobotanical data are now the result of cultural resource management work, samples may be small in size or number, and the results are often buried in contract reports. As noted by Maslowski (1985) for the mid and upper Ohio valley of West Virginia, Middle and Late Woodland period sites appear to be less well studied than larger late Late Woodland sites and late prehistoric cultures such as the Monongahela of southwestern Pennsylvania or the Clemson's Island of the Susquehanna River basin of north-central Pennsylvania. This paper will discuss primarily plant remains from the upper Ohio drainage in southwestern Pennsylvania and the Susquehanna drainage in central Pennsylvania.

## MEADOWCROFT ROCKSHELTER

Although Meadowcroft Rockshelter is probably the best known, and potentially the most significant, archaeological site in Pennsylvania, the data are somewhat difficult to integrate with those from other sites. Radiocarbon dates from the site have been questioned repeatedly because of their extreme antiquity: firepits dating back as far as 14,225 B.P., and a charcoal concentration and a carbonized, cut bark-like possible basketry fragment dating to more than 19,000 B.P. (Adovasio et al. 1980; Cushman 1982; Cushman Volman 1981).

**Table 2.1. Plant Remains from Four Monongahela Village Sites.**

| No. Samples | Early Gnagey | Early Wylie | Middle McJunkin | Late Sony |
|---|---|---|---|---|
| Total Volume (l) | 18.5 | 374.5 | – | 72.0 |
| Maize ubiquity | | | | |
|    % of samples of occurrence | 50.0 | 34.3 | 67.7 | 50.0 |
|    % of total charcoal | 0.8 | 0.1 | 2.3 | 14.0 |
| Nutshell | | | | |
|    % of total charcoal | 0.2 | 2.5 | 3.6 | 0.4 |
| Beans | 34 | – | – | 2 |
| Squash | 4 | 5 | – | 1 |
| Sunflower | 2 | – | 1 | 1 |
| Chenopod | 2 | – | 6 | – |
| Knotweed | 3 | 6 | 6 | 1 |
| Purslane | – | – | – | 11 |
| Fleshy fruit | 5 | 6 | 16 | 16 |
| Sumac | – | – | – | – |
| Tick-trefoil | 29 | 8 | – | 3 |
| Bedstraw | 2 | – | – | – |

In addition to extremely early dates for cultural remains, Meadowcroft has maize in strata dated to as early as 375-340 B.C. (Adovasio and Johnson 1981:Table 2; Cushman 1982). This is not an impossible date. Riley et al. (1994) reported AMS-dated maize in the age range of cal 170 B.C.-A.D. 10 from the Holding site in the American Bottom near East St. Louis. Maize has also been directly dated to A.D. 220 at the Edwin Harness site in Ohio and A.D. 175 at the Icehouse Bottom site in Tennessee (Chapman and Crites 1987). However, direct AMS dating of maize specimens has also disproved numerous other purported Early and Middle Woodland occurrences of maize (Fritz 1994). Until the maize from Meadowcroft is directly dated, its age will remain questionable. Likewise, there are relatively large, (i.e., domesticated-size) squash seeds from Meadowcroft dating to about 850 B.C. (Adovasio and Johnson 1981:Table 3; Cushman 1982) that should be directly dated. Because of the controversy the radiocarbon dates from Meadowcroft have generated, direct dating of the cultigens is essential before their antiquity can either be accepted or dismissed.

## MIDDLE WOODLAND

The Dunsfort Site, a Middle Woodland site in Washington County, southwestern Pennsylvania, excavated by Richard George of the Carnegie Museum of Natural History, fits very well with the Middle Woodland of Ohio or Illinois. Sixty percent of the seeds (King 1993a) represent the Eastern Agricultural Complex, and include erect knotweed, which is most common, as well as marshelder, goosefoot, and maygrass. Maygrass, which strongly dominates the Early, Middle, and early Late Woodland of central Ohio, is represented at Dunsfort by only a single seed (King 1993a). This could be attributable either to local differences in the use of Eastern Agricultural Complex plants or to preservation and sampling. No remains of squash, little barley, or sunflower were recovered from the Dunsfort site.

## LATE WOODLAND AND LATE PREHISTORIC

Data on the use of plants during the Late Woodland (ca. A.D. 400-1000) of southwestern Pennsylvania are overshadowed by the later (post-A.D. 1000) Monongahela, a culture of the lower upper Ohio River basin in southwestern Pennsylvania and adjacent states that is contemporaneous with the Fort Ancient of Ohio. The culture is characterized by a number of distinctive traits. One trait of particular interest to ethnobiologists and human ecologists is an apparently heavy reliance on maize agriculture demonstrated by human biological evidence. In a mass spectrometric analysis of bone from four Monongahela sites in the West Virginia panhandle, Farrow found that maize comprised at least 70 percent of the diet at all four sites, suggesting that the Monongahela subsistence base was highly specialized and nutritionally inadequate. This would have been mitigated by the use of beans, however, which were recovered from two of the four sites discussed here. In Farrow's sample, although maize was apparently heavily used throughout the period, it seems to have increased in importance from about 70 percent of the diet at A.D. 1050 to about 80 percent at A.D. 1225. In a comparison of caries and other dental pathologies with carbon isotope data from a number of Pennsylvania Monongahela sites, Sciulli (1995) and Sciulli and Carlisle (1975, 1977) found that maize comprised about 52 percent of the Monongahela diet and that there is no statistical difference between upland and lowland populations that might indicate dietary differences. Sciulli's data, as well as that of Church and McDaniel (1992), suggest that maize was somewhat less important in the diet than for the populations studied by Farrow (1986), but still dominant enough in the diet to cause health problems. Greenlee (1990:69-70) found some relationship between $\delta^{13}C$ and available arable land suitable for the growing of maize. Plant remains have been analyzed from only a few of the sites used for stable isotope analysis. However, the often small quantity of maize and the overall diversity of plants found at the Pennsylvania Monongahela sites also suggest that maize use may have been somewhat less at the eastern Monongahela sites or that its storage and/or use was not conducive to the preservation and recovery of amounts of carbonized maize reflecting its importance in the diet.

A high percentage of Monongahela sites occur in uplands, far removed from large river valleys with fertile, tillable soil. The villages are palisaded and occur as larger permanently occupied villages and smaller hamlets occupied for shorter periods and/or used for special purposes. Neither Greenlee (1990) nor Sciulli (1995) found any correlation in $\delta^{13}C$ values and topographic position that might indicate a difference in maize usage. One of the most notable features of Monongahela houses is the presence of small attached semi-subterranean pit features that have most often been interpreted as having been used for storage, although other uses have also been suggested. There is a definite progression through time in the number and distribution of these features. Early Monongahela houses lacked attached pits, although unattached subterranean storage features were present (Hart 1993). During the Middle Monongahela period, storage features appeared that were attached to the houses. However, it was during the Late Monongahela that large structures with numerous attached storage structures, termed "petal structures," appear. At some, but not all village sites, there are as many as 20 or more storage structures attached to a single house (Davis and Wilks 1998; Hart 1993) with few present elsewhere in the village, suggesting a centralization of control over stored goods.

The following discussion is of plant remains from four Monongahela village sites in southwestern Pennsylvania excavated by Richard George of the Carnegie Museum of Natural History or Christine Davis of Christine Davis Associates (Table 2.1). The Wylie and Sony sites have numerous flotation samples, the Gnagey site two relative large flotation samples coupled with earlier analyses by Cutler and Blake (1973), and the McJunkin site several early flotation samples of an unknown volume. Wylie and Gnagey are Early Monongahela (George 1983), McJunkin is Middle Monongahela (George 1978), and Sony is Late Monongahela (Davis and Wilks 1998). As exemplified by these sites, the tremendous variation in

**Table 2.2. Summary of Cultigens from Monongahela Sites with recovered Plant Remains.**

| | Site | Reference | Maize | Beans | Pepo gourd / squash | Sunflower | Chenopod | Little Barley | Maygrass | Erect Knotweed |
|---|---|---|---|---|---|---|---|---|---|---|
| Early/ Somerset | Gnagy | Blake and Cutler 1983 | X | X | X | X | X | – | – | – |
| Early/ Drew | Drew | Buker 1970, Cutler and Blake 1973 | X | – | – | – | – | – | – | – |
| | Duvall | Dunnell 1980; George 1974 | X | – | – | – | – | – | – | – |
| | Grays Landing-1 | Goodwin et al. 1990 | X | – | – | – | – | – | – | – |
| | Ryan 36WM231200 | Cutler and Blake 1973 | X | X | – | – | – | – | – | – |
| | Saddle | Church and McDaniel 1992 | X | X | – | – | – | – | – | – |
| | Wylie | Eisert 1981; King 1990 | X | – | X | – | X | – | – | X/? |
| Middle | Grays Landing-2 | Raber et al. 1990 | X | – | — | – | – | – | – | – |
| | Household | George et al. 1990 | – | – | – | – | – | – | – | – |
| | Mon City | Moeller 1990 | X | X | – | – | X | – | – | X/? |
| | McJunkin | King 1994 | X | – | X | X | X | – | – | X/? |
| | Bonnie Brook | Blake 1981 | X | – | – | – | – | – | – | – |
| Late | Sony | King 1993b | X | X | X | X | – | – | – | X/po |
| | Martin | Yarnell 1964 | X | – | – | – | – | – | – | – |
| | Phillips | Yarnell 1964 | X | – | – | – | – | – | – | – |
| | Reckner | Yarnell 1964 | X | – | – | – | – | – | – | – |
| | Powell 1 | Yarnell 1964 | X | – | – | – | – | – | – | – |
| | Emerick | Yarnell 1964 | X | X | – | – | – | – | – | – |
| | Buchanan Shelter | Yarnell 1964 | X | – | – | – | – | – | – | – |
| Fort Ancient | McKees Rocks | Jones 1968; Cutler and Blake 1973 | X | – | – | – | – | – | – | – |

processing and analysis of botanical samples from the majority of Monongahela and other sites precludes any but the most general comparisons.

The plant remains from these sites are shown in Table 2.1. Maize is common, occurring in between 34 and 68 percent of all features from the four sites discussed here. Although it occurs in the greatest percentage of samples at the McJunkin site, it has by far the greatest percentage by weight in the Late Monongahela Sony site. When measurable cob fragments occur, maize from Monongahela sites is typical of Eastern Eight-Row, also known as Northern Flint. It is very similar to that found in Fort Ancient sites. Analysis of well-preserved cob fragments from Meadowcroft Rockshelter indicate that maize with a higher row number was also present in southwestern Pennsylvania (Adovasio and Johnson 1981). Squash rind fragments occur in three of the four sites discussed here; bottle gourd was also recovered from McJunkin. Squash rind or seeds have been recovered from about one-third of Monongahela sites with published botanical remains, including Wylie, Gnagey (Blake and Cutler 1983), and Sony (Table 2.2). The beans from the Gnagey site are similar in every way to those of Fort Ancient (Wagner 1987). Beans have also been recovered from the Monongahela (ca. A.D. 1000-1300) Drew site (36AL62) (Buker 1970; Cutler and Blake 1973). Although sunflower is common in Fort Ancient sites, the achenes/seeds from the Gnagey, Sony, and McJunkin sites seem to be the first reported from Monongahela sites. Based on their sizes, these all appear to represent domesticated sunflower.

Nuts, represented by hickory (*Carya* sp.), black walnut (*Juglans nigra*), butternut (*Juglans cinerea*), acorns (*Quercus* sp.), and hazelnut (*Corylus americana*), occur in most Monongahela sites, but in surprisingly small amounts. Nuts, other than acorns, are a potentially important food resource because they contain a large amount of oil. Their low abundance suggests that nuts were either being ignored as being relatively too labor intensive or that they were being processed away from the sites discussed here. Studies have shown that by far the most efficient way to process hickory nuts is to bash them up and heat them in water,

skimming off the nutmeats and oil (Talalay et al. 1984). This would be especially true for shagbark hickory (*Carya ovata*) nuts in western Pennsylvania because they are much smaller and contain a relatively small nutmeat compared to those from Indiana or Illinois.

Starchy seeds occur in all the sites discussed here, as well as other of Monongahela sites (Table 2.2). Chenopod occurs in two sites, with that from the McJunkin site appearing to represent the domesticated *Chenopodium berlandieri*. Knotweed occurs in all four sites, and in the McJunkin site, six seeds represent at least three different species. While none of them is erect knotweed, the possible native cultigen, the presence of three distinct species suggests that seeds of wild species of knotweed were also used as food. Purslane (*Portulaca* sp.) is found in fairly large amounts in Fort Ancient and other sites.

Fleshy fruits occur in all of the sites with the most common taxa being grape and blackberry. Interestingly, there are no seeds of sumac, which Wagner (1987) found to be the most common fruit seed found in Fort Ancient sites. They have been found in numerous other sites as well (McAndrews et al. 1974; Yarnell 1964), including coprolites of Ozark Bluff-dwellers (Wakefield and Dellinger 1936). The hairs on the fruit are very sour and, although they tend to accumulate dust and small insects, the fruit can be steeped to make a lemonade-like drink or boiled to make a medicine used among historic Indians to treat diarrhea and other ailments (Moerman 1986:402-406).

The distribution of various types of plant remains is similar between Monongahela and Fort Ancient sites. This, coupled with the similarity of measurable cultigen specimens, suggests the two cultural groups had similar diets and agricultural practices, whatever their political relationship might have been. Fort Ancient diet may have been somewhat less diverse, and agriculture may have been more important than it was for at least some Monongahela villages. There are more descriptions of seed caches at Fort Ancient villages. If such caches represent stored food that was destroyed, they may indicate greater social risk among the Fort Ancient than among the Monongahela peoples. Alternatively, they may merely represent the effects of differing food-storage techniques on preservation.

George et al. (1990) have suggested that the Monongahela were decimated and subjugated by Fort Ancient peoples, with evidence including the presence of a large Fort Ancient village, the McKees Rocks site, in the floodplain of the Ohio in southwestern Pennsylvania, and a Fort Ancient projectile point associated with a Monongahela burial at the Household site. If the Monongahela were threatened by the Fort Ancient, there should be more evidence of warfare on the western edge of Monongahela territory than on the east where, presumably, Fort Ancient peoples infiltrated less often. We may see this in the comparison of plant remains from the more easterly Gnagey site, which has a somewhat richer variety of plants than the roughly contemporaneous Wylie site which lies considerably closer to Fort Ancient territory. In addition, the plant remains that I have examined from Monongahela sites tend to consist of maize kernels and very few cobs, suggesting that the hilltop sites were indeed defensive and that maize may have been grown on better agricultural soils in the steam valleys, removed from the cobs, and transported to the more secure upland sites. The work by Greenlee (1990) and Sciulli (1995) indicate that there was no significant difference in the importance of maize in the diet in skeletal populations from upland and lowland sites.

## CENTRAL PENNSYLVANIA

The major drainage system of both central Pennsylvania and portions of New York State is the Susquehanna River system, which lies just east of the Ohio River system and could have been used as a transportation route over a wide area. In this region, the Clemson's Island culture (ca. A.D. 700/800 to A.D. 1200/1300) is related to the later part of the Middle Woodland and the early part of the Late Woodland period in Pennsylvania prehistory (Stewart 1990); the period is also referred to as early Late Prehistoric by Hart and Asch Sidell (1996). Clemson's Island and the subsequent Stewart phase Shenks Ferry (ca. A.D. 1250-1350) are roughly equivalent to the Monogahela and

Fort Ancient of southwestern Pennsylvania and Ohio. Clemson's Island settlement types included primarily single-household farmsteads, multi-household hamlets, and fortified, multi-household hamlets (Custer et al. 1994). It has been suggested that sites were more likely to be located on highly productive floodplain soils after ca. A.D. 800, and Clemson's Island is generally viewed as having had the first agriculturally oriented subsistence systems in the West Branch basin (Custer 1986; Hay and Hatch 1980:88; Stewart 1990, 1994). Most early Late Prehistoric farmsteads and hamlets in the West Branch basin contain large subterranean storage facilities (Hart and Asch Sidell 1996; Stewart 1990), and stone hoes were recovered at the Memorial Park site (Hart and Asch Sidell 1996). Maize remains occur consistently, although in usually small amounts, on Clemson's Island sites (Hatch 1980a; Hay and Hamilton 1984; Stewart 1988, 1990, 1994), furthering the argument that agriculture was an important aspect of the subsistence system (Stewart 1990).

The Memorial Park site on the West Branch of the Susquehanna yielded botanical remains from early (ca. A.D. 890), middle (ca. A.D. 1015), and late (ca. A.D. 1170) Clemson's Island, as well as Stewart phase Shenks Ferry (ca. A.D. 1330) contexts (Hart and Asch Sidell 1996). Hart and Asch Sidell (1996) reported maize and two types of domesticated goosefoot, as well as sunflower, little barley, tobacco and a potentially important non-cultivated starchy seed, wild rice (*Zizania aquatica*). There are also numerous other wild plant taxa represented, including a wide diversity of nuts and fruits. The percent of starchy cultivated seeds (i.e., chenopod and little barley) increases with time from 69 percent in early Clemson's Island to 97 percent in middle and late Clemson's Island, before falling to 25 percent in Stewart phase (Hart and Asch Sidell 1996:Table 4). Likewise, the density of maize fragments is highest in early Clemson's Island and lower in the later components. However, the presence of little barley in the Stewart phase features suggests that the agricultural complex used during the Clemson's Island occupations remained in use at this later date (Hart and Asch Sidell 1996). Storage pits, similar to those designated as silos at the St.

Anthony site (Stewart 1988, 1994), were present in all components.

The Fisher Farm site (35CE35) is a Late Woodland/early Late Prehistoric farming hamlet on Bald Eagle Creek southwest of Milesburg. The site is of interest because it records the transition from Clemson's Island to Shenks Ferry, with an occupation using principally Clemson's Island and early Shenks Ferry (Blue Rock phase/ Stewart phase) ceramics dating from ca. A.D. 705 ± 70 to A.D. 1350 ± 50, roughly contemporaneous with the Memorial Park site. Maize was recovered from a pit dating to A.D. 705 ± 70, and a single structure was found with an attached semi-subterranean feature, termed a "keyhole structure," associated with a date of 1350 ± 105 (Hatch 1980b) and a preponderance of Shenks Ferry ceramics. This feature was particularly productive of plant remains, including maize, beans, squash, sunflower, goosefoot, and knotweed, as well as nutshell and seeds of blackberry/raspberry. Although goosefoot and knotweed were third and fourth in importance by weight of remains (following maize and hickory nut), it was not possible to ascertain whether the goosefoot and knotweed were domesticated or wild (Hatch and Daugirda 1980; Willey 1980:136-139).

Other early Late Prehistoric sites in the West Branch area with plant remains include the Bald Eagle, St. Anthony, and West Water Street sites. The Bald Eagle site yielded maize, beans, and squash (Hay and Hamilton 1984), the Clemson's Island St. Anthony site yielded maize in three dated pit features (Stewart 1988, 1994), and the Clemson's Island component at the West Water Street site produced maize, beans, and goosefoot with one type of pit filled completely with carbonized maize cobs (Custer et al. 1994; Hart and Asch Sidell 1996). Hart and Asch Sidell (1996) noted that, in the West Branch basin, maize may have been used as early as the eighth century and it is found consistently in sites dating to after the ninth century.

Beans were present in a feature at the Bald Eagle site dated to cal A.D. 910 ± 85 (cal A.D. 1162) (Hay and Hamilton 1984), the Clemson's Island component at the West Water Street site (Custer et al. 1994; Hart and Asch Sidell 1996), and a Fisher Farm feature dating A.D. 1350 ± 150 (cal A.D. 1328, 1333, 1395). *Pepo* squash and/or gourd were recovered from the Late Archaic and Early Woodland components at the Memorial Park site; it was also found at the Bald Eagle site in the earliest components, which date as early as A.D. 850, and at Fisher Farm in the feature dating A.D. 1350 ± 150 (Hatch 1980a).

In the West Branch basin, sunflower has been recovered from the Memorial Park site in a feature dated to A.D. 810 (cal A.D. 892, 925, 936) (Hart and Asch Sidell 1996) and at Fisher Farm along with beans and squash in the feature dated to A.D. 1350 (Hart and Asch Sidell 1996; Hatch 1980b).

Hart and Asch Sidell (1996) found two types of domesticated *Chenopodium* at the Memorial Park site, as well as cultivated little barley, indicating their presence in the West Branch basin by at least the ninth century A.D. The recovery of wild chenopod seeds from a number of sites suggests that starchy seeds contributed to early Late Prehistoric diets even when domesticated plants were not sown (Hart and Asch Sidell 1996).

In the southern Susquehanna drainage, Sheep Rockshelter, an early Historic Shenks Ferry and Susquehannock site in Huntington County, yielded maize, beans, squash, bottle gourd, sunflower, peach (a Spanish introduction to the New World), and a variety of nuts, fleshy fruits, and other wild resources (Cutler and Blake 1973; Yarnell 1964).

On the North Branch of the Susquehanna, considerably to the east of the Memorial Park site, the Clemson's Island occupation of the Catawissa site (ca. A.D. 900-1125) also produced a large number of carbonized plant remains (Table 2.3; King 1988, 1991). The Catawissa site was excavated in 1984 by the Cultural Resources Management Program of the Department of Anthropology at the University of Pittsburgh (East et al. 1988). Although there are some questions about the stratigraphy of the site (four major, more or less discrete occupational surfaces), most of the plant remains came from a Middle Woodland/early Late Woodland occupation (Stratum III, ca. A.D. 400-500 to ca. A.D. 900) and the overlying early Late Woodland Clemson's Island (Stratum IV, ca.

**Table 2.3. Plant Remains from the Catawissa Bridge Site.**

| | STR III -A.D. 400-900 | | STR IV -A.D. 900-1125 | |
| --- | --- | --- | --- | --- |
| | No. | % | No. | % |
| Maize | 59 | 30.1 | 42 | 9.4 |
| Beans | | | 1 | 0.2 |
| Squash rind fragments | 1 | 0.5 | 5 | 1.2 |
| Starchy EAC: | | | | |
| Little barley | 52 | 26.5 | 167 | 37.3 |
| Chenopod | 3 | 1.5 | 3 | 0.7 |
| Wild rice | 2 | 1.0 | 2 | 0.4 |
| Other dry seeds | 52 | 26.5 | 176 | 39.2 |
| | (5 taxa) | | (6 taxa) | |
| Fleshy fruit | 21 | 10.7 | 51 | 11.4 |
| | (5 taxa) | | (6 taxa) | |
| Aquatic | 6 | 3.1 | 1 | 0.2 |
| | (2 taxa) | | | |

*Notes*
Maize and squash rind fragments are equated with seeds for the purposes of this table.
After King 1991.

A.D. 900-1125) (East et al. 1988). Stratum III plant remains, which unfortunately represent a long temporal span, include maize, squash, little barley, and apparently undomesticated goosefoot, as well as wild rice and a variety of wild resources (Table 2.3; King 1988, 1991). Maize at the North Branch Catawissa site by A.D. 900 coupled with that from the West Branch Fisher Farm site (Hatch 1980a) suggests that maize may have been widely known, if not heavily grown, in the eighth century in central Pennsylvania.

The Clemson's Island cultigens include maize, beans, and squash; native cultigens include 167 seeds of little barley, 3 chenopod seeds, 3 knotweed (not erect knotweed), wild rice, and again, a wide variety of nuts and fruits and berries, as well as bulbs of wild onion. There are also two carbonized maygrass-like seeds, although they were too distorted for a positive identification.

Finds of starchy seeds at a number of sites in central Pennsylvania, including goosefoot,

knotweed, and assorted grasses, have generally, and probably correctly, been assumed to represent the harvesting of wild stands (Custer et al. 1994; Hart and Asch Sidell 1996; Hatch 1980a; Hay and Hamilton 1984; Stewart 1990). Although the identification of a small number of fragmentary and distorted seeds is extremely problematic, reexamination of the material identified before the recognition of native cultigens for this region might add new identifications of such material in additional sites. Likewise, the use of flotation techniques for the recovery of plant remains from sites excavated in the future will also add significantly to the database.

## SUMMARY AND CONCLUSIONS

Although far less numerous than plant remains from Midwestern sites, botanical remains from Pennsylvania sites indicate that squash was present from the Late Archaic and Early Woodland and that maize, beans, and members of the Eastern Agricultural Complex were present during the Late Woodland/early Late Prehistoric. In answer to the questions posed earlier, available evidence indicates that maize was an important crop after ca. A.D. 900/1000 in central Pennsylvania, and that beans, squash, tobacco, and members of the Eastern Agricultural Complex (chenopod, little barley, sunflower) were also used as were some of their wild counterparts. Based on the limited available data, however, usage may have been lighter and/or more variable than that in the Ohio River drainage. Chenopod and knotweed occur on several sites, although they are not always the domesticated forms, and several sites have at least three species of knotweed. We may be seeing a use of wild taxa related to cultivated ones in cases where the domesticated forms were not available or did not grow well.

Maize was introduced into Pennsylvania by at least ca. A.D. 750, possibly much earlier considering its presence in Ohio sites by about A.D. 425. Analysis of stable carbon isotopes from skeletal remains indicate that maize consumption increased after approximately A.D. 1000 (Scuilli 1995:Table 1).

A number of conclusions can be reached that may apply to the archaeobotanical record of New England. *Pepo* squash/gourd was present at the Memorial Park site in central Pennsylvania by 5,400 B.P. and squash by 2,625 B.P. (Hart and Asch Sidell 1997). It appears that indigenous cultivated plants (i.e., members of the Eastern Agricultural Complex) were present in western and central Pennsylvania during the Late Woodland/early Late Prehistoric and possibly the Middle Woodland.

Fort Ancient and Monongahela both began about A.D. 950 to 1000, corresponding to a period of warm temperatures known in Europe as the Medieval Warm period. This is the period during which the Vikings settled on Iceland, Greenland, and the Labrador coast only to be later frozen out of Greenland by the Little Ice Age. Maize had already been present in eastern North America for several hundred to a thousand years, presumably being grown at an extremely low level and becoming slowing acclimatized to marginal environments. It has been suggested that maize may have initially attained widespread importance in the Southeast as a sacred item (Scarry 1988) rather than a food staple. This may also have been the case in the Northeast where, for example, the long, slender eight-rowed Iroquois maize did have a sacred value. In the Northeast, at least, climatic warming may have extended the growing season, making maize agriculture reliable enough to evolve into a major food crop. Climate was undoubtedly a more important factor in maize agriculture in the mountainous parts of central Pennsylvania or to the north in New England than it was in the Southeast or Midwest. If climate was critical and human selection for hardier varieties inadequate, we might expect to see a peak in the number of sites with maize during the period from about A.D. 900 to 1200, followed by a local or regional declines in maize use as the climate cooled. There is evidence from the Catawissa, Memorial Park, and Fisher Farm sites that maize was present, and at least at the Memorial Park site, common by about A.D. 900; if so, the increase in its use coincided, for whatever reason, with climatic warming. The adoption of maize as a crop staple was probably followed closely by the adoption of lye processing, which alters the amino acid ratios of maize and makes it more nutritious. Most historic/modern cultures that rely on maize as a food staple do utilize some form of alkali processing (Katz et al. 1974). Whether or not stress caused by climatic change or by human population growth were factors human subsistence in the Northeast, this is a region of great environmental variability and a tremendous diversity of natural resources. The relationship between these factors has varied through time and space across the Northeast, as undoubtedly did the relative use of cultigens versus wild plant and animal foods.

## ACKNOWLEDGEMENTS

I would like to thank Richard L. George of the Carnegie Museum of Natural History, Pittsburgh, Pennsylvania, and Christine Davis of Christine Davis, Consultants, Inc., Verona, Pennsylvania. As reviewers, Michael Stewart and Dee Anne Wymer had many excellent comments and suggestions. The analysis of plant remains from the Catawissa Bridge Replacement site was conducted while I was a Research Associate of the Cultural Resources Management Program (now Center for Cultural Resource Research), Department of Anthropology, University of Pittsburgh.

## REFERENCES CITED

Adovasio, J. M., J. D. Gunn, J. Donahue, R. Stuckenrath, J. E. Guilday, and K. Cushman Volman. 1980. Yes Virginia, It Really Is That Old. *American Antiquity* 45:588-95.

Adovasio, J. M., and W. C. Johnson. 1981. The Appearance of Cultigens in the Upper Ohio Valley: A View from Meadowcroft Rockshelter. *Pennsylvania Archaeologist* 51(1-2): 63-80.

Asch, D. L., and N. B. Asch. 1985. Prehistoric Plant Cultivation in West-Central Illinois. In *Prehistoric Food Production in North America*, edited by R. I. Ford, pp. 149-204. Anthropological Papers No. 75. Museum of Anthropology, University of Michigan, Ann Arbor.

Asch, N. B., and D. L. Asch. 1985a. Archaeobotany. In *Deer Track: A Late Woodland Village in the Mississippi Valley*, edited by C. R. McGimsey and M. D. Connor, pp. 44-117. Technical Report 1. Center for American Archaeology, Kampsville Archaeological Center, Kampsville, Illinois.

—————. 1985b. Archaeobotany. In *The Hill Creek Homestead and the Late Mississippian Settlement in the Lower Illinois Valley*, edited by M. D. Conner, pp. 115-170. Research Series No. 1. Center for American Archaeology, Kampsville Archaeological Center, Kampsville, Illinois.

—————. 1986. Woodland Period Archaeobotany of the Napoleon Hollow Site. In *Woodland Period Occupations of the Napoleon Hollow Site in the Lower Illinois Valley*, edited by M. D. Wiant and C. R. McGimsey, pp. 427-512. Research Series No. 6. Center for American Archaeology, Kampsville Archaeological Center, Kampsville, Illinois.

Bernabo, J. C. 1981. Quantitative Estimates of Temperature Changes over the Last 2700 Years in Michigan Based on Pollen Data. *Quaternary Research* 15:143-159.

Blake, L. W. 1981. Carbonized Plant Remains from the Bonnie Brook Site (36BT43). *Pennsylvania Archaeologist* 51(3)52-54.

Blake, L. W., and H. C. Cutler. 1983. Plant Remains from the Gnagey Site (36SO55). *Pennsylvania Archaeologist* 53(4):83-88.

Broida, M. O. 1983. *Maize in Kentucky Fort Ancient Diets and Analysis of Carbon Isotope Ratios in Human Bone*. Unpublished Masters Thesis, Department of Anthropology, University of Kentucky, Lexington.

—————. 1984. An Estimate of the Percents of Maize in the Diets of two Kentucky Fort Ancient Villages. In *Late Prehistoric Research in Kentucky*, edited by D. Pollack, C. Hockensmith, and T. Sanders, pp. 68-82. Kentucky Heritage Council, Frankfort.

Buker, W. E. 1970. The Drew Site (36-AL-62). *The Pennsylvania Archaeologist* 40(3-4):21-66.

Chapman, J., and G. Crites. 1987. Evidence for Early Maize (*Zea mays*) from the Icehouse Bottom Site, Tennessee. *American Antiquity* 52:352-354.

Church, F., and G. McDaniel. 1992. *The Saddle Site (46 Mr 95): Upland Monongahela Occupations in Marshal County, West Virginia*. Report prepared for Soil Conservation Service, Morgantown, WV, by Archaeological Services Consultants, Inc., Columbus, Ohio (cited in Hart 1993).

Cushman, K. A. 1982. Floral Remains from Meadowcroft Rockshelter, Washington County, Southwestern Pennsylvania. In *Collected Papers on the Archaeology of Meadowcroft Rockshelter and the Cross Creek Drainage*, edited by R. C. Carlisle and J. M. Adovasio, pp. 207-220. Department of Anthropology, University of Pittsburgh.

Cushman Volman, K. A. 1981. *Paleo-environmental Implications of Botanical Data from Meadowcroft Rockshelter, Pennsylvania*. Unpublished Ph.D. dissertation, Department of Botany, Texas A&M University, College Station.

Custer, J. F., S. C. Watson, and D. N. Bailey. 1994. *Recovery Investigations of the West Water Street Site 36CN175 Lock Haven, Clinton County, Pennsylvania*. Prepared by KFS Historic Preservation Group, Philadelphia, Pennsylvania for U.S. Army Corps of Engineers, Baltimore.

Cutler, H. C., and L. W. Blake. 1973. *Plants from Archaeological Sites East of the Rockies*. Missouri Botanical Garden, St. Louis.

————. 1983. Plant Remains from the Gnagey Site (36SO55). *Pennsylvania Archaeologist* 53(4):83-88.

Dailey, P. W. 1975. *Climates of the States: Pennsylvania*. In *Climates of the States*, Vol. 2, pp. 832-835. National Oceanic and Atmospheric Administration. Gale Research Company, Detroit.

Davis, C.E. and A.K. Wilks. 1998. *Phase III Date Recovery, Sony Site, 36WM151*, Westmoreland County Pennsylvania. Report Prepared by Christine Davis Consultants, Inc., Verona, Pennsylvania for Westmoreland County Development Corporation, Pennsylvania.

Dunnell, R. C. 1980. Duvall: A Monongahela Settlement in Central Ohio County, West Virginia. *West Virginia Archaeologist* 29:1-37.

East, T. C., J. M. Adovasio, W. C. Johnson, and D. R. Pedler. 1988. *The Prehistory of the Catawissa Bridge Replacement Site (36CO9), Columbia County, Pennsylvania*. Prepared by the Cultural Resource Management Program, Department of Anthropology, University of Pittsburgh, for Parsons Brinkerhoff-Quade and Douglas, Inc. and the Pennsylvania Department of Transportation.

Eisert, R. W. 1981. The Wylie Site (36WH274). *Pennsylvania Archaeologist* 51(1-2):11-62.

Farrow, D. C. 1986. A Study of Monongahela Subsistence Patterns Based on Mass Spectrometric Analysis. *Midcontinental Journal of Archaeology* 11:153-180.

Fritz, G. J. 1994. Are the First American Farmers Getting Younger? *Current Anthropology* 35:305-309.

Gajewski, K. 1987. Climatic Impacts on the Vegetation of Eastern North America during the Past 2000 years. *Vegetation* 68: 179-190.

————. 1988. Late Holocene Climate Changes in Eastern North America Estimated from Pollen Data. *Quaternary Research* 29: 255-262.

George, R.L. 1974. Monongahela Settlement Patterns and The Ryan Site. *Pennsylvania Archaeologist* 44(1-2):1-22.

————. 1978. The McJunkin Site, a Preliminary Report. *Pennsylvania Archaeologist* 48(4):33-47.

————. 1983.The Gnagey Site and The Monongahela Occupation of the Somerset Plateau. *Pennsylvania Archaeologist* 53(4):1-97.

Goodwin, R. C., and T. W. Neumann, W. C. Johnson, J. Cohen, and N. H. Lopinot. 1990. *Archaeological Data Recovery from Prehistoric Site 36FA363, Grays Landing Lock and Dam*, 2 vols. by R. Christopher Goodwin and Associates, Inc., Frederick, Maryland. Prepared for U.S. Army Corps of Engineers, Pittsburgh District.

Greenlee, D. M. 1990. *Environmental and Temporal Variability in $\delta^{13}C$ Values in Late Prehistoric Subsistence Systems in the Upper Ohio Valley*. Master's thesis, Department of Anthropology, University of Washington.

Hart, J. P. 1990. Modeling Oneota Agricultural Intensification: A Cross-Cultural Evaluation. *Current Anthropology* 31:569-577.

————. 1993. Monongahela Subsistence-Settlement Change: The Late Prehistoric Period in the Lower Upper Ohio River Valley. *Journal of World Prehistory* 7:71-120.

Hart, J. P., and N. Asch Sidell. 1996. Prehistoric Agricultural Systems in the West Branch of the Susquehanna River Basin, A.D. 800 to A.D. 1350. *Northeast Anthropology* 52:1-30.

————. 1997. Additional Evidence for Early Cucurbit Use in the Northern Eastern Woodlands East of the Allegheny Front. *American Antiquity* 62:523-537.

Hatch, J. W. (editor). 1980a. *The Fisher Farm Site: A Late Woodland Hamlet in Context.* Occasional Papers in Anthropology No. 3. Department of Anthropology, The Pennsylvania State University, University Park.

Hatch, J. W. 1980b. Radiocarbon Dates from the Fisher Farm Site. In *The Fisher Farm Site: A Late Woodland Hamlet in Context*, edited by J.W. Hatch, pp. 257-263. Occasional Papers in Anthropology No. 3. Department of Anthropology, The Pennsylvania State University, University Park.

Hatch, J.W. and J. Daugirda. 1980. The Semi-Subterranean Keyhole Structure At Fisher Farm—Feature 28. In *The Fisher Farm Site: A Late Woodland Hamlet in Context*, Edited by J.W. Hatch, pp.171-190. Occasional Papers in Anthropology, Number 12, Department of Anthropology, The Pennsylvania State University, University Park, Pennsylvania.

Hay, C. A., and C. Hamilton. 1984. *The Bald Eagle Township Sewage Collection System Archaeological Project: Final Mitigation Research.* Technical Report No. 2. Department of Anthropology, The Pennsylvania State University, University Park.

Hay, C. A., and J. W. Hatch. 1980. Predictive Models of Site Distribution within the Bald Eagle Creek Watershed. In *The Fisher Farm Site: A Late Woodland Hamlet in Context*, edited by J. W. Hatch, pp. 83-91. Occasional Papers in Anthropology No. 3. Department of Anthropology, The Pennsylvania State University, University Park.

Johannessen, S. 1984. Paleoethnobotany. In *American Bottom Archaeology*, edited by C. J. Bareis and J. W. Porter, pp. 197-214. University of Illinois Press, Urbana.

Johnson, W.C., W.P. Athens, M.T. Fuess, L.G. Jaramillo, K.R. Bastianni, and E. Ramos. 1989. *Late Prehistoric Period Monongahela Culture Site and Cultural Resource Inventory.* Cultural Resource Management Program, Department of Anthroplogy, University of Pittsburgh. Pittsburgh, Pennsylvania.

Jones, V. H. 1968. Corn from the McKees Rocks Village Site. *Pennsylvania Archaeologist* 38(1-4):81-86.

Katz, S. H, M. L. Hediger, and L. A. Valleroy. 1974.Traditional Maize Processing Techniques in the New World. *Science* 184:765-773.

King, F. B. 1988 Floral Remains. In *The Prehistory of the Catawissa Bridge Replacement Site (36CO9), Columbia County, Pennsylvania*, edited by T. C. East, J. M. Adovasio, W. C. Johnson, and D. R. Pedler, pp. 303-312. Prepared by the Cultural Resource Management Program, Department of Anthropology, University of Pittsburgh, for Parsons Brinkerhoff-Quade and Douglas, Inc. and the Pennsylvania Department of Transportation.

————. 1990 Plant Remains Recovered from the 1989 Excavations at the Wylie Farm #3 Site, 36WH283, Washington Co., Pennsylvania. Report prepared for R. L. George, Carnegie Museum of Natural History, Pittsburgh.

————. 1991. Plant Remains from the Catawissa Bridge Replacement Site. Report prepared for the Center for Cultural Resource Research, Department of Anthropology, University of Pittsburgh, Pittsburgh.

————. 1993a. Plant Remains from the Dunsfort Site, Washington Co., Pennsylvania. Report prepared for the Carnegie Museum of Natural History.

————. 1993b. Preliminary Report on Archaeobotanical Remains from the Sony Site. Report prepared for Christine Davis Consultants, Inc., Pittsburgh.

———. 1994. *Plant Remains from the McJunkin Site*. Report prepared for R. George, Division of Anthropology, Carnegie Museum of Natural History, Pittsburgh.

Maslowski, R.F. 1985. Woodland Settlement Patterns in the Mid and Upper Ohio Valley. *West Virginia Archaeologist* 37(2):23-34.

McAndrews, J. H., R.T. Byrne, and W.D. Finlayson. 1974. Report on the Investigation at Crawford Lake. Canada Council Grant. Royal Ontario Museum. Toronto.

Moeller, R.A. 1990. Flotation Analysis. In *Phase III Data Recovery at the Monongahela City Bridge Site (36WH737), L.R., Section 14M, Washington County, Pennsylvania*, edited by J.P. Hart, pp. 61-81. Prepared by GAI Consultants, Inc., Monroeville, Pennsylvania, for the Pennsylvania Department of Transportation, Greentree (cited in Hart 1993).

Moerman, D. E. 1986. *Medicinal Plants of Native America*. 2 vols. Technical Reports No. 19, Research Reports in Ethnobotany Contribution 2. Museum of Anthropology, University of Michigan, Ann Arbor.

Raber, P. S., C. M. Stevenson, and C. A. Hay. 1990. *Archaeological Data Recovery at Site 36Fa368, Grays Landing Lock and Dam, Fayette County, Pennsylvania, E.R. No. 81-1129-051*, 3 vols. by Archaeological and Historical Consultants, Inc., Centre Hall, Pennsylvania. Prepared for U.S. Army Corps of Engineers, Pittsburgh District (cited in Hart 1993).

Riley, T. J., G. R. Walz, C. J. Bareis, A. C. Fortier, and K. E. Parker. 1994. Accelerator Mass Spectrometry (AMS) Dates Confirm Early *Zea mays* in the Mississippi River Valley. *American Antiquity* 59:490-498.

Scarry, C. M. 1988. Variability in Mississippian Crop Production Strategies. Paper presented at the 45th Southeastern Archaeological Conference, New Orleans.

Scuilli, P. W. 1995. Biological Indicators of Diet in Monongahela Populations. *Pennsylvania Archaeologist* 65(2):1-18.

Scuilli, P. W., and R. C. Carlisle. 1975. Analysis of the Dentition from Three Western Pennsylvania Late Woodland Sites. I. Descriptive Statistics, Partition of Variation of Asymmetry. *Pennsylvania Archaeologist* 45(1):47-54.

———. 1977. Analysis of the Dentition from Three Western Pennsylvania Late Woodland Sites. II. Wear and Pathology. *Pennsylvania Archaeologist* 47(4):53-59.

Stewart, M. 1988. *Clemson's Island Cultures in the West Branch Valley: Phase II and Phase III Archaeological Investigations (36Un11) of the St. Anthony Street Bridge Replacement, L.R. 59024, Section 007, Union County, Lewisburg, Pennsylvania*. The Cultural Resource Group, Berger Burkavage, Inc., Clarks Summit, Pennsylvania.

———. 1990. Clemson's Island Studies in Pennsylvania: A Perspective. *Pennsylvania Archaeologist* 60(1):79-107.

———. 1994. *Prehistoric Farmers of the Susquehanna Valley: Clemson's Island Culture and the St. Anthony Site*. Occasional Publications in Northeastern Anthropology 13, Bethlehem, Connecticut.

Talalay, L., D. R. Keller, and P. J. Munson. 1984. Hickory Nuts, Walnuts, Butternuts, and Hazelnuts: Observations and Experiments Relevant to Their Aboriginal Exploitation in Eastern North America. In *Experiments and Observations on Aboriginal Wild Plant Food Utilization in Eastern North America*, edited by P. J. Munson, pp. 338-359. Prehistory Research Series 6(2). Indiana Historical Society, Indianapolis.

Wagner, G. 1987. *Uses of Plants by Fort Ancient Indians*. Unpublished Ph.D. dissertation, Department of Anthropology, Washington University, St. Louis.

———. 1989. The Corn and Cultivated Beans of the Fort Ancient Indians. In *New World Paleoethnobotany: Collected Papers in Honor of Leonard W. Blake*, edited by E. E. Voigt and D. M. Pearsall, pp. 107-135. *The Missouri Archaeologist* 47.

Wakefield, E. G., and S. C. Dellinger. 1936. Diet of Bluff Dwellers of the Ozark Mountains and Its Skeletal Effects. *Annals of Internal Medicine* 9:1412-1418.

Willey, L.M. 1980. The Analysis of Flotation Samples from the Fisher Farm Site. In *The Fisher Farm Site: A Late Woodland Hamlet in Context*, edited by J.W. Hatch, pp. 136-139. Occasional Papers in Anthroplogy, Number 12, Department of Anthropology, The Pennsylvania State University, University Park, Pennsylvania.

Wymer, D. 1987. The Middle Woodland-Late Woodland Interface in Central Ohio: Subsistence Continuity Amid Cultural Change. In *Emergent Horticultural Economies of the Eastern Woodlands*, edited by W. F. Keegan, pp. 201-216. Center for Archaeological Investigations, Occasional Papers No. 7. Southern Illinois University at Carbondale.

————. 1992. Trends and Disparities: The Woodland Paleoethnobotanical Record of the Mid-Ohio Valley. In *Cultural Variability in Context: Woodland Settlements of the Mid-Ohio Valley*, edited by M. F. Seeman, pp. 65-76. The Kent State University Press, Kent.

————. 1993. Cultural Change and Subsistence: The Middle and Late Woodland Transition in the Mid-Ohio Valley. In *Foraging and Farming in the Eastern Woodlands*, edited by C. M. Scarry, pp. 138-156. University Press of Florida, Gainesville.

Yarnell, R. A. 1964. *Aboriginal Relationships Between Culture and Plant Life in the Upper Great Lakes Region*. Anthropological Papers No. 23. Museum of Anthropology, University of Michigan, Ann Arbor.

# Chapter 3

# Sunflower in the Seneca Iroquois Region of Western New York

Connie Cox Bodner

In the 1978 festschrift for Volney Jones, Richard Yarnell (1978:289) noted that at that time two plants, sunflower and sumpweed, were generally considered to have been domesticated aboriginally in eastern North America, although neither case was universally accepted. Paleoethnobotanical work in the two decades since has demonstrated to the satisfaction of most that not only were sunflower (*Helianthus annuus* L.) and sumpweed *(Iva annua* var. *macrocarpa* Jackson) domesticated by Native Americans in eastern North America, but so were goosefoot (*Chenopodium berlandieri* Moq.) and one or more forms of gourd (*Cucurbita* sp.) (Cowan and Smith 1993; Decker 1986, 1988; Fritz 1990, 1995; Fritz and Smith 1988; Smith 1985, 1987, 1989; Smith and Cowan 1987; Smith et al. 1992; Yarnell 1993; Yarnell and Black 1985). Strong arguments based on observations of morphological changes in seeds have been made to include erect knotweed (*Polygonum erectum* L.) as a fifth member of this group (Fritz 1987 in Smith 1992). Completing the suite of indigenous plants now generally viewed as constituting the basis of pre-maize Native American plant husbandry in much of the East are the cultigens maygrass (*Phalaris caroliniana* Walt.) and little barley (*Hordeum pusillum* L.) (Cowan 1978b; Fritz 1995; Smith 1992).

In short, we have come to realize that prehistoric Native American agriculture in eastern North America was a complex process, long-evolving, and based at first on several indigenous rather than introduced plants. We now have the data to support the notion that the Eastern Woodlands was an independent center of plant domestication and that the maize-beans-squash triad, which once commonly defined all Native American plant husbandry (and probably still does among the public-at-large), was added incrementally to a system of clearing, planting, cultivating, harvesting, processing, and storing plant foods that had begun 1,000 years earlier. It has also now been documented that Native American plant husbandry in eastern North America did not develop uniformly but rather evolved to reflect the region's diversity of environmental, social, and cultural conditions, resulting in a highly intricate mosaic of localized phenomena. Much of the effort in paleoethnobotanical work currently being undertaken in the Northeast is directed at defining this mosaic by first identifying plant remains recovered from securely dated, culturally meaningful contexts and then assessing evidence of spatial and temporal patterning.

For several reasons, sunflower is likely to be an important element in this work in the Northeast, much as it was twenty years ago when issues pertaining to subsistence change and agricultural origins became research priorities in the Midwest and Southeast. First, because of their relatively large size, sunflower seeds are readily recoverable via flotation, assuming adequate preservation. Second, Yarnell (1978) has shown that it is possible to assess the domestication status of particular specimens by simply measuring the lengths and widths of seeds and achenes. Third, as one of the few domesticated plants whose wild progenitor still exists in nature, sunflower is particularly well suited to recently developed DNA-based analyses that make it possible to determine the degrees of relatedness among specific populations of biological organisms. These studies, in turn, have already been used to provide new data relevant to the mechanisms of domestication as well as the origins and subsequent movements of sunflower throughout North America (Arias and Rieseberg 1995; Bretting 1990; Heiser 1951:432; Rieseberg et al. 1996; Rieseberg and Seiler 1990).

As interest in the recovery and analysis of plant remains from archaeological sites increases in the Northeast, so do reports of the occurrences of sunflower. Although the number of occurrences is small and the picture is still very preliminary, a pattern is developing. The purpose of this paper is to report the presence of sunflower seeds and achenes recovered from a series of seventeenth-century Seneca Iroquois sites in Western New York and to offer some interpretation of their significance. To establish a framework for interpreting these materials, this chapter presents a brief summary of sunflower botany; a consideration of the ethnohistorical record pertaining to sunflower cultivation and use in the Northeast; and a discussion of the reported occurrence of sunflower in archaeological sites throughout eastern North America. The Seneca Iroquois materials are then described with regard to both their physical attributes and the archaeological contexts from which they were recovered, and interpretations of their occurrences are offered.

## SUNFLOWER BOTANY

The sunflower is a member of the Asteraceae or Composite Family, the largest family of flowering plants with about 1,535 currently accepted genera and some 23,000 species (Bremer 1994:13). The family is widely distributed except in the Antarctic mainland and is especially well represented in the semiarid regions of the tropics and subtropics; the woodland, wooded grassland, grassland, and bushlands of Africa, South America, and Australia; and the arctic, arctic-alpine, temperate, and montane floras throughout the world. It is poorly represented only in tropical rain forests (Heywood 1993:263). Besides sunflower, other economically important members of the family include lettuces, artichokes, artemisias, chrysanthemums, daisies, and dahlias.

The family is undergoing taxonomic revision in response to recent discoveries in biochemistry, micromorphology, anatomy, and cytology, and assignments from tribes through species are in a state of flux. Bremer (1994) has used an arrangement employing three subfamilies and 17 tribes that places sunflower within the subfamily Asteroideae and the tribe Heliantheae. The latter contains 35 subtribes, 189 genera, and nearly 2,500

species, most of which are native to the New World (Karis 1993). The genus *Helianthus* L. contains about 50 species of annual and perennial herbs (Rieseberg et al. 1991:50), all native to North America. Twenty-one species are reported as occurring within the broadly defined northeastern United States and adjacent Canada (Gleason and Cronquist 1991:527-529). The genus is typically divided into four sections: *Helianthus, Agrestes* Schilling and Heiser, *Ciliares* Schilling and Heiser, and *Divaricati* Schilling and Heiser (Schilling and Heiser 1981). *Helianthus annuus* is placed in section *Helianthus*. The section includes diploids, tetraploids, and hexaploids, all with the basic chromosome number of x = 17 (Rieseberg et al. 1991:50). *Helianthus annuus* includes not only the domesticated form but also weedy and wild types. Some authors have separated these at the subspecies level, but other schemes have synonymized all forms to *Helianthus annuus* L. All are annuals; all are diploids.

Morphologically, the modern cultivated sunflower is easily distinguished from its wild and weedy relatives. Reflecting intentional human selection, it is typically a much larger plant, it has a single rather than a branched stalk, and it is monocephalic in that it produces a single massive flower head rather than several small ones.[1] This tendency toward single unbranched stalks bearing single very large terminal heads has been dubbed the "sunflower effect" and is seen in many cereals with side seed-bearing branches, including maize, pearl millet, and sorghum (Harlan 1975:127-128). The advantage of such a change to the farmer who wishes to maximize seed production and streamline harvesting is obvious; collecting the seeds from one large head per plant is far easier than collecting from many small heads.[2]

The cultivated form of sunflower produces larger achenes (i.e., the dry fruit which contains a single seed), which are not only more variable in their shapes and color patterns but also tend to remain in the head rather than fall from the plant at maturity, again assisting farmers in harvesting. Lastly, seeds of the domesticated form germinate rapidly and uniformly, whereas those of wild and weedy forms germinate very slowly and unevenly (Heiser 1951:432, 1981:187, 1985:59). That the domesticated sunflower is a diploid suggests that the achene length increased without the involvement of polyploidy and was accomplished solely through gene mutation and human selection.

Heiser (1951, 1965, 1969, 1976, 1985) combined morphological, geographical, and archaeological data in his hypothesis regarding the origin of the domesticated sunflower. He suggested that wild *H. annuus* was used by early humans for food and became a camp-following weed. The taxon's success as a weed was not due to the features that typically characterize weeds (e.g., production of large numbers of small seeds, long-lived seeds, presence of an efficient dispersal mechanism, and self-compatibility), none of which holds for the sunflower; rather the key factor was its great variability, both morphologically and physiologically (Heiser 1965:391-392). Native Americans most likely introduced the plant (accidentally or deliberately) to areas where it came into contact with other annual species of *Helianthus,* and in hybridizing with these species, *H. annuus* acquired genes that allowed it to become adapted to many different regions.

Heiser has posited that humans were also responsible for bringing the weedy sunflower to the Midwest, but that introgression may not have played so important a role in sunflower's actual domestication, which took place there. A form with a large number of recessive genes, as the modified weedy annual *H. annuus* would have had, would be most easily domesticated where wild sunflowers were not abundant, a condition met in the Midwest. After its domestication, sunflower was carried both to the East and Southwest.

Recent studies of genetic variation as evidenced in isozymes and chloroplast DNA of numerous sunflower accessions have supported Heiser's hypothesis (Rieseberg and Seiler 1990). It has been determined that wild and domesticated *H. annuus* are very similar in their enzymatic and chloroplast DNA sequences, and domesticated *H. annuus* has been found to contain a subset of the alleles and chloroplast DNAs found in the wild forms. The extensive polymorphism in the wild plants and the virtual monomorphism in cultivat-

ed lines further suggest a single origin of the domesticated sunflower from a very limited gene pool; in other words, the domesticated sunflower originated only once. These studies have also shown that Native American varieties of the domesticated sunflower were genetically more variable than other cultivated lines, suggesting that they gave rise to other cultivated stocks. Molecular evidence has not, however, allowed a determination of the exact geographic origin of the domesticated sunflower.

Other studies of randomly amplified polymorphic DNA (RAPD) loci for sunflower accessions have not only confirmed the origin of domesticated sunflower as from wild *H. annuus,* but have also quantified degrees of relatedness between and among certain Native American varieties, old landraces, and modern cultivars (Arias and Rieseberg 1995). Not surprisingly, Native American varieties and old landraces form a genetically cohesive group, whereas modern cultivars are not genetically cohesive. The cohesiveness of the former is attributed to their origin prior to the use of interspecific hybridization in the development of sunflower cultivars.

## NATIVE AMERICANS AND SUNFLOWERS

Historic reports of the Native American use of sunflower, both wild and domesticated, are fairly numerous. Seeds of the wild form were gathered for food by Native Americans in Idaho, Wyoming, Utah, and New Mexico (Heiser 1951:432). The seeds were variously eaten raw; pounded with other substances and made into flat cakes that were dried in the sun; and roasted, ground into a flour, and then made into cakes or mush. Alternatively, they were ground to a paste and then rolled into balls for travel food. Roasted hulls were boiled to produce a coffee-like beverage. There are records of the Hopi using the purple pigment (anthocyanin) of seed husks as a dye for coloring earthenware, basketry, and skin. The Blackfoot used oil from the seed as a hair ointment, and certain Southwest groups used the petals and pollen to make face paint.

Moerman (1986:217-218) included *Helianthus*

species in his compendium of medicinal plant use by Native Americans. Using preparations of the plant to treat snake bite has been recorded for the Apache and the Zuni. The Dakota employed the flowers as an analgesic and as a pulmonary aid. Wild forms have been documented as used in ceremonial medicine and as a stimulant by the Gros Ventres, the Mandans, and the Rees. The Hopi and the Ramah Navaho used the plant as a dermatological aid. Navaho used the seeds as a dietary aid "to give appetite" (Moerman 1986:217). There are reports of the Kayenta Navaho using sunflower as a ceremonial medicine, a disinfectant, and as a pediatric aid, the latter two relating to prenatal infections brought about by solar eclipses (Wyman and Harris 1951:48). Other recorded Native American uses of the sunflower include as an antirheumatic (Paiute), a gynecological aid (Pawnee), an anthelmintic (Pima), a febrifuge (Pima), a veterinary aid (Pima), and dermatological aid in treating sores and swellings (Thompson Indians).

In the Northeast, all reports of the taxon refer to the domesticated form. In 1615, Champlain observed the cultivated sunflower at a village with 200 large cabins near what is now Loretto, Canada.

> [The country] is very extensively cleared up. They plant in it a great quantity of Indian corn, which grows there finely. They plant likewise squashes, and sunflowers, from the seed of which they make oil, with which they anoint the head [Champlain 1907 (1604-18):284].

In his *Resa til Norra America*, Pehr Kalm, the Swedish naturalist, noted that in 1750, Native Americans cultivated sunflower in maize fields (Kalm 1966 [1937]).

A century and a half later, Waugh reiterated both the use of the oil in anointing and the cultivation of the crop in maize fields.

> The sunflower … was frequently cultivated, either together with corn and beans, or in patches by itself, and fur-

nished an oil which was highly esteemed. The Hurons and Iroquois generally are said to have sown but little of it, though they made from it an oil "to annoint [*sic*] themselves."

> The oil was said, by a Mohawk informant, to have been made by roasting the seeds slightly, then pounding them in a mortar, after which the material was boiled and the oil skimmed off.

> The oil, at present, is used principally for ceremonial purposes, such as the anointing of the masks used by the Falseface society. It was also stated by Chief Gibson to be good for the hair and to prevent it from falling out or changing colour [Waugh 1916:78].

These same themes occur in Jenness' description of early twentieth-century Iroquois agriculture.

> Although the Iroquoian tribes subsisted very largely on maize, they raised also beans and squashes … In the same fields they often planted the sunflower, which yielded an oil esteemed by the Indians of Virginia for making bread and soup, but by the Iroquois mainly as an ointment [Jenness 1934:40-41].

Heiser cited a letter dated March 9, 1948, from Col. E.P. Rendle, Indian Superintendent at Brantford, Canada, as stating that

> generations of Iroquoian tribes [had] used oil of sunflower achenes for dressing their hair at tribal ceremonies conducted during the special festival they have at the planting season. Sunflower seeds were also used in the False Face ceremonies, during which they were roasted over a fire, then pounded and cooked with roasted white corn, sweetened with maple sugar, and used in somewhat the same way we use lard. It

was also used for medicinal purposes particularly for bad coughs [Heiser 1951:433-435].

In his *Iroquois Uses of Maize and Other Food Plants*, Arthur Parker described the process by which Iroquois isolated sunflower oil.

> Sunflower oil was used in quantities by the Iroquois, with whom it was a favorite food oil. It was prepared by bruising the ripe seed in a mortar, heating the mass for a half hour and then throwing it into boiling water until most of the oil had been separated from the pulp. The water was cooled and strained and then the oil skimmed off [Parker 1968:102].

In sum, it appears that historic Native American relationships with sunflower in the West focused on use of the wild plant as food and medicine. In the Northeast, the focus was on the cultivated form as a source of oil used primarily in ceremonial contexts and to a lesser extent as food.

## ARCHAEOLOGICAL SUNFLOWER

Over the past two decades, much information about sunflower husbandry has come to light as the result of archaeological investigations incorporating flotation and paleoethnobotany in their research designs. The oldest remains of domesticated sunflower reported to date are carbonized seeds from the Hayes site, a stratified multicomponent Archaic period site in the central Duck River valley in Tennessee. Six complete seeds were recovered, and one of these yielded an accelerator date of 4,265 ± 60 B.P. (Crites 1993). Table 3.1 summarizes the results of a survey of the published reports of sunflower seeds and achenes recovered from archaeological sites in the Eastern Woodlands.

It may be instructive to consider the locations of archaeological sites from which domesticated sunflower seeds and achenes have been recovered by date. Figure 3.1 depicts the locations

**Figure 3.1** Sunflower recovered from archaeological contexts dating to 2,300 B.C.-A.D. 200: (1) Salts Cave; (2) Mammoth Cave; (3) Cloudsplitter; (4) Newt Kash Hollow; (5) Higgs; (6) Rose Island; (7) Big Bone Cave; (8) Hayes; (9) Marble Bluff; (10) Napoleon Hollow; (11) Riverton.

of such sites dating to between 2,300 B.C. and A.D. 200. There is a clustering in the Midcontinent with Marble Bluff and Napoleon Hollow on the west and Cloudsplitter, Newt Kash Hollow, Higgs, and Rose Island on the east.

A plot of sites that have produced sunflower dating to between A.D. 200 and A.D. 900 (Figure 3.2) illustrates an expansion from this core area into Iowa, Missouri, Indiana, and Ohio. Included are Iowa's Hadfields Cave, a series of upland sites corresponding to the Prairie Peninsula in western Illinois, several sites excavated as part of the FAI-270 Project in the American Bottom, a series of Ozark Plateau rockshelters, and the Waterplant and Zencor sites in Ohio.

Yet further expansion is noted when we examine the locations of sites producing sunflowers dating to between A.D. 900 and A.D. 1700 (Figure 3.3). In the north, the margin extends to Wisconsin and New York; in the east, it stretches to Connecticut; and one seed has been recovered

**Table 3.1. Sunflower Seeds and Achenes Recovered from Selected Eastern Woodland Archaeological Sites.**

| Site Name | Associated Date | Reference |
|---|---|---|
| Hayes | 2,300 B.C. | Crites 1993 |
| Riverton | 1,250 B.C. | Yarnell 1993 |
| Higgs | 900 B.C. | Shea (Yarnell 1978) |
| Marble Bluff | 893 B.C. | Fritz 1993 |
| Cloudsplitter | 840 B.C. | Cowan 1985 |
| Newt Kash Hollow | 650 B.C. | Jones 1936, Cowan (Yarnell 1978) |
| Salts Cave | 650-250 B.C. | Yarnell 1978 |
| Mammoth Cave | 650-250 B.C. | Yarnell 1978 |
| Rose Island | 300 B.C.-A.D. 200 | Yarnell 1993 |
| Big Bone Cave | 227 B.C. | Yarnell 1993 |
| Napoleon Hollow | 200 B.C. | Yarnell 1993 |
| Owl Hollow Phase sites | A.D. 200-600 | Crites 1978 |
| Hadfields Cave | A.D. 300-400 | Benn 1980 |
| Haystack Rockshelter | A.D. 400-700 | Cowan 1978a, 1979 |
| Mund | A.D. 500-600 | Johannessen 1983 |
| Boyd | A.D. 500 | Yarnell 1978 |
| Rogers | A.D. 500-700 | Cowan (Yarnell 1978) |
| Waterplant | A.D. 500 | Wymer 1987, 1993 |
| Zencor | A.D. 750 | Wymer 1987, 1993 |
| Range | A.D. 600-900 | Johannessen 1987, 1993 |
| Old Monroe | A.D. 700-900 (est.) | Pulliam 1987 |
| Dohack | A.D. 800-850 | Johannessen 1985, 1993 |
| Memorial Park | A.D. 881-1404 | Hart and Asch Sidell 1996 |
| Sand Ridge | A.D. 900 | Featherstone 1977 (Johannessen 1993) |
| Leonard Haag | A.D. 900 | Reidhead 1976, 1980 |
| BBB Motor | A.D. 950-1100 | Whalley 1984, Johannessen 1993 |
| 36Ti58 | A.D. 900-1300 | Gardner 1993b |
| Gnagey | A.D. 1000-1250 | King et al. 1994 |
| Sponemann | A.D. 1050-1100 | Johannessen 1993 |
| Turner | A.D. 1050-1150 | Whalley 1983 |
| Fred Edwards | A.D. 1050-1150 | Arzigian 1987 |
| Julien | A.D. 1150-1400 | Johannessen 1984 |
| Hill Creek | A.D. 1200 | King 1993 |
| McJunkin | A.D. 1250-1550 | King et al. 1994 |
| Morton | A.D. 1250-1550 | King 1993 |
| Turner-Snodgrass | A.D. 1300 | L. Blake (Yarnell 1978) |
| Burnham-Shepard | A.D. 1300-1450 | Bendremer and Dewar 1994 |
| Brompton 2 | A.D. 1500 | Gardner 1993a |
| Sony | A.D. 1550-Contact | King et al. 1994 |
| Zimmerman | Historic Period | King 1993 |
| St. Augustine | 17th century | Ruhl 1993 |

**Figure 3.2** Sunflower recovered from archaeological contexts dating to A.D. 200-900: (1) Leonard Haag; (2) Waterplant; (3) Zencor; (4) Sand Ridge; (5) Haystack Rockshelter; (6) Owl Hollow phase sites; (7) Ozark Plateau rockshelter sites; (8) Mund; (9) Range; (10) Dohack; (11) Old Monroe; (12) Prairie Peninsula upland sites; (13) Hadfields Cave.

**Figure 3.3** Sunflower recovered from archaeological contexts dating to A.D. 900-1700: (1) Brompton 2; (2) Seneca Iroquois sites; (3) Burnham-Shepard; (4) Memorial Park; (5) 36Ti58; (6) Gnagey; (7) McJunkin; (8) Sony; (9) St. Augustine; (10) Radic; (11) BBB Motor; (12) Range; (13) Sponemann; (14) Hill Creek; (15) Morton; (16) Zimmerman; (17) Fred Edwards.

from St. Augustine in Florida.

Many of the sites in the Northeast have produced fewer than five seeds; in fact, one or two is typically the case. An exception is the Burnham-Shepard site in Connecticut from which 34 seeds were recovered from a lined storage pit (Bendremer and Dewar 1994).

Throughout the time spanned by these sites, there has been a general tendency toward increased achene size. This increase is interpreted as the result of human selection pressure in favor of larger seeds. Yarnell (1978) quantified size distribution in wild, ruderal, and cultigen sunflower achenes, and these breaks are followed by most analysts in determining the status of archaeological sunflower specimens. Achenes of wild forms generally fall between 3.0 and 5.5 mm; those of ruderal forms measure between 4.0 and 7.0 mm; and fruits of cultivated sunflower measure anywhere from 6.3 to over 20 mm in length by 3.2 to

over 12.0 mm in width. Because carbonized seeds and achenes have undergone shrinkage, most researchers convert their measurements of these materials to those of uncarbonized achenes and seeds. Again, following Yarnell (1978), this is done for carbonized achenes by multiplying the length x 1.11 and the width x 1.27. For carbonized seeds the length is multiplied by 1.30 and the width by 1.45. Table 3.2 demonstrates the range of variation in size that has been documented for archaeological sunflower achenes in the Eastern Woodlands.

## SENECA IROQUOIS SUNFLOWER

The primary purpose of this section is to report descriptively the existence of archaeological sunflower materials in the Rochester Museum & Science Center's Seneca Iroquois collections. What follows is by no means a complete accounting of

**Table 3.2. Measurements of Sunflower Achenes Recovered from Eastern Woodland Sites.[a]**

| Site Name | Associated Date | Length (mm) | Width (mm) |
|---|---|---|---|
| Hayes | 2,300 B.C. | 5.7-7.4 | 2.2-3.8 |
| Higgs | 900 B.C. | 5.7-10.1 | 1.8-4.2 |
| Marble Bluff | 893 B.C. | 8.8-9.3 | —— |
| Newt Kash Hollow | 650 B.C. | 7.0-11.1 | 3.0-4.2 |
| Salts Cave | 650-250 B.C. | 5.3-9.8 | 2.2-4.8 |
| Mammoth Cave | 650-250 B.C. | 5.1-12.4 | 2.3-5.7 |
| Haystack Rockshelter | A.D. 500-700 | 9.0 | 4.0 |
| Boyd | A.D. 500 | 5.9-8.4 | 2.3-3.1 |
| Rogers | A.D. 500-700 | 6.6-10.0 | 3.0-5.0 |
| Memorial Park[b] | A.D. 881-1404 | 3.9 | 1.7 |
| 36Ti58[b] | A.D. 900-1300 | 3.9-7.0 | 2.5-3.2 |
| Turner-Snodgrass | A.D. 1300 | 10.5-13.1 | 4.5-5.7 |
| Burnham-Shepard | A.D. 1300-1450 | 7.3 | —— |
| Brompton 2 | A.D. 1500 | 5.8 (incompl.) | 3.6 |

*Notes*

[a] These measurements have not been adjusted to reflect shrinkage due to carbonization.

[b] These are seeds, not achenes.

all the sunflower material in these collections, although making such an accounting is certainly a long-term goal. Rather, these discoveries were made in the course of efforts to identify specific sets of archaeobotanical materials recovered from a series of Historic Period Seneca sites as part of the Seneca Archaeology Research Project (Wray et al. 1987, 1991). The sites occur south and east of Rochester in the Genesee region of Western New York (Figure 3.4), and they are believed to represent the remains of Seneca Iroquois villages dating from A.D. 1540 to 1687.[3] The sites are also thought to represent eastern and western "sequences" of inhabited villages. This notion of sequence is based on the thesis that two principal Seneca villages coexisted simultaneously from at least the latter half of the sixteenth century through the end of the seventeenth century, and that these villages were abandoned and relocated approximately every twenty years (Wray et al. 1987:2). Most of the material in these collections, both botanical and artifactual, was donated to the Museum; very little of it was excavated in accordance with current professional archaeological standards.

Nevertheless, the collection has considerable value, to which the information presented here will attest, and its documentation and analysis are worthwhile endeavors.

The Seneca Archaeology Research Project has proceeded in a chronological fashion, starting with the materials from the oldest sites. Most of the archaeobotanical materials examined to date have consisted of berry seeds, squash seeds, gourd fragments, maize, beans, wood charcoal, bark, and nutshell. A collection of sunflower seeds from the Fugle site, which dates to about A.D. 1615, provided a new taxon for the Seneca sequence and prompted a search for comparative data. Because reports of archaeological sunflower in Northeast sites were uncommon, it appeared appropriate to review the RMSC collections in greater detail to determine what other, if any, sunflower materials they might contain.

A cursory examination of the collections, only some of which have been inventoried and next to none of which have been examined by a paleoethnobotanist, revealed that sunflower achenes had been collected from at least seven Seneca

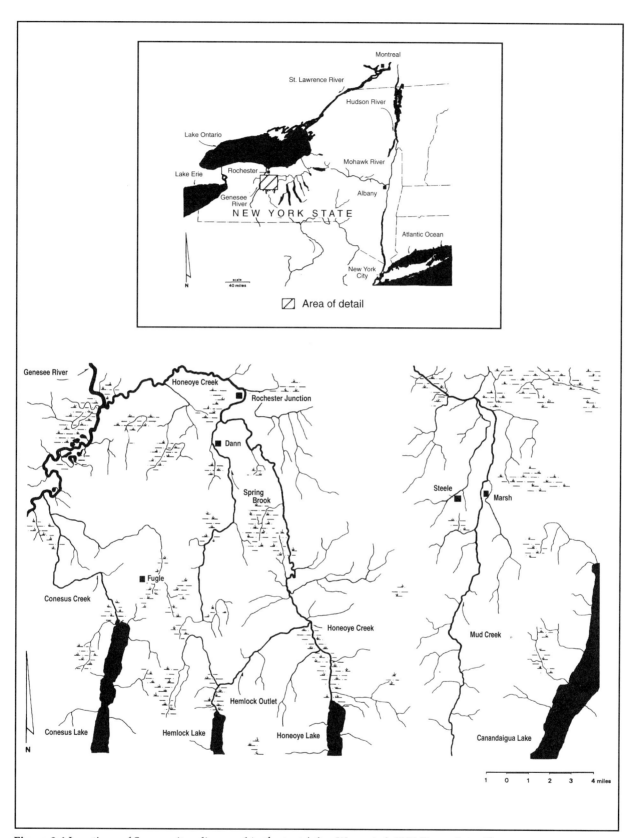

**Figure 3.4** Locations of Seneca sites discussed in the text (after Wray et al. 1991:Figure Intro-2).

Iroquois region sites, which range in date from A.D. 1520 to A.D. 1715 (Figures 3.5 and 3.6). Numbers of sunflower achenes per site vary, but with the exception of the Alhart site, common to all are their proveniences within burials, reflecting a bias in collection technique as well as in preservation. Many uncarbonized achenes were found in brass kettles and were preserved because of it. Table 3.3 shows the ranges of achene length and width measurements by site, and documents a general tendency toward larger achene sizes through time.

For many of these sunflower samples, there is virtually no information on provenience other than the collector's name. In other cases, we know more. For example, some of the Alhart site (RMSC 202/305; RMSC 72/305) (A.D. 1520) material came from a circular, round-bottomed feature interpreted as a roasting pit from which fire-cracked rock, carbonized hickory nuts, beans, maize, and squash seeds were also recovered. Alhart is interpreted as a small Iroquoian agricultural village that was destroyed by a major fire in the fall or early winter. The presence of skeletal material exhibiting signs of severe trauma suggest that the village may have been purposely set on fire, perhaps in connection with a raid by an outside (and probably Iroquoian) group.

The 14 Fugle site (RMSC 10266/95) (A.D. 1615) sunflower achenes are from a burial and were associated with a plum pit, squash seeds, and strawberry seeds, but nothing else is known about their context.

Three collections of sunflower achenes were made at the Steele site (A.D. 1650), but only one (RMSC 12722/100) has associated information. These achenes were found in a small woven basket within a brass kettle associated with the burial of a 12-14 year old. Nearby were a section of a wooden ladle; hematite; fish and bird bone; an iron knife, a large shell bead; several frog skeletons, a large quantity of wampum beads; feathers; and two sets of deer legs. Larger collections have been assigned accession numbers RMSC 12254/100 and RMSC 525/100.

Two collections of sunflower achenes were recovered from the Dann site (A.D. 1660), but again, information is available for only one of

them (RMSC 3103/28). This collection was from a small brass kettle in the disturbed burial of a small child or infant. Beneath the kettle was a trade blanket fragment, and nearby were a pewter spoon and porringer. The burial had been previously disturbed. The second collection has neither an accession number nor any contextual information other than site name.

Achenes from the Marsh site (RMSC 1796/99) (A.D. 1660) are probably from the disturbed burial of an adult. Also associated with this burial were a large brass kettle containing two iron knives, an iron awl, a wooden ladle, and a canoe-shaped tray. Archaeobotanical materials included a quantity of bark, squash seeds, and what the notes list as "the usual verdigris of preserved organic materials."

Sunflower achenes from the Rochester Junction site (RMSC 740/29) (A.D. 1680) are of uncertain provenience, although they may have come from a brass kettle associated with the group burial of three children.

Finally, sunflower achenes were recovered from the surface of the Townley Read site (RMSC 6503/160) (A.D. 1715), which must have been disturbed only very shortly before the find was made. The achenes were located within a small brass kettle which appeared to have been plowed from the burial of a 10-12 year old. Also present were glass seed beads; catlinite beads, pipe, and pendant; a glass mirror; and brass finger rings.

In total, this very quick survey resulted in the documentation of 1,672 sunflower achenes and the measurement of 140 of them. Most of the achenes were uncarbonized, all were domesticated, and all but 16 came from burial contexts.

## INTERPRETATION

When we attempt to compare the Seneca sunflower with material from other archaeological sites in the Eastern Woodlands, we are immediately faced with several interpretive problems. First, the contexts of these materials are unusual in that most are from burials, whereas sunflower reported elsewhere is not. Sunflowers placed in a burial presumably reflect a ritual and/or spiritual con-

**Figure 3.5** Sunflower achenes recovered from the Alhart, Fugle, and Steele sites.

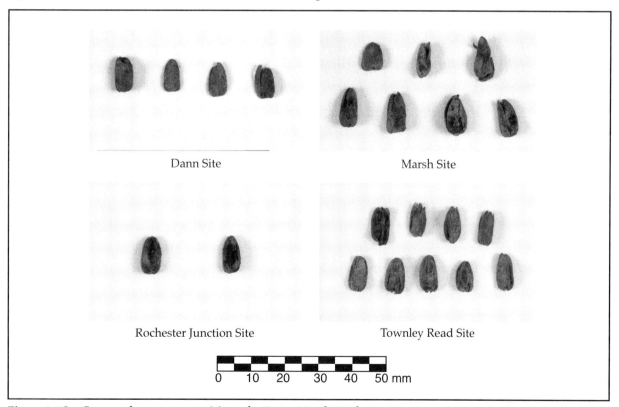

**Figure 3.6** Sunflower achenes recovered from the Dann, Marsh, Rochester Junction, and Townley Read sites.

**Table 3.3. Measurements of Sunflower Achenes Recovered from Seneca Iroquois Sites.**

| Site Name | Site Numbers | Catalogue Number | Approximate Date of Site Occupation | Date Reference | Total No. Achenes | No. Achenes Measured | Range Length (mm) | Range Width (mm) |
|---|---|---|---|---|---|---|---|---|
| Alhart | RMSC Bgn 015 Wray 305 | 202/305 72/305 | A.D. 1520 | a | 13 3 | 13 3 | 6.7-9.4 11.0-12.0 | 3.2-4.8 5.5-6.0 |
| Fugle | RMSC Hne 032 Wray 95 | 10266/95 | A.D. 1615 | b | 13 | 13 | 7.5-9.5 | 3.0-5.0 |
| Steele | RMSC Can 008 Wray 100 | 12722/100 12254/100 525/100 | A.D. 1650 | b | 31 40 1384 | 22 23 48 | 7.5-11.0 8.0-11.0 8.0-12.0 | 4.0-6.0 4.0-6.0 3.0-6.0 |
| Dann | RMSC Hne 003 Wray 28 | 3103/28 No # | A.D. 1660 | b | 5 3 | 3 2 | 9.1-9.8 10.5-11.0 | 4.8-5.5 4.5-5.0 |
| Marsh | RMSC Can 007 Wray 99 | 1796/99 | A.D. 1660 | b | 11 | 4 | 9.0-11.0 | 5.0-6.0 |
| Rochester Junction | RMSC Hne 011 Wray 29 | 740/29 | A.D. 1680 | b | 2 | 2 | 10.5 | 5.0-5.5 |
| Townley Read | RMSC Plp 016 Wray 160 | 6503/160 | A.D. 1715 | c | 164 | 7 | 9.8-10.0 | 4.0-5.5 |

*Date References*

a: Date based upon three radiocarbon age determinations on materials excavated from the Alhart site by Rochester Museum & Science Center archaeologists in 1976. The uncorrected dates normalized for 13C are 405 ± 75 B.P. (I-9774); 415 ± 75 B.P. (I-9775); and 480 ± 75 B.P. (I-9776) (Teledyne Isotopes).

b: Date based upon the chronology of eastern and western Seneca site sequences proposed by Wray et al. (1991:5).

c: Date based upon an assessment of the European artifacts recovered from the site.

notation, while those from a habitation midden or storage pit signify only that the plant was used and/or stored. Unless all possible contexts are sampled, it is very difficult to assess the relative cultural importance of the plant between and among sites.

Second, the numbers are small for absolute counts of achenes as well as types of archaeological contexts, which renders almost any statistical treatment of the data inappropriate. Third, the time span covered by the Seneca materials is very restricted. There is a maximum spread of 195 years, and most of this material dates to a 100-year period.

Looking at our nearest neighbors does little to help us with regard to either absolute numbers or time depth. The single achene found at Brompton 2 in Amherst, New York, is associated with a date of A.D. 1500, and the 74 charred sunflower seeds that Monckton (1992) reported from historic Huron villages date to the same general time period. The problems of context, sample size, and temporal span will most assuredly be alleviated when numerous achenes are available from a wide variety of sites in each kind of context spread over a long period of time, but accumulating such data may be a slow process.

For now, there is a significant gap of some 3,800 years between the time sunflower appears as a domesticated plant in Tennessee and the time it appears as a grave offering in New York. The question is what underlies the apparent discontinuities in time and space that seem to characterize sunflower in the Midcontinent and the Northeast, or more explicitly, Iroquoia?

1. One possible answer is that there is no real discontinuity, but rather what we are seeing is simply a function of inadequate recovery techniques in archaeology. After all, one does not find what one does not seek. If this is the correct explanation, then the problem will soon fade, because we are getting better at looking.

2. Alternatively, the apparent discontinuity may be due to inadequate reporting. That too is being alleviated as paleoethnobotany becomes part of mainstream archaeology in the Northeast and as the opportunities for disseminating the results of our work increase in number.

3. A third possible answer to our question is that the different patterns of deposition we see on archaeological sites are the result of significantly different plant use. The ethnohistorical accounts of sunflower among Iroquoians indicate that sunflower was valued for its oil which was used in rituals. Mention of sunflower as a food plant is nearly incidental and relatively late. Clearly, this distinguishes the Iroquoian usage of sunflower from that of western Native Americans, who used the wild form for food, and from that of Midcontinent groups, among whom sunflower was one of a suite of cultivated crops that collectively supported populations long before maize was known. If this is true, then we would expect sunflower to appear less frequently in routine food- and/or storage-related contexts at Iroquois sites. The validity of this explanation can be better evaluated once there are more recoveries of sunflower from good contexts at securely dated sites, but in the meantime, this is something to consider.

4. A fourth explanation for the apparent discontinuities in time and space characterizing sunflower distributions might be simple time lag. After all, groups living in the Midwest and Southeast simply became agricultural a long time before Iroquoian groups, and so naturally we would not expect to see something like sunflower until much later in time (ca. A.D. 1000-1400) when agriculture became the predominant subsistence mode. This answer is short, simple, straightforward–and worrisome. It might be the most comfortable answer in the tradition of the "Three Sisters" understanding of Iroquois agriculture, but it most likely masks some of the complexities which we now know characterize human-plant interrelationships. Furthermore, a failure to consider the true nature of Iroquois agricultural systems may well obfuscate details germane to the understanding of diffusion and migration issues relating to Iroquoian people, plants, or both. We should scrutinize every detail and carefully evaluate each possibility before accepting any explanation, especially simplistic ones.

One such issue that we may be wise to consider in this regard pertains to the divers relationships between sunflower and maize that occur in the Eastern Woodlands. The ethnohistorical accounts of sunflower among Iroquoians indicate that sunflower was typically grown in Iroquois maize fields rather than in separate plots. This distinguishes the Iroquoian case from that of the Midcontinent where the crops were separated in time and thus in space, at least early on. Yarnell (1978) and Johannessen (1993) have noted that sunflower was less common after the intensification of maize agriculture in the Midcontinent, which suggests a segregation of some sort later as well. We may never know precisely when or if it was ever common practice to cultivate maize and sunflower together in the Midcontinent, but current data suggest that for the first 2,200 years of sunflower cultivation, it was not even a possibility, and for the last 400 years prior to the Contact period, it was not common. In contrast, to date, there have been no instances reported of domesticated sunflower recovered *without* maize in Iroquoia.

Why might Iroquoians have grown sunflower and maize in the same field? A hint comes from a look at current agribusiness in the U.S. Corn-belt farmers today are good customers of that segment of the agrochemical industry which is geared toward the production of herbicides that kill sunflowers. A known mangler of combines, sunflower is one of the most serious weeds in maize.[4] It is next to impossible to detect because its similar germination time and its upright, unbranched habit allow it to successfully masquerade as a maize plant until it flowers, and by then the maize is tall enough to hide the sunflower. In addition, the growth requirements of the two plants are nearly identical. Home gardeners are advised to plant sunflower at the same time they plant their maize, in the same kind of soil, to water it with the same intensity and at the same frequency, and to provide it with the same drainage. Biologically and ecologically, maize and sunflower make good companion plants.[5]

Thus, it is possible that sunflower and maize were coincidentally linked in the Iroquois region as companion plants, perhaps something akin to a crop-weed pair in which the weed turned out to be valuable for a purpose other than food. Alternatively, the two cultigens might have been linked as part of an established agricultural pattern that was diffused as an intact unit into Iroquoia from elsewhere. Just as we have identified discontinuities between the Iroquoian and Midcontinent uses and cultivation practices associated with sunflowers, perhaps there is an as-yet unidentified place in which uses and cultivation practices are similar to that observed in Iroquoia. It is certainly something of which we should be aware as we continue to recover, analyze, and interpret archaeobotanical remains from increasing numbers of sites.

## CONCLUSION

Surely, among the most interesting and thought-provoking intellections to emerge from the analysis of the large body of paleoethnobotanical data produced in the Eastern Woodlands over the past two decades have been the realization that numerous processes were at work in agricultural systems at any one time and that this resulted in considerable regional variation. In the Northeast, the convergence of the increasingly frequent incorporation of paleoethnobotany in archaeological research designs with the recent resurrection of Northern Iroquoian migration vs. in situ development debate is particularly fortunate.

Snow's (1995) argument for links among horticulture, matrilocality, migration, and compact villages, in connection with an hypothesis that Northern Iroquoians migrated into the lower Great Lakes region sometime after A.D. 900, has been effectively countered by Crawford and Smith (1996), who used paleoethnobotanical data from their work on the Princess Point Complex in southern Ontario as their first line of evidence (see also Crawford et al. 1997). Snow (1996) has subsequently revised his hypothesis and suggested that the migration took place some three centuries earlier than he had first proposed with agriculture still identified as an factor of major significance. We all stand to benefit from the fertile dialog that has begun here.

As has been the case so often elsewhere in the world, it is very likely that securely dated plant remains from culturally meaningful archaeological contexts will be important in the evaluation of these and other migration and diffusion hypotheses in Iroquoian studies. Clearly, we must strive to define Iroquoian agricultural systems in as much detail as possible (Harris 1994). We must resist the temptation to generalize where we should not and make an attempt not to "transplant" the model of Midcontinent prehistoric agriculture, as interesting as it is, into our area where it might not be appropriate. It is unlikely that agriculture was developed indigenously in the Northeast as it was in the Midcontinent, and we should follow the example set by Smith and Crawford (1993) at the commencement of their Princess Point work by focusing upon crop acquisition mechanisms and the body of theory relating to secondary agricultural origins. We must look beyond (or perhaps more accurately, "behind") Three Sisters agriculture to consider each taxon and each element of each agricultural system independently and then try to determine what patterns are in evidence and what they might mean for larger culture-historical issues. Sunflower, today as twenty years ago, is very likely to help us find our way.

## ACKNOWLEDGEMENTS

I thank Martha Sempowski, Lorraine Saunders, Charles F. Hayes III, and the anonymous reviewer for reading and commenting on earlier drafts of this paper. Figure 3.4 is based on a map originally drafted by Patricia L. Miller of PM Design, Portsmouth, New Hampshire.

## END NOTES

1. Recent efforts in breeding garden varieties of sunflower, however, have been aimed toward the development of cultivars with numerous smaller heads. The goal here is to produce a maximum number of colorful flowers with little regard for ease in seed harvesting.

2. The monocephalic form is most appropriately viewed as a point on a continuum with wild forms which have never been subjected to human selection on one end and forms which have undergone intensive and intentional human selection on the other. Wilson (1987) related a Hidatsa account of cultivated sunflowers with one large head and several smaller ones on the same stalk. Clearly, such forms lay somewhere between the two extremes.

3. All dates presented here for Seneca sites are in calendar years.

4. This is most common, of course, where maize and sunflower are rotated in the same field.

5. This contrasts with the allelopathy experienced by many plants other than maize growing in the vicinity of sunflowers. Allelopathy is the destruction of plants from the effect of certain toxic chemicals produced and released by other plants.

## REFERENCES CITED

Arias, D. M. and L. H. Rieseberg. 1995. Genetic Relationships among Domesticated and Wild Sunflowers (*Helianthus annuus*, Asteraceae). *Economic Botany* 49:239-248.

Arzigian, C. 1987. The Emergence of Horticultural Economies in Southwestern Wisconsin. In *Emergent Horticultural Economies of the Eastern Woodlands*, edited by W. F. Keegan, pp. 217-242. Center for Archaeological Investigations, Occasional Papers No. 7. Southern Illinois University at Carbondale.

Bendremer, J. C. M., and R. E. Dewar. 1994. The Advent of Prehistoric Maize in New England. In *Corn and Culture in the Prehistoric New World*, edited by S. Johannessen and C. A. Hastorf, pp. 369-393. Westview Press, Boulder.

Benn, D. W. 1980. *Hadfields Cave: A Perspective on Late Woodland Culture in Northeastern Iowa*. Report 13. Office of the State Archaeologist, University of Iowa, Iowa City.

Bremer, K. (editor). 1994. *Asteraceae Cladistics and Classification.* Timber Press, Portland, Oregon.

Bretting, P. K. 1990. New Perspectives on the Origin and Evolution of New World Domesticated Plants: Introduction. *Economic Botany* 44(3 Supplement):1-5.

Champlain, S. de. 1907. [1625]*Voyages of Samuel de Champlain,* 1604-1618,edited by W. L. Grant. Charles Scribner's Sons, New York.

Cowan, C. W. 1978a. Seasonal Nutritional Stress in a Late Woodland Population: Suggestions from Some Eastern Kentucky Coprolites. *Tennessee Anthropologist* 3:117-128.

——————. 1978b. The Prehistoric Use and Distribution of Maygrass in Eastern North America: Cultural and Phytogeographical Implications. In *The Nature and Status of Ethnobotany,* edited by R. I. Ford, pp. 263-288. Anthropological Papers No. 67. Museum of Anthropology, University of Michigan, Ann Arbor.

——————. 1979. Excavations at the Haystack Rockshelters, Powell County, Kentucky. *Midcontinental Journal of Archaeology* 4:3-33.

——————. 1985. Understanding the Evolution of Plant Husbandry in Eastern North America: Lessons from Botany, Ethnography, and Archaeology. In *Prehistoric Food Production in North America,* edited by R. I. Ford, pp. 205-244. Anthropological Papers No. 75. Museum of Anthropology, University of Michigan, Ann Arbor.

Cowan, C. W., and B. D. Smith. 1993. The Wild Gourd of the Ozarks. *The World & I* 8(10):200-205.

Crawford, G. W., and D. G. Smith. 1996. Migration in Prehistory: Princess Point and the Northern Iroquoian Case. *American Antiquity* 61:782-790.

Crawford, G. W., D. G. Smith, and V. E. Bowyer. 1997. Dating the Entry of Corn (*Zea mays*) into the Lower Great Lakes. *American Antiquity* 62:112-119.

Crites, G. D. 1993. Domesticated Sunflower in Fifth Millennium B.P. Temporal Context: New Evidence from Middle Tennessee. *American Antiquity* 58:146-148.

Decker, D. S. 1986. *A Biosystematic Study of Cucurbita pepo.* Unpublished Ph.D. dissertation, Biology Department, Texas A&M University, College Station.

——————. 1988. Origin(s), Evolution, and Systematics of *Cucurbita pepo* (Cucurbitaceae). *Economic Botany* 42:4-15.

Featherstone, B. J. 1977. A Report on the Floral Remains from Two Archaeological Sites in Southwestern Ohio. Paper presented at the 53rd Annual Meeting of the Central States Anthropological Society, Cincinnnati.

Fritz, G. J. 1987. The Trajectory of Knotweed Domestication in Prehistoric Eastern North America. Paper presented at the 10th Annual Conference of the Society of Ethnobiology, Gainesville, Florida.

——————. 1990. Multiple Pathways to Farming in Precontact Eastern North America. *Journal of World Prehistory* 4:387-435.

——————. 1993. Early and Middle Woodland Period Paleoethnobotany. In *Foraging and Farming in the Eastern Woodlands,* edited by C. M. Scarry, pp. 39-56. University Press of Florida, Gainesville.

——————. 1995. New Dates and Data on Early Agriculture: The Legacy of Complex Hunter-Gatherers. *Annals of the Missouri Botanical Garden* 82:3-15.

Fritz, G. M., and B. D. Smith. 1988. Old Collections and New Technology: Documenting the Domestication of Chenopodium in Eastern North America. *Midcontinental Journal of Archaeology* 13:3-27.

Gardner, P. S. 1993a. Carbonized Plant Remains from a Circa A.D. 1500 Western New York Chert Quarry. In *Stage 3 Cultural Resource Investigation of the Brompton 2 Site (UB 2412), Town of Amherst, Erie County, New York* by D. J. Perrelli, F. L. Cowan, and N. R. Herter. Reports of the Archaeological Survey, Volume 25, Number 19, Department of Anthropology, State University of New York at Buffalo, Buffalo.

—————. 1993b. Carbonized Plant Remains from 36Ti58, ca. A.D. 900-1300, Tioga County, Pennsylvania. In *Archaeological Data Recovery: Site 36Ti58*, edited by P. Miller. Archaeological and Historical Consultants, Inc., Centre Hall, Pennsylvania.

Gleason, H. A., and A. Cronquist. 1991. *Manual of Vascular Plants of Northeastern United States and Adjacent Canada*. 2nd edition. The New York Botanical Garden, Bronx.

Harlan, J. R. 1975. *Crops and Man*. American Society of Agronomy Crop Science Society of America, Madison, Wisconsin.

Harris, D. R. 1994. Agricultural Origins, Beginnings and Transitions: The Quest Continues. *Antiquity* 68:873-877.

Hart, J. P., and N. Asch Sidell. 1996. Prehistoric Agricultural Systems in the West Branch of the Susquehanna River Basin, A.D. 800 to A.D. 1350. *Northeast Anthropology* 52:1-30.

Heiser, C. B., Jr. 1951. The Sunflower among the North American Indians. *Proceedings of the American Philosophical Society* 95:432-448.

—————. 1965. Sunflowers, Weeds, and Cultivated Plants. In *The Genetics of Colonizing Species*, edited by H.G. Baker and G. L. Stebbins, pp. 391-401. Academic Press, New York.

—————. 1969. The North American Sunflowers (*Helianthus*). *Memoirs of The Torrey Botanical Club* 22(2).

—————. 1976. *The Sunflower*. University of Oklahoma Press, Norman.

—————. 1981. *Seed to Civilization: The Story of Food*. 2nd edition. W.H. Freeman and Company, San Francisco.

—————. 1985. Some Botanical Considerations of the Early Domesticated Plants North of Mexico. In *Prehistoric Food Production in North America*, edited by R. I. Ford, pp. 57-72. Anthropological Papers No. 75. Museum of Anthropology, University of Michigan, Ann Arbor.

Heywood, V. H. (consulting editor). 1993 *Flowering Plants of the World*. Oxford University Press, New York.

Jenness, D. 1934. *The Indians of Canada*. 2nd edition. National Museum of Canada Bulletin 65. Anthropological Series No. 15.

Johannessen, S. 1983. Plant Remains from the Mund Phase. In *The Mund Site*, by A. C. Fortier, F. A. Finney, and R. B. Lacampagne, pp. 299-318. American Bottom Archaeology FAI-270 Site Reports Volume 5, University of Illinois Press, Urbana.

—————. 1984. Plant Remains from the Julien Site. In *The Julien Site*, by G. R. Milner, pp. 244-273. American Bottom Archaeology FAI-270 Site Reports Volume 7, University of Illinois Press, Urbana.

—————. 1985. Plant Remains. In *The Dohack Site*, by A. B. Stahl, pp. 249-269. American Bottom Archaeology FAI-270 Site Reports Volume 12, University of Illinois Press, Urbana.

—————. 1987. Patrick Phase Plant Remains. In *The Range Site: Archaic through Late Woodland Occupations*, by J. E. Kelly, A. C. Fortier, S. J. Ozuk, and J. A. Williams, pp. 404-416. American Bottom Archaeology FAI-270 Site Reports Volume 16, University of Illinois Press, Urbana.

—————. 1993. Farmers of the Late Woodland. In *Foraging and Farming in the Eastern Woodlands*, edited by C. M. Scarry, pp. 57-77. University Press of Florida, Gainesville.

Jones, V. H. 1936. The Vegetal Remains of Newt Kash Hollow Shelter. In *Rock Shelters in Menifee County*, Kentucky, edited by W. S. Webb and W. D. Funkhouser. University of Kentucky Reports in Archaeology and Anthropology 3(4):147-167.

Karis, P. O. 1993. *Heliantheae* sensu lato (*Asteraceae*), Clades and Classification. *Plant Systematics and Evolution* 188:139-195.

Kalm, P. 1966. [1937] *Peter Kalm's Travels in North America*, the Engilsh version of 1770, revised from the original Swedish and edited by Adolph B. Benson. Dover, New York.

King, F. B. 1993. Climate, Culture, and Oneota Subsistence in Central Illinois. In *Foraging and Farming in the Eastern Woodlands*, edited by C. M. Scarry, pp. 232-254. University Press of Florida, Gainesville.

King, F. B., R. L. George, and C. E. Davis. 1994. Monongahela Subsistence and Maize Usage in Southwestern Pennsylvania. Paper presented at the Ethnobiology Conference, Rochester Museum & Science Center, Rochester, New York.

Moerman, D. E. 1986. *Medicinal Plants of Native America*. 2 vols. Technical Reports No. 19, Research Reports in Ethnobotany Contribution 2. Museum of Anthropology, University of Michigan, Ann Arbor.

Monckton, S. G. 1992. *Huron Paleoethnobotany*. Ontario Archaeological Reports 1. Ontario Heritage Foundation, Toronto.

Parker, A. C. 1968. *Parker on the Iroquois*. Edited with an introduction by W. N. Fenton. Syracuse University Press, Syracuse.

Pulliam, C. B. 1987. Middle and Late Woodland Horticultural Practices in the Western Margin of the Mississippi River Valley. In *Emergent Horticultural Economies of the Eastern Woodlands*, edited by W. F. Keegan, pp. 185-199. Center for Archaeological Investigations, Occasional Papers No. 7. Southern Illinois University at Carbondale.

Reidhead, V. A. 1976. *Optimization and Food Procurement at the Prehistoric Leonard Haag Site, Southeast Indiana: A Linear Programming Approach*. Ph.D. dissertation, Indiana University. University Microfilms, Ann Arbor.

—————. 1980. A Test of an Optimization Model. In *Modeling Change in Prehistoric Subsistence Economies*, edited by T. K. Earle and A. Christenson, pp. 141-186. Academic Press, New York.

Rieseberg, L. H., S. M. Beckstrom-Sternberg, A. Lison, and D. M. Arias. 1991. Phylogenetic and Systematic Inferences from Chloroplast DNA and Isozyme Variation in *Helianthus* sect. *Helianthus* (Asteraceae). *Systematic Botany* 16:50-76.

Rieseberg, L. H., B. Sinervo, C. R. Linder, M. C. Ungerer, and D. M. Arias. 1996. Role of Gene Interactions in Hybrid Speciation: Evidence from Ancient and Experimental Hybrids. *Science* 272:741-745.

Rieseberg, L. H., and G. J. Seiler. 1990 Molecular Evidence and the Origin and Development of the Domesticated Sunflower (*Helianthus annuus*, Asteraceae). *Economic Botany* 44(3 Supplement):79-91.

Ruhl, D. L. 1993. Old Customs and Traditions in New Terrain: Sixteenth- and Seventeenth-Century Archaeobotanical Data from *La Florida*. In *Foraging and Farming in the Eastern Woodlands*, edited by C. M. Scarry, pp. 255-283. University Press of Florida, Gainesville.

Schilling, E. E., and C. B. Heiser. 1981. An Infrageneric Classification of *Helianthus* (Compositae). *Taxon* 30:393-403.

Smith, B. D. 1985. The Role of *Chenopodium* as a Domesticate in Pre-Maize Garden Systems of the Eastern United States. *Southeastern Archaeology* 4:51-72.

—————. 1987. The Economic Potential of *Chenopodium berlandieri* in Prehistoric Eastern North America. *Ethnobiology* 7:29-54.

—————. 1989. Origins of Agriculture in Eastern North America. *Science* 246:1566-1571.

—————. 1992. Prehistoric Plant Husbandry in Eastern North America. In *The Origins of Agriculture: An International Perspective*, edited by C. W. Cowan and P. J. Watson, pp. 101-119. Smithsonian Institution Press, Washington, D.C.

Smith, B. D., and C. W. Cowan. 1987. The Age of Domesticated *Chenopodium* in Prehistoric Eastern North America: New Accelerator Dates from Eastern Kentucky. *American Antiquity* 52:355-357.

Smith, B. D., C. W. Cowan, and M. P. Hoffman. 1992. Is It an Indigene or a Foreigner? In *Rivers of Change: Essays on Early Agriculture*, edited by B. D. Smith, pp. 67-100. Smithsonian Institution Press, Washington, D.C.

Smith, D. G., and G. W. Crawford. 1993. The Origins of Agriculture in Ontario. Paper presented at the 26th Annual Meeting of the Canadian Archaeological Association, Montreal, Quebec.

Snow, D. R. 1995. Migration in Prehistory: The Northern Iroquoian Case. *American Antiquity* 60:59-79.

—————. 1996. More on Migration in Prehistory: Accommodating New Evidence in the Northern Iroquoian Case. *American Antiquity* 61:791-796.

Waugh, F. W. 1916. *Iroquois Foods and Food Preparation*. Geological Survey Memoir 86, Anthropological Series No. 12, Ottawa. (Facsimile edition published by National Museums of Canada in 1973).

Whalley, L. A. 1983. Plant Remains from the Turner Site. In *The Turner and DeMange Sites*, by G. R. Milner, pp. 213-233. American Bottom Archaeology FAI-270 Site Reports Volume 4, University of Illinois Press, Urbana.

—————. 1984. Plant Remains from the Stirling Phase. In *The BBB Motor Site*, by T. E. Emerson and D. K. Jackson, pp. 321-335. American Bottom Archaeology FAI-270 Site Reports Volume 6, University of Illinois Press, Urbana.

Wilson, G. L. 1987. *Buffalo Bird Woman's Garden: Agriculture of the Hidatsa Indians*. Minnesota Historical Society Press, St. Paul. [Originally published as *Agriculture of the Hidatsa Indians: An Indian Interpretation*, 1917, University of Minnesota.]

Wray, C. F., M. L. Sempowski, L. P. Saunders, and G. C. Cervone. 1987. *The Adams and Culbertson Sites*. Charles F. Wray Series in Seneca Archaeology Volume I. Research Records No. 19. Rochester Museum & Science Center, Rochester, New York.

Wray, C. F., M. L. Sempowski, and L. P. Saunders. 1991. *Tram and Cameron: Two Early Contact Era Seneca Sites*. Charles F. Wray Series in Seneca Archaeology Volume II. Research Records No. 21. Rochester Museum & Science Center, Rochester, New York.

Wyman, L. C., and S. K. Harris. 1951. *The Ethnobotany of the Kayenta Navaho*. The University of New Mexico Press, Albuquerque, New Mexico.

Wymer, D. 1987. The Middle Woodland-Late Woodland Interface in Central Ohio: Subsistence Continuity Amid Cultural Change. In *Emergent Horticultural Economies of the Eastern Woodlands*, edited by W. F. Keegan, pp. 201-216. Center for Archaeological Investigations, Occasional Papers No. 7. Southern Illinois University at Carbondale.

—————. 1993. Cultural Change and Subsistence: The Middle and Late Woodland Transition in the Mid-Ohio Valley. In *Foraging and Farming in the Eastern Woodlands*, edited by C. M. Scarry, pp. 138-156. University Press of Florida, Gainesville.

Yarnell, R. A. 1978. Domestication of Sunflower and Sumpweed in Eastern North America. In *The Nature and Status of Ethnobotany*, edited by R. I. Ford, pp. 289-299. Anthropological Papers No. 67, Museum of Anthropology, University of Michigan, Ann Arbor.

—————. 1993. The Importance of Native Crops during the Late Archaic and Woodland Periods. In *Foraging and Farming in the Eastern Woodlands*, edited by C. M. Scarry, pp. 13-26. University Press of Florida, Gainesville.

Yarnell, R. A., and J. Black. 1985. Temporal Trends Indicated by a Survey of Archaic and Woodland Plant Food Remains from Southeastern North America. *Southeastern Archaeology* 4:93-106.

# CHAPTER 4

# DATING ROUNDTOP'S DOMESTICATES: IMPLICATIONS FOR NORTHEAST LATE PREHISTORY

John P. Hart

In most regions where there have been long-term, extensive archaeological research programs, there is a handful of sites that most archaeologists in those regions recognize by name. These are sites that have contributed lasting, important information on one or more aspects of the region's history or prehistory. There are a number of such sites in the Northeast, one of which is the Roundtop site located in the upper Susquehanna River basin in Broome County, New York (Figure 4.1). Roundtop is one of many sites excavated by William Ritchie and field crews from the New York State Museum during the 1960s. The importance of Roundtop in the Northeast includes its apparent association with early agriculture. Ritchie (1969, 1973) reported a radiocarbon date of 880 ± 60 B.P. and the recovery of a quantity of charred maize (*Zea mays*), beans (*Phaseolus vulgaris*), and squash (*Cucurbita pepo*) remains from the site. He described Roundtop as being occupied primarily during the early Owasco Carpenter Brook phase (950 B.P. to 850 B.P.). As a result of Ritchie's publications, the domesticate remains are associated with the early Owasco occupation of Roundtop in the literature on Northeast archaeology. The remains have been cited frequently since as the oldest or among the oldest evidence for maize, and/or beans, and/or squash in the Northeast (Bendremer and Dewar 1994; Brown 1977; Chapdelaine 1993; Ford 1985; Funk 1993; McBride and Dewar 1987; Riley et al. 1990; Snow 1980, 1995; Versaggi 1986; Yarnell 1976).

A careful reading of Ritchie's (1973) summary of the site indicates that the radiocarbon date he reported, contrary to a number of statements in the literature by other authors (e.g. Funk 1993:208), was not from Feature 35 that produced the maize, beans, and squash remains. Rather, the date is from Feature 30, which produced no domesticate remains. As a result, given the importance of Roundtop in discussions of early agricul-

ture in the Northeast, I considered obtaining direct dates on the maize and beans from Feature 35 and other contexts important. In this chapter, I present accelerator mass spectrometry (AMS) dates which cluster during the mid-seventh century B.P. on domesticate remains and associated wood charcoal from Feature 35. I also report AMS dates that range in age from the ninth to fourth centuries B.P. on maize and beans from three other contexts at the site. An examination of the New York State Museum's collections from Roundtop, including artifacts and Ritchie's field and lab notes, makes it apparent that (1) the pottery assemblage from Feature 30 is earlier than that from Feature 35, and (2) the multicomponent nature of the site has been under emphasized in the literature.

The results of the AMS dating and review of pottery collections confirm that Ritchie's original assessment found in his lab notes was correct;

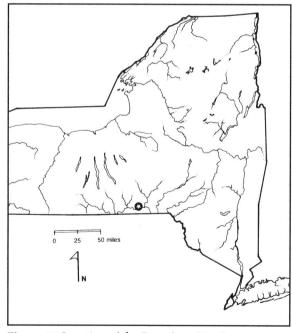

**Figure 4.1** Location of the Roundtop Site, Broome County, New York.

Feature 35 represents a later occupation than Feature 30. There is no connection between the radiocarbon date obtained by Ritchie for Feature 30 and the domesticate remains recovered from Feature 35. An AMS date on a maize kernel from Feature 235 is not significantly different from the date reported by Ritchie for Feature 30 and therefore confirms the presence of maize at the site during the earlier occupations. The domesticates recovered from Roundtop can no longer be cited as evidence for ninth-century B.P. maize-beans-squash agriculture in New York and the Northeast. However, these remains are now the earliest direct-dated occurrence of the triad in the Northeast.

The mid-seventh-century B.P. date on beans from Feature 35 raises important issues about the timing of the introduction to and archaeological visibility of beans in the Northeast. No direct dates that are earlier than the one reported here have been published for beans in the Northeast. The Roundtop Feature 35 bean date has the potential to extend our knowledge of the "developmental mosaic across the East" in maize-bean-squash agriculture (Smith 1992:111) if corroborated by direct AMS dates on beans in other apparently early contexts in the Northeast. The domesticates from Roundtop's Feature 35, then, remain an important part of our knowledge of prehistoric agricultural evolution in the Northeast.

## THE ROUNDTOP SITE

The Roundtop site was located in the village of Endicott, in Broome County, New York. As described by Ritchie (1973:179), Roundtop "occupies about two-thirds of an acre on a nearly flat terrace rising between 15 and 20 feet above normal water level. It is on the north bank of the Susquehanna River, in close proximity to a steep knoll of glacially eroded shale, 260 feet higher than the terrace, which gives its name to the site." The site had been investigated by local amateurs who, beginning in 1958, excavated more than 100 pit features (Laccetti 1965, 1966, 1974). As related by Ritchie (1973:179), the New York State Museum became involved with Roundtop after the village

of Endicott purchased the property on which the site was located. The village anticipated making extensive ground disturbance in the site area during the construction of a park. After Roundtop and its impending destruction were reported to Ritchie, he convinced the village to allow the Museum to do salvage excavations at the site before construction. In the summer of 1964, Ritchie and a crew of three graduate students and several local amateurs excavated 464 m$^2$ of the site. Ritchie's crew documented and excavated 70 pit features and several hundred post molds. Of the 70 features, 52 were determined to have been excavated previously by amateurs. During the following two summers, William Lipe directed archaeological field schools at the site for the State University of New York (SUNY) at Binghamton. The two field schools excavated 437 m$^2$ adjacent to Ritchie's, exposing an additional 156 pit features. According to Ritchie (1973:179), many of these features also had been excavated previously by amateurs.

Ritchie's first published summary of the site appeared in the preface to the 1969 second edition of *The Archaeology of New York State*. Ritchie published a longer and more definitive summary of the site in his 1973 volume with Robert Funk, *Aboriginal Settlement Patterns in the Northeast*. This summary deals primarily with the results of Ritchie's excavations but contains a site plan showing both Ritchie's and Lipe's excavations, reproduced here as Figure 4.2. Ritchie also included Lipe's materials, along with those recovered by amateurs, in a trait list for the site (Ritchie 1973:179, 192). Laccetti (1965, 1966, 1974) published several articles on Roundtop based on both amateur excavations and those by Ritchie. The following review will concentrate on Ritchie's publications because they have been the basis for interpretations of Roundtop's domesticates in the literature.

## FEATURE 35 AND THE ROUNDTOP DOMESTICATES

Roundtop's Feature 35 is perhaps the best known feature from a prehistoric site in New York. The feature was discovered during Ritchie's excavations and was one of the few features inves-

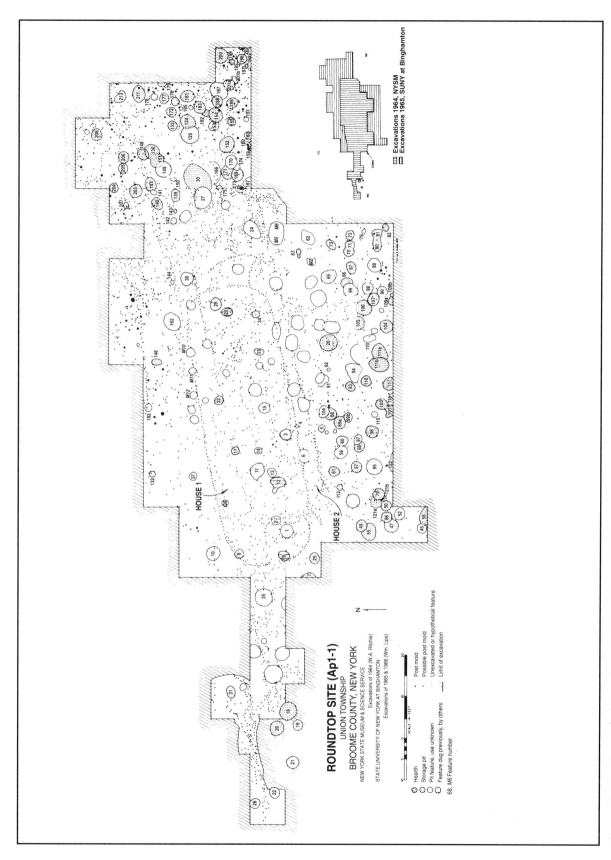

**Figure 4.2** Site plan of the Roundtop site (from Ritchie 1973).

tigated by his field crew that had not been previously excavated by amateurs. Ritchie (1973:183-184) published a detailed description of the feature based on field notes by Frank Schambach. The profile of the pit published by Ritchie (1973:184) is reproduced here with minor modifications as Figure 4.3. The feature measured 1.6 m in diameter and 1.2 m deep and had a U-shaped profile. It contained eight distinct layers, numbered consecutively from bottom to top (1-8), reflecting a series of uses that Ritchie attributed to a single occupation of the site. Layers 1-4 have no direct bearing on the context and interpretation of the domesticate remains, which were recovered from Layer 5, a bark lining. As related by Ritchie, above Layer 4:

> [T]he pit bottom and sides were partially covered with flat sandstone slabs 1 to 2 inches thick. A lining, 1 to 2 inches thick, of coarse (hemlock?) bark was next placed over the stones, completely investing the bottom and sides of the pit [Layer 5]. The feature then became an underground granary … the pit was again fired, producing a burned red band [Layer 6] and carbonizing the bark lining with many vegetable remains adhering to it … the pit seems next to have been used as a trash receptacle. About 8 inches of dark brown soil with scattered burned rock, charcoal, and potsherds were accumulated [Layer 7] [Ritchie 1973:184].

In his notes on the feature, Schambach stated that:

> [P]ractically all the pottery found in this pit came from layer 7 which seems to have accumulated when the befouled storage pit was used for refuse or as a hearth. For the most part, the sherds were lying up against or right in the bark lining on the bottom and sides of the pit. Very little time could have elapsed between the time the pit was used for storage and the time it was used for refuse … all of the pottery from

this pit with the exception of one sherd … and all of the suspected vegetable remains occurred *unquestionably* in direct association with each other in and around the bark lining [Schambach 1964:6, emphasis in original].

This fortuitous recovery of charred domesticate remains, before the advent of flotation retrieval, became the foundation for Ritchie's subsequent discussions of Roundtop's evidence for agriculture. In the preface to the second edition of *The Archaeology of New York State* in 1969, Ritchie summarized the evidence for prehistoric agriculture at Roundtop as follows:

> Of primary importance was the discovery by the Science Survey party of carbonized plant remains *constituting the earliest radiocarbon-dated evidence for cultigens in New York State. The material came from Feature 35, a large, deep U-shaped pit, sixty-two inches in diameter and forty-six inches deep, with unequivocal charcoal and ceramic associations.* The radiocarbon date of A.D. 1070 ± 60 years (Y-1534) is the earliest so far obtained for an Owasco site [Ritchie 1994:xxv, emphasis added].

Later in that volume, Ritchie (1994:276) stated, "Corn has been found on the village sites of every [Owasco] phase; beans and squash are only recently known from the early or Carpenter Brook horizon of this culture, which marks the beginning, so far as we are presently aware, of a diversified economy wherein an accelerating emphasis was accorded hoe tillage of garden crops." These comments are obviously based on the recovery of maize, beans, and squash from Roundtop.

In his 1973 summary, Ritchie (1973:186, 193) stated that this was "the earliest date thus far obtained for a site of the Owasco culture," making Roundtop the "oldest radiocarbon-dated site of the Carpenter Brook phase." Ritchie (1973:193, 186) asserted that the site "has produced the earliest and largest series of cultigens thus far discovered in New York and probably in the entire

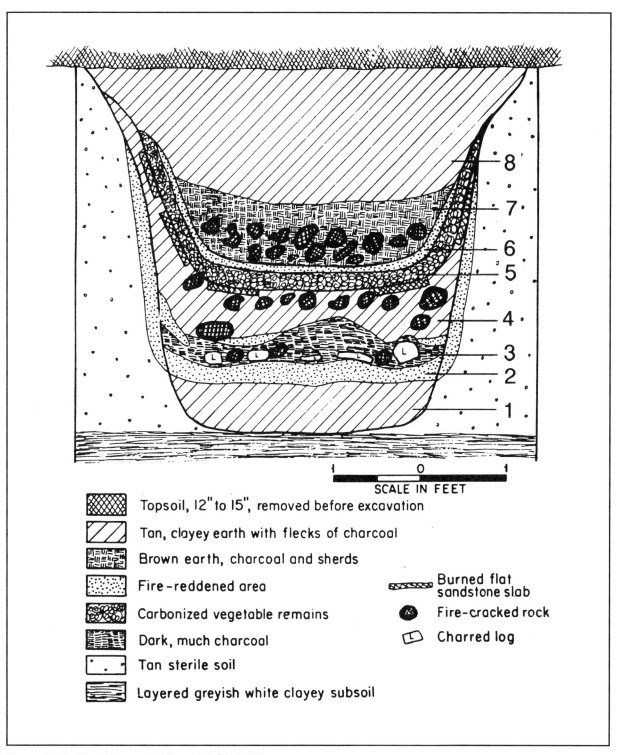

Figure 4.3 Profile of Feature 35 (from Ritchie 1973).

The legend entries for the figure are:

- Topsoil, 12" to 15", removed before excavation
- Tan, clayey earth with flecks of charcoal
- Brown earth, charcoal and sherds
- Fire-reddened area
- Carbonized vegetable remains
- Dark, much charcoal
- Tan sterile soil
- Layered greyish white clayey subsoil
- Burned flat sandstone slab
- Fire-cracked rock
- Charred log

SCALE IN FEET

Northeast area" and that "the cultigens found on the site represent the oldest known evidence of agriculture in New York State and probably in the whole Northeast."

Samples of the Roundtop Feature 35 domesticates were submitted to Richard Yarnell, then of Emory University, for identification. Ritchie reported Yarnell's results as follows:

> Most of the carbonized plant vestiges were fortuitously preserved in a large, deep pit, Feature 35, excavated by the State Museum ... These specimens were identified by Richard A. Yarnell of Emory University as corn cob fragments and kernels of typical "Northern Flint" variety, bean cotyledons (*Phaseolus vulgaris*), squash seeds (probably *Cucurbita pepo*), 'squash" [sic] seed (probably *Cucurbita pepo*, variety *ovifera*, the egg gourd or yellow flowering gourd), hawthorn seeds and fruits (*Crataegus*), plum seeds and fruits (probably *Prunus americana*), acorn meats, butternut shells (*Juglans cinerea* L.), and walnut shells (*Juglans nigra* L.) (Letter of June 28, 1967) [Ritchie 1973:186].

Ritchie (1973:186) noted that Paul Mangelsdorf identified the maize as eight-rowed flint corn. He also reported that the SUNY Binghamton excavations had yielded "eight corn kernels, six bean cotyledons, a plum pit, an acorn, a butternut, and a hawthorn seed" (Ritchie 1973:186). No radiocarbon assay was obtained for the SUNY Binghamton excavations. The botanical remains from these field schools were reindentified and tabulated by Margaret Scarry of the University of North Carolina at Chapel Hill and are discussed below.

Despite the fact that Feature 35 produced large quantities of charred bark and wood, it was not selected for radiocarbon dating, presumably because live groundnuts were present in the feature and there were concerns that groundnut rootlets had contaminated the charcoal samples (Schambach 1964). Rather, Ritchie submitted char-

coal from Feature 30 for radiocarbon assay. He described Feature 30 as a "large, oval pit (72 inches long, 60 inches wide, 36 inches deep), with sloping walls and flat bottom, apparently a corn cache, *although no trace of a lining or food remained*" (Ritchie 1973:183, emphasis added). In discussing the selection of Feature 30 charcoal for radiocarbon dating, Ritchie stated that "[m]ost of the sherds of Carpenter Brook Cord-on-Cord were intermingled with a good quantity of clean charcoal which was carefully collected and provided the dated sample for this site ... *As this ceramic type (Carpenter Brook Cord-on-Cord, herringbone design) occurred in direct association in Feature 35 with the vegetable remains ...the C-14 determination for Feature 30 is considered a reliable date for the agricultural vestiges at this site*" [Ritchie 1973:183, emphasis added].[1]

In their concluding chapter to the volume, Ritchie and Funk (1973:360) suggested, "The Roundtop investigations disclosed unmistakable evidence that corn, beans, and squashes were cultivated by Carpenter Brook people." At the time of this publication, it is clear that Ritchie believed that Features 30 and 35 were contemporaneous (i.e., they both dated to the Carpenter Brook phase) because they each contained sherds of the Carpenter Brook Cord-on-Cord, herringbone type. The Carpenter Brook phase was believed by Ritchie to date between ca. 950 and 850 B.P. (Ritchie 1994:274-275; also see Snow 1995:64-66).

Following Ritchie's publications, Roundtop's domesticates from Feature 35 were, and continue to be, cited frequently as among the earliest in the Northeast. The maize has been frequently cited as the oldest recovered from a New York site (Ceci 1979-80:47; Versaggi 1986:18) or more recently as among the oldest in the Northeast (Bendremer and Dewar 1994:381). Roundtop's beans (Ford 1985:353; Riley et al. 1990:531; Yarnell 1976:272) and squash (Chapdelaine 1993:194) are also cited as the earliest examples of those domesticates in the East, Northeast or associated with the Iroquois. The site has also been cited as having the earliest evidence in New York for the co-occurrence of maize, beans, and squash (Snow 1995:65; Winter 1971:8).

The extent to which Roundtop's Feature 35

domesticates are associated with early agriculture in the Northeast is emphasized by the misattribution of the radiocarbon date from Feature 30 to Feature 35 by a number of authors. For example, McBride and Dewar (1987:308) stated, "Maize, beans, and squash are directly dated to A.D. 1070 at the Roundtop site." Funk (1993:269, 208) stated, "Considerable subsistence evidence was present at the Roundtop site (Ritchie and Funk 1973) including ... carbonized corn kernels, beans, and squash," and "Radiocarbon dates for Carpenter Brook components at Fortin site locus 2, zone 4, and on feature 35 at the Roundtop site were, respectively, A.D. 1080 ± 75 years and A.D. 1070 ± 60 years."

## AMS DATING

### Rationale and Sample Selection

Before the advent of flotation recovery, finds of domesticate remains in the Eastern Woodlands were rare, and large quantities of charcoal were needed for radiocarbon assays. As a result, the domesticates from Feature 35 and other contexts at Roundtop were not directly dated by Ritchie. Given the concerns over rootlet contamination of the charred bark lining on which the domesticates were found, charcoal from Feature 35 was not dated. Not enough charcoal was recovered from other contexts with domesticates to enable radiocarbon dating. Rather, Ritchie relied on a radiocarbon date from Feature 30 and the occurrence of Carpenter Brook Cord-on-Cord, herringbone pottery sherds in both Features 30 and 35 to date the Feature 35 domesticates.

Since the early 1980s, accelerator mass spectrometry (AMS) dating has allowed direct dating of very small charcoal samples. As little as 5 mg of charcoal is needed for AMS dating compared to a minimum of around 2 g, or 400 times more, for standard radiocarbon dating. This is possible because the AMS technique counts atoms of $^{14}$C rather than radioactive disintegration as is done in standard radiocarbon dating (Gowlett 1987:130). As few as one or two maize kernels or cupules or one bean cotyledon can be dated directly through this method. As a result, AMS dating of domesti-

cate remains in potentially early contexts is now done routinely in the Eastern Woodlands (Bendremer et al. 1991; Chapman and Crites 1987; Conard et al. 1984; Crawford et al. 1997; Crites 1993; Hart and Asch Sidell 1996, 1997; Petersen and Asch Sidell 1996; Riley et al. 1994).

There are several reasons to date domesticates directly. These include (1) avoiding the "old-wood" problems associated with dating associated wood charcoal (Creel and Long 1986; Schiffer 1987; Shott 1992), (2) the possibility that domesticates and associated wood charcoal do not represent contemporaneous events, and (3) the possibility that the domesticates represent later prehistoric or modern contaminants (Conard et al. 1984; Gowlett 1987). AMS dating was, of course, not available to Ritchie at the time of his Roundtop excavations. However, it is a technique that now can be used to assess the reliability of previously obtained wood-charcoal dates associated with apparently early domesticates, as in the Roundtop case. Given the importance that has been placed on the Roundtop domesticates, direct dating of several samples of the Feature 35 domesticates and several samples from other contexts was deemed appropriate.

A search of the New York State Museum's collections from the Roundtop site failed to locate the botanical remains identified by Yarnell as reported by Ritchie in 1973. They were tracked to Yarnell's collections at the University of North Carolina at Chapel Hill where Margaret Scarry retabulated the material before returning it to the New York State Museum. Scarry also identified and tabulated several samples from Feature 35 maintained in the New York State Museum's Roundtop collections since Ritchie's excavations. Scarry's tabulations are presented in Table 4.1. Those listed with an RLA catalog number are from the sample originally identified by Yarnell, and the others are from the New York State Museum samples. Unfortunately, the glass vial in Yarnell's collections labeled "beans" was empty, and the original bean sample could not be relocated for this study. However, Scarry identified beans in a charcoal sample from Feature 35 that had been maintained in the New York State Museum's collections since Ritchie's excavations.

**Table 4.1 List of Botanical Remains Identified from Feature 35, Layer 5 Samples.**

| Catalog No. | Common Name | Scientific Name | Count | Weight (g) |
|---|---|---|---|---|
| RLA[a] | Maize cupule | *Zea mays* | 197 | 3.91 |
| RLA | Maize kernel[c] | *Zea mays* | 13 | 0.34 |
| RLA | Bean cf. (small fragments, tentative id) | *Phaseolus vulgaris* | 2 | 0.01 |
| RLA | Squash (possibly two varieties) | *Cucurbita pepo* | 2 | 0.08 |
| RLA | Acorn meat | *Quercus* sp. | 1 | 0.08 |
| RLA | Butternut shell | *Juglans cinerea* | 1 | 0.64 |
| RLA | Walnut shell | *Juglans nigra* | 1 | 0.19 |
| RLA | Hawthorn | *Crataegus* sp. | 38 | 1.59 |
| RLA | Plum | *Prunus americana* | 3 | 0.50 |
| RLA | Unidentifiable | Unidentifiable | 6 | 0.19 |
| 427464-C[b] | Maize cupule | *Zea mays* | 1 | 0.03 |
| 427464-C | Maize kernel[d] | *Zea mays* | 35 | 1.51 |
| 427464-C | Hawthorn | *Crataegus* sp. | 9 | 0.29 |
| 427464-C | Serviceberry | *Amelanchier canadensis* | 1 | 0.01 |
| 427464-C | Unidentifiable | Unidentifiable | 2 | 0.05 |
| 427464[b] | Maize cupule | *Zea mays* | 2 | 0.03 |
| 427464 | Maize kernel | *Zea mays* | 16 | 0.86 |
| 427464 | Squash | *Cucurbita pepo* | 1 | 0.06 |
| 427464 | Butternut | *Juglans cinerea* | 1 | 0.18 |
| 427464 | Hawthorn | *Crataegus* sp. | 3 | 0.18 |

*Notes*

[a] Sample originally identified by Yarnell, now in New York State Museum collections.

[b] Sample held in New York State Museum collections.

[c] 2 kernels used for AMS Sample 1.

[d] 2 kernels used for AMS Sample 2.

Four samples were selected from Feature 35 for AMS dating and submitted to the National Science Foundation (NSF) Arizona AMS facility. Two of these samples consisted of maize kernels, one of charred wood, and one of bean. These samples were chosen to represent several different materials and both the Yarnell sample and those maintained at the New York State Museum. All the samples were recovered from Layer 5 of Feature 35. Samples 1 (AA21978) and 2 (AA21979) each consisted of two maize kernels weighing a total of 92 mg and 128 mg, respectively. Sample 1 was chosen from kernels in the collection originally identified by Yarnell, and Sample 2 was chosen from the collection maintained at the New York State Museum since Ritchie's excavations. Sample 3 (AA21980) consisted of a small fragment of a charred twig weighing 181 mg from the New York State Museum's collections. Finally, Sample 4 (AA23106) consisted of a bean cotyledon weighing 50 mg recovered by Scarry from the charcoal sample in the New York State Museum's collections.

**Results**

The results of the AMS dating of Feature 35 are presented in Table 4.2. The AMS dates clearly indicate that most of the domesticates from Feature 35 originated around 650 B.P. Samples 2, 3, and 4 cluster very tightly, and their calibrated ages and $2\sigma$-ranges suggest a single event. The three dates are statistically the same at the 95 percent level of confidence, and each is statistically different from Ritchie's date at the 95 percent level of confidence (Stuiver and Reimer 1993). Sample 1 is about 350 years later, statistically different at the 95 percent level of confidence from the other three dates, and clearly anomalous. It may represent a later Iroquoian occupation of the site. This explanation is supported by the presence of a small rim sherd from Feature 35 that is reminiscent of later Iroquoian pottery (see below). The date is consistent with two dates reported below, one of a maize kernel and one of a bean cotyledon, recovered from post molds by the SUNY field schools.

There are several possible explanations for the difference between the original radiocarbon assay on Feature 30 and the AMS dates obtained

on Feature 35: (1) the AMS dates are in error and the two features are contemporaneous; (2) the original radiocarbon assay is in error and the two features are contemporaneous; (3) the original and AMS dates are both valid and the features represent different occupations of the site. Explanation 1 is not supported since three of the four AMS dates, all on different material, are virtually identical. The only way to determine whether Explanation 2 or 3 is valid is to evaluate independent data sets. The largest data set available from the two features is their pottery assemblages.

## POTTERY

Ritchie's discussions of Features 30 and 35, the domesticate remains, and the original radiocarbon date, both in publications and in correspondence, suggest that he was certain of the contemporaneity of the two features. That is, in culture-historical terms, they both originated during the early Owasco Carpenter Brook phase. However, in examining Ritchie's laboratory notes, it became apparent that at some point he thought the two features represented different occupations–Feature 35 was later than Feature 30.

### Feature 35

In his 1973 summary, Ritchie (1973:184) described the pottery from Feature 35 as follows: "Practically all of the pottery found in the pit came from this layer [Layer 7]. It included three rims and a body sherd of Carpenter Brook Cord-on-Cord type, two rims of Owasco Corded Horizontal, three corded and two comb-marked body sherds, and eight sherds too small to identify." Ritchie did not mention any pottery in his description of Layer 5. A pottery collection like this would be consistent with the 880 B.P. date obtained on charcoal from Feature 30. Culture historians consider Carpenter Brook Cord-on-Cord to be a predominantly early Owasco type, while Owasco Corded Horizontal occurs in early Owasco pottery assemblages, although it is more frequently found in later assemblages (Prezzano 1992:145; Ritchie and MacNeish 1949:112, 121). However, Ritchie's published description is at

**Table 4.2 Results of Roundtop AMS Dating.**

| Sample | Lab No. | Material | Provenience | Age (B.P.)[a] | Calibrated Date (A.D.)[b] | Calibrated 2σ Range (A.D.)[b] |
|---|---|---|---|---|---|---|
| 1 | AA21978 | maize kernels | Feature 35, Layer 5 | 330 ± 45 | 1525, 1558, 1631 | 1452-1660 |
| 2 | AA21979 | maize kernels | Feature 35, Layer 5 | 675 ± 55 | 1299 | 1264-1404 |
| 3 | AA21980 | charred twig | Feature 35, Layer 5 | 670 ± 55 | 1300 | 1268-1406 |
| 4 | AA23106 | bean cotyledon | Feature 35, Layer 5 | 658 ± 48 | 1303 | 1279-1405 |
| 5 | AA26539 | maize kernel | Post Mold, E100N70 | 440 ± 45 | 1446 | 1414-1622 |
| 6 | AA26540 | bean cotyledon | Post Mold, E110N70 | 315 ± 45 | 1636 | 1464-1665 |
| 7 | AA26541 | maize kernel | Feature 235 | 830 ± 45 | 1225 | 1063-1285 |
| Ritchie | Y-1534 | charcoal | Feature 30 | 880 ± 60 | 1176 | 1022-1281 |

*Notes*

a AMS dates normalized to a δ13C = -25‰ (relative to PDB).
b Stuiver and Reimer (1993).

**Table 4.3. Pottery Type Identifications by Feature for State Museum Excavations Transcribed from Ritchie's Lab Notes.[a]**

| Feature | Levanna Corded | Carpenter Brook Cord on Cord | Levanna Corded Collar | Owasco Corded Horizontal | Owasco Platted | Owasco Corded Collar | Incised Iroquoian | Linear Punctate | Collared Plain | Collared Cord Dec. | Cultural Attribution |
|---|---|---|---|---|---|---|---|---|---|---|---|
| 1 | X | X | – | – | – | – | – | – | – | – | Early Owasco |
| 8 | – | X | – | – | – | – | – | – | – | – | Early Owasco |
| 18 | X | – | – | – | – | – | – | – | – | – | Early Owasco |
| 19 | X | X | – | – | – | – | – | – | – | – | Early Owasco |
| 20 | – | X | X | – | – | – | – | – | – | X | Middle Owasco? |
| 25 | – | – | – | – | X? | – | – | – | X | – | Middle Owasco? |
| 26 | X | X | – | – | – | – | – | – | – | – | Early Owasco |
| 27 | – | – | X | – | – | – | X | X | – | – | Late Iroquois |
| 28 | X | X | – | X? | – | – | – | – | – | – | Early Owasco |
| 30 | X | X | – | – | – | – | – | – | – | – | Early Owasco |
| 31 | – | X | – | X? | – | – | – | – | – | – | Early Owasco |
| 35, Layer 7 | – | X | X? | – | – | – | – | Trailed Body S. | X | – | Middle Owasco? |
| 35, Layer 5 | – | X | – | – | – | X | – | – | – | – | Late Owasco? |
| 36 | X | X | – | – | – | – | – | – | – | – | Late Owasco? |

*Notes*

a Features 21 and 29 were removed from the transcribed table since they contained no pottery. Ritchie's column for secondary provenience information was not transcribed. Ritchie's columns for Dentate-on-Cord and Point Peninsula Cordlike were not included because Ritchie did not identify these types in the museum-excavated features.

odds with both his lab notes and with the pottery that is in the New York State Museum's collection from Feature 35.

In lab notes for the Museum's 1964 Roundtop excavations, a handwritten table by Ritchie, initialed "W.A.R." and transcribed here as Table 4.3, lists pottery types and "Cultural Attribution" by feature. In his tabulation of Feature 35's Layer 5, Ritchie identified Carpenter Brook Cord-on-Cord, Owasco Corded Collar, and trailed body sherds. Those pottery types listed for Feature 35's Layer 7 are Carpenter Brook Cord-on-Cord, Levanna Corded Collar?, and Collared Plain. Ritchie attributed Layer 5 to late Owasco (ca. 750 to 650 B.P.) and Layer 7 to middle Owasco (ca. 850 to 750 B.P.), appending question marks to both attributions. In separate lab notes, Ritchie indicated that Feature 35 contained both early and late Owasco pottery.

Rim sherds from Feature 35's Layers 5 and 7 are illustrated in Figures 4.4-4.8. The rim sherds from Layer 5 represent at least four vessels. The first vessel is collared with a smooth exterior surface and cord-impressed designs on and below the collar (Figure 4.4a). Three, horizontal cord impressions occupy the collar. This pattern is broken by oblique cord impressions. A band of oblique cord impressions begins at the base of the collar and terminates at the vessel's shoulder. The flat lip is decorated with widely spaced cord impressions oriented perpendicularly to the vessel's orifice. The smooth interior surface of the rim is decorated by oblique cord impressions. The body sherds have vertical trailing or combing over a smooth exterior surface. This vessel represents the Owasco Corded Collar type in Table 4.3 and would be classified as Kelso Corded in Prezzano's (1992:145-146) terminology (also see Lenig 1965). This type has been dated by Prezzano (1992:146) primarily to the period 750-650 B.P. and by Ritchie and MacNeish (1949:114) primarily to late Owasco.

The second vessel also has a collared rim. It is represented in Layer 5 by one small rim sherd and several body sherds. Many more sherds from this vessel were recovered from Layer 7, and it is described in more detail below. The remaining two rim sherds recovered from Layer 5 (Figure

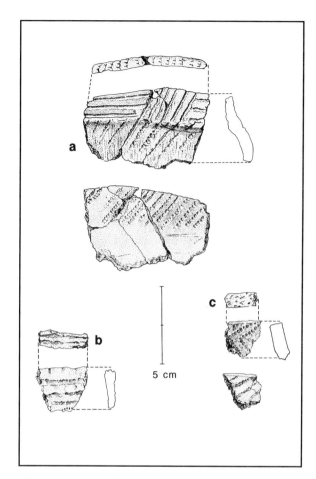

**Figure 4.4** Pottery from Feature 35, Layer 5 (a. Owasco Corded Collar, b. and c. Carpenter Brook Cord-on-Cord).

4.4b,c) are very small with cord-impressed designs over vertical cordmarking. These sherds correspond to Ritchie's Carpenter Brook Cord-on-Cord type designation in Table 4.3. One of the sherds (Figure 4.4b) was collected separately by Schambach during his excavations of Feature 35 because it was found in direct association with the domesticate remains.

The rim sherds from Layer 7 represent three vessels. The first (Figure 4.5) is the collared vessel from which only a single rim sherd was recovered in Layer 5. This is probably the Levanna Corded Collar? type listed by Ritchie in Table 4.3. Although more crudely rendered, the design of this vessel is very similar to that of the vessel designated by Ritchie as Owasco Corded Collar in

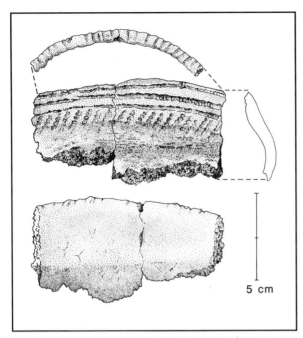

**Figure 4.5** Owasco Corded Collar Rim Sherd from Feature 35, Layer 7.

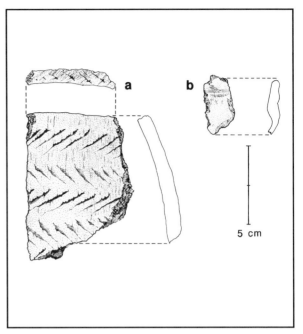

**Figure 4.6** Pottery from Feature 35, Layer 7 (a. Carpenter Brook Cord-on-Cord, b. Collared Plain).

Layer 5. The primary differences are as follows: (1) the collar of this vessel is not as pronounced, (2) the exterior surface of the body has partially smoothed over cord or fabric impressions rather than a smooth surface with trailing, and (3) there is a band of horizontal cord impressions on the neck, below which is possibly a second band of oblique cord marks. The horizontal cording on the collar and the smooth rim and collar surfaces suggest an attribution to Owasco Corded Collar or Kelso Corded in Prezzano's (1992) terminology. In a separate set of lab notes, Ritchie identified this vessel as "O.C. Collar?", by which he probably meant Owasco Corded Collar. Presumably, the rim sherds from this vessel are those identified by Ritchie (1973) in his published description of Feature 35 as Owasco Corded Horizontal. However, the Owasco Corded Horizontal type does not have collared rims (Prezzano 1992:144-145; Ritchie and MacNeish 1949:112), so this vessel cannot be attributed to that type.

The second vessel is represented by a single, relatively large rim sherd with a herringbone pattern of cord impressions over a vertically cord-marked surface (Figure 4.6a). The flat lip of this sherd is decorated with oblique cord impressions over a cordmarked surface. The interior surface is smooth. This sherd can be attributed to the Carpenter Brook Cord-on-Cord type in Table 4.3. The third vessel from Layer 7 is represented by one small, collared rim sherd with smooth exterior and interior surfaces (Figure 4.6b). Small, shallow notches are present at the base of the collar and there is an oblique, incised line below the collar. The angle of the lip relative to the base of the collar suggests that a castellation was present on this portion of the rim. This sherd corresponds to Ritchie's designation of Collared Plain in Table 4.3. It may represent later Iroquoian materials corresponding to the younger of the two AMS dates on maize kernels.

Feature 35's pottery assemblage, then, contains a mixture of earlier and later pottery types according to the generally accepted culture-historical pottery chronology for New York. Ritchie recognized this in his lab notes, but not in his published account. The presence of the late type Owasco Corded Collar or Kelso Corded in Layers 5 and 7 is consistent with the AMS dates and helps to establish the domesticates as representing a mid-seventh-century B.P. occupation of the site. The potentially earlier pottery in this feature may

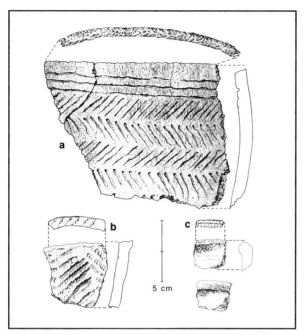

**Figure 4.7** Owasco Cord-on-Cord Sherds from Feature 30.

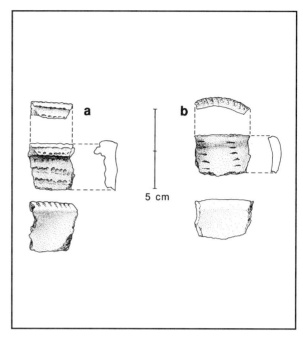

**Figure 4.8** Pottery from Feature 30 (a. Owasco Corded Horizontal, b. Owasco Platted).

represent continued use of particular decorative motifs beyond those times in which they are most commonly associated or secondary inclusions in the feature fill as a result of excavations through earlier deposits.

**Feature 30**

In Table 4.3, Ritchie listed the pottery types for Feature 30 as Levanna Corded and Carpenter Brook Cord-on-Cord. Ritchie attributed this feature to early Owasco. In notes accompanying the table, Ritchie indicated that Feature 30 was one of nine features excavated by the Museum that contained only early Owasco pottery. In his published account of the feature, Ritchie (1973:183) described the pottery assemblage as containing "numerous Owasco sherds (10 Carpenter Brook Cord-on-Cord, two Levanna Cord-on-Cord, two Owasco Corded Horizontal, one Owasco Platted, four corded body sherds)." Both the lab notes and published description are in general agreement with the pottery from Feature 30 in the Museum's collections.

Rim sherds from Feature 30 are illustrated in Figures 4.7 and 4.8. Rim sherds recovered from

this feature represent eleven vessels. Most of the pottery from the feature originated from a large cordmarked jar with a cord-impressed herringbone design on the rim below a band of three horizontal cord impressions (Figure 4.7a). The flat lip of this vessel is cordmarked, while the interior surface is smooth. This vessel is consistent with Ritchie's designation of Carpenter Brook Cord-on-Cord in Table 4.3. The fact that large portions of this vessel were contained in Feature 30 suggests that it was a primary deposit. This type, Carpenter Brook Corded in Prezzano's (1992:142-143) terminology, is most frequently found in contexts dating to 950 to 850 B.P. and is therefore consistent with the 880 B.P. date obtained by Ritchie for Feature 30. Two small rim sherds with vertical cordmarked surfaces overprinted by cord impressions represent two other vessels that also can be assigned to this type (Figure 4.7b,c).

Of the remaining eight vessels, only one is represented by more than one rim sherd. This vessel, represented by two refitting rim sherds, has partially smoothed over, bi-directional cord impressions on the exterior surface. The flat lip is cord impressed, while the interior surface is smooth. This vessel corresponds to Ritchie's attribution of Levanna Cord-on-Cord in Table 4.3, or Levanna Rough in Prezzano's (1992:143-144) terminology. Three other small rim sherds recovered from Feature 30 can also be assigned to this type, which is most common in early Owasco contexts (Prezzano 1992:144). The remaining rim sherds can be assigned to the Sackett Series as defined by Prezzano (1992:144-145; also see Lenig 1965). Under Ritchie and MacNeish's (1949) typology, three of these sherds would be assigned to the Owasco Corded Horizontal type (one is illustrated in Figure 4.8a), and one would be assigned to the Owasco Platted type (Figure 4.8b). Ritchie and MacNeish (1949:111-112) suggested that both of these types occurred in early Owasco but were more common during later times. Prezzano (1992:145) suggested that the Sackett Series was most common in middle Owasco times, but also occurred in early and late Owasco times.

**Summary**

The pottery collections from Features 30 and 35 were examined to determine whether they support a conclusion that the radiocarbon assay from Feature 30 was in error and Feature 30 is contemporaneous with Feature 35 (Explanation 2), or whether the assay is correct and the two features represent different occupations of the site (Explanation 3). The pottery from Feature 35 is consistent with the three seventh-century B.P. AMS dates, with most of the pottery coming from two vessels that can be assigned to the Owasco Corded Collar type of Ritchie and MacNeish (1949) or the Kelso Corded type of Prezzano (1992). This is contrary to Ritchie's (1973) published description of the pottery from this feature, which suggests an early Owasco origin. The pottery from Feature 30 comes mostly from a single, large jar that can be assigned to the Carpenter Brook Cord-on-Cord type of Ritchie and MacNeish (1949) or Carpenter Brook Corded as redefined by Prezzano (1992), a type that occurs in primarily early Owasco contexts. This type is consistent with the 880 B.P. date obtained by Ritchie for this feature, and as noted by Ritchie (1973), was associated with the charcoal selected for dating. The other pottery from this feature can be assigned to the type Levanna Cord-on-Cord

(Ritchie and MacNeish 1949)/Levanna Roughened (Prezzano 1992), or to types that are members of the Sackett Series (Prezzano 1992). No pottery assignable to later types such as Owasco Corded Collar that could be associated with the Feature 35 AMS dates was recovered from Feature 30. As a result, the pottery collections from the two features support Explanation 3; the two features represent different occupations of the site.

## OTHER DOMESTICATES FROM ROUNDTOP

While Ritchie relied on the domesticate remains from Feature 35 to build his case for early agriculture at Roundtop, domesticates have been reported from Roundtop in other contexts. Even though the Feature 35 domesticate remains were determined to date to the mid-seventh century B.P. or later, it was possible that those from other proveniences would support Ritchie's contention of ninth-century B.P. evidence for agriculture at Roundtop. As a result, three samples of domesticate remains from other proveniences were submitted for AMS dating.

**Samples**

Ritchie (1973:186) provided a detailed list of domesticates recovered by the SUNY field schools at Roundtop in 1965 and 1966. SUNY field school samples in the New York State Museum's collections were examined and tabulated by Scarry (Table 4.4). The material listed in Table 4.4 is reasonably close to that listed by Ritchie, so it can be assumed it is the same collection. The SUNY field school materials included 11 samples. Six of these were from features, and five were labeled with general excavation unit proveniences. A check of the SUNY field catalog indicated that most of the latter were probably from post molds. Four samples included domesticate remains. Three of these were from post molds including one in Excavation Unit E110N70 that had 8 bean cotyledons, 1 whole bean, 5 bean fragments, 1 maize cupule, 3 maize kernels, 1 hawthorn (*Crataegus* sp.) seed, and wood charcoal. A post mold from Excavation Unit E100N70 contained 14 maize kernel fragments. A third post mold from Excavation Unit E140N50

**Table 4.4 List Of Prehistoric Botanical Remains Identified in SUNY Field School Samples.**

| Catalog No. | Provenience | Common name | Taxonomic name | Count | Weight (g) |
|---|---|---|---|---|---|
| 4527 | E110N70 post mold | Bean | *Phaseolus vulgaris* | 14 | 0.42 |
| | | Maize cupule | *Zea mays* | 1 | 0.01 |
| | | Maize kernel | *Zea mays* | 3 | 0.02 |
| | | Hawthorn | *Crataegus* sp. | 1 | 0.04 |
| | | Wood | unidentified | | 0.08 |
| 45341 | E140N50 post mold | Maize kernel | *Zea mays* | 2 | 0.04 |
| | | Wood | unidentified | | 0.04 |
| 45371 | E100N70 post mold | Maize | *Zea mays* | 14 | 0.47 |
| 45379 | Feature 69 | Bark | unidentified | | 3.53 |
| 45413 | Feature 111a | Acorn meat | *Quercus* sp. | 1 | 0.06 |
| | | Wood | unidentified | | 0.01 |
| 45422 | Feature 124 | Hawthorn | *Crataegus* sp. | 2 | 0.17 |
| | | Wood | unidentified | | 2.74 |
| 45441 | Feature 154 | Butternut | *Juglans cinerea* | 1 | 0.48 |
| | | Wood | unidentified | | 3.04 |
| 45500 | Feature 235 | Maize kernel | *Zea mays* | 3 | 0.06 |
| | | Bark | unidentified | | 0.06 |

contained 3 maize kernel fragments and wood charcoal. The fourth sample was from Feature 235 and contained 3 maize kernel fragments and charred bark. Other samples contained charred wood, bark, hawthorn seeds, butternut (*Juglans cinerea*) shell, and acorn (*Quercus* sp.) meat. Two samples not listed in Table 4.4 contained uncarbonized seeds that were probably not of prehistoric origin.

Three samples were submitted to the National Science Foundation Arizona AMS Facility for dating and are listed as Samples 5-7 in Table 4.2. Sample 5 (AA26540) was a maize kernel fragment from the post mold in Unit E100N70. This sample was chosen for dating because the large amount of material from the post mold suggested a primary deposit. That is, the material probably originated from a single depositional event rather than through one or more post-depositional processes. Sample 6 was a bean cotyledon from the post mold in Unit E110N70. This sample was chosen because of the importance of Roundtop in the literature for establishing early beans in the Northeast and because the large amount of material in the sample suggested a primary deposit. Sample 7 was a maize kernel fragment from Feature 235. This sample was chosen for dating because Feature 235 is the only pit feature other than Feature 35 to have yielded domesticate remains. Feature 235 contained a predominantly Sackett series pottery assemblage including the types Owasco Corded Horizontal, Owasco Herringbone, and Owasco Platted, as well as Carpenter Brook Cord-on-Cord and Levanna Cord-on-Cord.

**Results**

Along with Sample 1 from Feature 35, Samples 5 and 6 represent late occupations of the site with dates of $440 \pm 45$ B.P. and $315 \pm 45$ B.P., respectively (Table 4.2). Samples 1, 5, and 6 are statistically the same at the 95 percent level of confidence with a pooled radiocarbon age of $360 \pm 26$ B.P. (Stuiver and Reimer 1993). Sample 7 from Feature 235 has a radiocarbon age of $830 \pm 45$ B.P. This date is consistent with the feature's pottery assemblage. Sample 7 and Ritchie's date are statistically the same at a 95 percent level of confidence. This sug-

gests that the two features may be contemporaneous, supporting Ritchie's linkage of the Feature 30 radiocarbon date with maize agriculture. However, additional analysis of Roundtop's pottery assemblage is needed to clarify the chronological relationship of Features 30 and 235.

## IMPLICATIONS

Ritchie (1973) was convinced that the major occupation of Roundtop, and by extension the domesticates from Feature 35, pertained to his early Owasco Carpenter Brook phase. He acknowledged the existence of later components at Roundtop but downplayed their significance:

> The Iroquois stone maskette found by a collector, the six Madison type arrowpoints, two pipe fragments, and the few sherds of late Iroquois pottery types, probably pertain to the small, nearby Iroquois campsite on the river bank, reported to have been dug out prior to our work. There is also some small evidence in the pottery series at the site to indicate its minor use by people of late Owasco times [Ritchie 1973:187].

Ritchie (1973:193) also stated that "the river terrace which attracted the Roundtop people also offered advantages to other groups, apparently very small parties en route up or down river." Clearly, by the time of his 1973 publication, Ritchie did not seriously consider the possibility that a later occupation of the site could account for the domesticates that were recovered from Feature 35, despite the presence of what was obviously late pottery in that feature.

The results of the AMS dating, reexamination of a small portion of the site's pottery assemblage, and Ritchie's lab notes demonstrate that Ritchie under emphasized the importance of Roundtop's later occupations in his publications. More importantly for the present volume, the AMS dates fail to support Ritchie's assertions that the domesticate remains recovered from Roundtop's Feature 35 are evidence for ninth-century B.P.

maize-beans-squash agriculture in New York.

Based on the AMS dates from Feature 35, the earliest evidence for the co-occurrence of maize, beans, and squash at Roundtop is the mid-seventh century B.P. Roundtop has been cited as evidence for the establishment of this triad in New York and the Northeast by the ninth century B.P. (Snow 1995). Other purported pre-seventh-century B.P. occurrences of the triad (Heckenberger et al. 1992) lack direct dating of domesticates. As a result, the timing of its establishment in the Northeast is now an open question, although the Feature 35 material is now the earliest directly dated occurrence of the triad in the Northeast.

Based on recent AMS dating of *Cucurbita pepo* remains from mid-Holocene and early late Holocene contexts (Hart and Asch Sidell 1997; Petersen and Asch Sidell 1996), gourd and squash were present in the Northeast by at least the sixth and third millennium B.P., respectively, well before maize and beans. The 830 B.P. direct date on maize from Feature 235 does not change current thinking on the timing of maize's entry into New York and the Northeast. Ritchie's original date is no longer the oldest date associated with maize in the Northeast (Cassedy and Webb, this volume; Crawford et al. 1997; Hart and Asch Sidell 1996). For example, Crawford et al. have reported AMS dates on maize in Southern Ontario as early as 1570 B.P. ± 90 B.P., and Cassedy and Webb (this volume) have reported an AMS date on maize of 1050 ± 50 B.P. from eastern New York. As a result, the establishment of the maize, beans, and squash triad in the Northeast is dependent on the entry of beans and its subsequent evolution with maize and squash in northeastern agroecologies.

The original ninth-century B.P. date for the site established a precedent for the occurrence of beans in the Northeast equivalent to its initial occurrence in the American Midwest (Riley et al. 1990; Yarnell 1993). As stated by Riley et al. (1990:335), "Beans appear to arrive at virtually the same time in New York, at Owasco period sites" (also see Fritz 1990:398). The presence of beans without direct dates in apparently early contexts has been accepted in the Susquehanna River basin and elsewhere in the Northeast based on the apparent strength of its association with the early

Owasco component at Roundtop (Hart and Asch Sidell 1996; Heckenberger et al. 1992; Scarry 1990). However, the only other published direct date on beans in the Northeast is 550 ± 60 B.P. at the Burnham-Shepard site in Connecticut (Bendremer et al. 1991).

There are several references in the literature to beans in pre-seventh-century B.P. contexts in the Susquehanna River basin (Custer et al. 1994; Hart and Asch Sidell 1996; Hay and Hamilton 1984; King 1992; Scarry 1990). These occurrences make drawing strong conclusions from the Roundtop dates on the timing of the introduction of beans into the Northeast problematic. Only by directly dating beans from purportedly pre-seventh-century B.P. contexts at other sites can the question of bean's introduction into the Northeast be addressed. By the same token, only by directly dating domesticates from contexts where maize, beans, and squash co-occur at other sites can the timing of the evolution of maize-beans-squash agriculture be ascertained. Substantiation of the Roundtop dates by direct dates from purported pre-seventh-century contexts at other sites will help elucidate late prehistoric maize-beans-squash agricultural variability in the Eastern Woodlands (Smith 1992:111).

## DISCUSSION

My examination of Ritchie's lab notes suggests that he was convinced at some point prior to his published accounts of Roundtop that Feature 35 was associated with a later occupation of the site than was Feature 30, which yielded the ninth-century B.P. date. Ritchie's notes clearly indicate that he recognized the multicomponent nature of the site as confirmed in my examination of the pottery assemblages from three Roundtop features. Why, then, did Ritchie publish accounts of the site that downplayed the post early Owasco occupations? Why did he associate the date from Feature 30 with domesticates from Feature 35 when he had previously determined that Feature 30 was earlier than Feature 35?

Developing full answers to these questions would require the development of the complete historical and intellectual contexts under which Ritchie worked and is thus outside the scope of this chapter. However, there are important clues to these contexts in the publications in which Ritchie presented his accounts of Roundtop. The following represents an initial and admittedly tentative attempt to answer questions about Ritchie's motives. My goal is neither to attack Ritchie nor to diminish his considerable legacy. Rather it is to present a preliminary analysis of his interpretive framework that can be built on in future, more in-depth treatments.

Throughout most of his career, Ritchie was primarily a culture-historical taxonomist. He developed systematics for New York prehistory (Ritchie 1944, 1969) that is still in use today (Snow 1995). The goal of culture-historical systematists was to create internally homogeneous units at various scales that were chronologically and spatially discrete from other units at the same scale (Lyman et al. 1997). The methods for defining culture historic taxa were very successful at this task, and chronological ordering of taxa became the primary activity of archaeologists working under the paradigm (Dunnell 1986:175).

By the mid-1960s with the publication of the first volume of *The Archaeology of New York*, Ritchie, following developments in Americanist archaeology that began in the late 1940s and intensified in the 1950s and early 1960s (Lyman et al. 1997; Trigger 1989), desired to move beyond chronological ordering and become more anthropologically oriented. As Ritchie stated in the introduction to that volume, citing Taylor's (1948) conjunctive approach, his emphasis had "shifted from a primary concern with taxonomy, chronology, culture content and relationships, to the examination of whole cultures, within the relatively narrow limits afforded by their archaeological survivors" (Ritchie 1994:xxvii). By culture, Ritchie (1994:xxvii) meant "the particular strain of social heredity of a group of individuals … united by the sharing of a common tradition or traditions." The goal of this approach was to interpret archaeological cultures in a manner equivalent to ethnographic studies of living groups.

In the introduction to their 1973 volume *Aboriginal Settlement Patterns in the Northeast*,

Ritchie and Funk stated that their primary goal was the identification of the settlement patterns of specific components at archaeological sites. They defined component as "the totality of traits of a single occupation by a single community or social group, inferred from material remains at a site or level of site" (Ritchie and Funk 1973:1). Citing Deetz (1967) and Chang (1968), they defined settlement pattern as "that aspect of a component which reflects the structuring of the community at the site, and comprises the individual houses and other constructions, their arrangement, and associated features" (Ritchie and Funk 1973:1). Ritchie and Funk's (1973:2) settlement pattern analysis was geared towards "comprehending the extinct society and its relationship to other groups."

The goal of Ritchie's analysis of Roundtop, then, was to identify the primary component at the site. Since the culture-historical taxa he had previously defined for chronological purposes became the equivalent of ethnographic groups, by identifying a Carpenter Brook component at the site, Ritchie was identifying a specific group of people who were responsible for the creation of those material remains. To Ritchie (1973:193), these were the "Roundtop people." All the remains associated with that taxon were interpreted as the result of the activities of a single group of people. The presence of diagnostic artifacts of the Carpenter Brook phase in a feature reflected the activities of that social group.

Other components at the site were minor and transient (Ritchie 1973:187) and could not in the final analysis account for the presence of the maize, beans, and squash remains in Feature 35. The few small Carpenter Brook Cord-on-Cord herringbone sherds in Feature 35 were probably enough to convince Ritchie that the domesticates were affiliated with the Carpenter Brook phase, Roundtop people. The later sherds in the pit became problematic. His earlier unpublished ascription of them to later culture-historical types and therefore taxa, was in error, and he reassigned some to earlier types. Alternatively, the later pottery was simply noise that interfered with Ritchie's identification and analysis of the primary component and therefore could be ignored in his published description of Feature 35.

## SUMMARY AND CONCLUSIONS

Ritchie's published accounts of the Roundtop site have had a considerable impact on the late prehistoric archaeology of New York specifically and the Northeast in general. One reason for this was his association of maize, beans, and squash remains from Feature 35 with the Carpenter Brook, early Owasco culture-historical taxon which was radiocarbon dated to the ninth century B.P. AMS dating of these domesticates disproves this association. The earliest dates on the domesticates in Feature 35 are in the mid-seventh century B.P. This also represents the earliest date on beans at the site. The AMS dates on Feature 35 now represent the earliest direct-dated occurrence of the maize-beans-squash triad and of beans in the Northeast.

The dates on Roundtop beans suggest that this domesticate did not enter New York until at least 400 years after the introduction of maize. In both instances, the earliest dates may represent the first archaeological visibility of the domesticates rather than their time of introduction (Hart 1999; Smith 1992). The age of beans in the Northeast needs to be clarified by direct dating of beans from pre-mid-seventh-century B.P. contexts at other sites. There are enough reports of beans in such contexts in the Susquehanna River basin to prevent the drawing of any broad conclusions from the Roundtop dates. However, it is evident that the acceptance of beans in pre-mid-seventh-century B.P. contexts in the Northeast has been influenced by Ritchie's association of Roundtop's Feature 35 domesticates with the 880 B.P. date from Feature 30.

The results of AMS dating Roundtop's domesticates emphasize the need to directly date domesticate remains from apparently early contexts in the Northeast. The analysis of Ritchie's interpretation of Roundtop and its domesticate remains emphasize that descriptions of sites in the literature are interpretations, not observations. These interpretations must be closely analyzed and evaluated before they are accepted and incorporated into new descriptions, analyses, and interpretations of the past.

## ACKNOWLEDGEMENTS

Margaret Scarry located and tabulated the Roundtop botanical samples originally sent to Richard Yarnell by Ritchie. She also helped to get samples to the NSF Arizona AMS facility for dating. The NSF Arizona AMS facility staff prioritized the SUNY field school samples for dating, which prevented delay of this publication. Christina Rieth and Susan Prezzano helped to identify the culture-historical types of the pottery from Features 30, 35, and 235. Gary Crawford, Christina Rieth, Margaret Scarry, and two anonymous reviewers read earlier drafts of this chapter and provided many useful comments. Patricia Kernan provided the artifact illustrations and helped prepare the other figures. The AMS dates were funded by the New York State Museum. I alone am responsible for the content and interpretations presented in this chapter.

## END NOTE

1. In a letter to Mangelsdorf dated April 19, 1965, Ritchie stated that the "material comes from the Roundtop site, Endicott, Broome County, N.Y. It was excavated in August 1964 by an expedition from the New York State Museum and Science Service led by me, from Feature 35. The site pertains to the Early Owasco culture. Charcoal from another feature on the site, of the same culture, has recently been radiocarbon dated at the Yale Radiocarbon Laboratory at A.D. 1070 ± 60 years (Y-1534)."

REFERENCES CITED

Bendremer, J. C. M., and R. E. Dewar. 1994. The Advent of Prehistoric Maize in New England. In *Corn and Culture in the Prehistoric New World*, edited by S. Johannessen and C.A. Hastorf, pp. 369-393. Westview Press, Boulder.

Bendremer, J. C.M., E. A. Kellogg, and T. B. Largy. 1991. A Grass-Lined Maize Storage Pit and Early Maize Horticulture in Central Connecticut. *North American Archaeologist* 12:325-349.

Brown, J. A. 1977. Current Directions in Midwestern Archaeology. *Annual Reviews in Anthropology* 6:161-179.

Ceci, L. 1979-80. Maize Cultivation in Coastal New York: The Archaeological, Agronomical, and Documentary Evidence. *North American Archaeologist* 1:45-73.

Chang, K. C. 1968. Toward a Science of Prehistoric Society. In *Settlement Archaeology*, edited by K. C. Chang, pp. 1-9. National Press Books, Palo Alto, California.

Chapdelaine, C. 1993. The Sedentarization of the Prehistoric Iroquois: A Slow or Rapid Transition? *Journal of Anthropological Archaeology* 12:173-209.

Chapman, J., and G. Crites. 1987. Evidence for Early Maize (*Zea mays*) from the Icehouse Bottom Site, Tennessee. *American Antiquity* 52:352-354.

Conard, N., D. L. Asch, N. B. Asch, D. Elmore, H. Gove, M. Rubin, J. A. Brown, M. D. Wiant, K. B. Farnsworth, and T. G. Cook. 1984. Accelerator Radiocarbon Dating of Evidence for Prehistoric Horticulture in Illinois. *Nature* 308:443-446.

Crawford, G. W., D. G. Smith, and V. E. Bowyer. 1997. Dating the Entry of Corn (*Zea mays*) into the Lower Great Lakes. *American Antiquity* 62:112-119.

Creel, D., and A. Long. 1986. Radiocarbon Dating of Corn. *American Antiquity* 51:826-836.

Crites, G.D. 1993. Domesticated Sunflower in Fifth Millennium B.P. Temporal Context: New Evidence from Middle Tennessee. *American Antiquity* 58:146-148.

Custer, J. F., S. C. Watson, and D. N. Bailey. 1994. *Recovery Investigations of the West Water Street Site 36CN175 Lock Haven, Clinton County, Pennsylvania*. Prepared by KFS Historic Preservation Group, Philadelphia, Pennsylvania for U.S. Army Corps of Engineers, Baltimore.

Deetz, J.. 1967. *Invitation to Archaeology*. Natural History Press, New York.

Dunnell, R. C. 1986. Methodological Issues in Americanist Artifact Classification. In *Advances in Archaeological Method and Theory*, Vol. 9, edited by M. B. Schiffer, pp. 149-207. Academic Press, New York.

Ford, R. I. 1985. Patterns of Prehistoric Food Production in North America. In *Prehistoric Food Production in North America*, edited by R. I. Ford, pp. 341-364. Anthropological Papers No. 75. Museum of Anthropology, University of Michigan, Ann Arbor.

Fritz, G. J. 1990. Multiple Pathways to Farming in Precontact Eastern North America. *Journal of World Prehistory* 4:387-435.

Funk, R. E. 1993. *Archaeological Investigations in the Upper Susquehanna Valley, New York State*. Persimmon Press, Buffalo.

Gowlett, J. A. J. 1987. The Archaeology of Radiocarbon Accelerator Dating. *Journal of World Prehistory* 1:127-170.

Hart, J. P. 1999. Maize Agriculture Evolution in the Eastern Woodlands of North America: A Darwinian Perspective. *Journal of Archaeological Method and Theory* 6: in press.

Hart, J. P., and N. Asch Sidell. 1996. Prehistoric Agricultural Systems in the West Branch of the Susquehanna River Basin, A.D. 800 to A.D. 1350. *Northeast Anthropology* 52:1-30.

————. 1997. Additional Evidence for Early Cucurbit Use in the Northern Eastern Woodlands East of the Allegheny Front. *American Antiquity* 62:523-537.

Hay, C. A., and C. E. Hamilton. 1984. *The Bald Eagle Township Sewage Collection System Archaeological Project: Final Mitigation Research*. Technical Report No. 2. Department of Anthropology, The Pennsylvania State University, University Park.

Heckenberger, M. J., J. B. Petersen, and N. Asch Sidell. 1992. Early Evidence of Maize Agriculture in the Connecticut River Valley of Vermont. *Archaeology of Eastern North America* 20:125-149.

King, F. B. 1992. Floral Remains. In *The Prehistory of the Catawissa Bridge Replacement Site (36CO9)*, Columbia County, Pennsylvania, by T.C. East, J. M. Adovasio, W.C. Johnson, and D.R. Pedler. Prepared for the Cultural Resource Management Program, Department of Anthropology, University of Pittsburgh.

Laccetti, M. F. 1965. The Round Top Site: A Postulated Early Owasco Component. *The Bulletin of the New York State Archaeological Association* 33:12-20.

——————. 1966. The Round Top Site: A Pre-Iroquoian Farming Village in South-Central New York: Amateurs Uncover Early Indian Village in Southern Tier. *The New York State Conservationist* 22(3):12-14.

——————. 1974. The Round Top Site: An Early Owasco Horticultural Stage. *The Bulletin of the New York State Archaeological Association* 62:4-26.

Lenig, D. 1965. *The Oak Hill Horizon and its Relation to the Development of Five Nations Iroquois Culture*. Researches and Transactions of the New York State Archaeological Association, Vol. XV, No. 1. Buffalo.

Lyman, R. L., M. J. O'Brien, and R. C. Dunnell. 1997. *The Rise and Fall of Culture History*. Plenum Press, New York.

McBride, K. A., and R. E. Dewar. 1987 Agriculture and Cultural Evolution: Causes and Effects in the Lower Connecticut River Valley. In *Emergent Horticultural Economies of the Eastern Woodlands*, edited by W. F. Keegan, pp. 305-328. Center for Archaeological Investigations, Occasional Papers No. 7. Southern Illinois University at Carbondale.

Petersen, J. B., and N. Asch Sidell. 1996. Mid-Holocene Evidence of *Cucurbita* sp. from Central Maine. *American Antiquity* 61:685-698.

Prezzano, S. C. 1992. *Longhouse, Village, and Palisade: Community Patterns at the Iroquois Southern Door*. Ph.D. dissertation. Department of Anthropology, State University of New York at Binghamton. University Microfilms, Inc. Ann Arbor.

Riley, T. J., R. Edging, and J. Rosen. 1990. Cultigens in Prehistoric Eastern North America: Changing Paradigms. *Current Anthropology* 31:525-542.

Riley, T. J., G. R. Walz, C. J. Bareis, A. C. Fortier, and K. E. Parker. 1994. Accelerator Mass Spectrometry (AMS) Dates Confirm Early *Zea mays* in the Mississippi River Valley. *American Antiquity* 59:490-498.

Ritchie, W. A. 1944. *The Pre-Iroquoian Occupations of New York State*. Rochester Museum of Arts and Sciences, Rochester.

——————. 1969. *The Archaeology of New York State*. Revised edition. Natural History Press, Garden City.

——————. 1973. The Roundtop Site (Apl.1). In *Aboriginal Settlement Patterns in the Northeast*, by W. A. Ritchie and R. E. Funk, pp. 179-194. Memoir 20, New York Museum and Science Service. The University of the State of New York, Albany.

——————. 1994. *The Archaeology of New York State*. Revised edition. Purple Mountain Press, Fleischmanns, New York.

Ritchie, W. A., and R. E. Funk. 1973. *Aboriginal Settlement Patterns in the Northeast*. Memoir 20, New York Museum and Science Service. The University of the State of New York, Albany.

Ritchie, W. A., and R. MacNeish. 1949. The Pre-Iroquoian Pottery of New York State. *American Antiquity* 15:97-124.

Scarry, C. M. 1990. Plant Remains: 1985-1987 Seasons. In *Excavations at the Boland Site 1984-1987: A Preliminary Report*, by S. Prezzano and V. P. Steponaitis, pp. 143-460. Research Report 9, Research Laboratories of Anthropology, University of North Carolina, Chapel Hill.

Schambach, F. 1964. Round top Site, Fea 35, sec W10 N10, August 22/23, 1964. Notes on file, New York State Museum, Albany.

Schiffer, M. B. 1987. *Formation Processes of the Archaeological Record*. University of New Mexico Press, Albuquerque.

Shott, M. J. 1992. Radiocarbon Dating as a Probabilistic Technique: The Childers Site and Late Woodland Occupation in the Ohio Valley. *American Antiquity* 57:202-230.

Smith, B. D. 1992. Prehistoric Plant Husbandry in Eastern North America. In *The Origins of Agriculture: An International Perspective*, edited by C. W. Cowan and P. J. Watson, pp. 101-119. Smithsonian Institution Press, Washington, D.C.

Snow, D. R. 1980. *The Archaeology of New England*. Academic Press, New York.

—————. 1995. Migration in Prehistory: The Northern Iroquoian Case. *American Antiquity* 60:59-79.

Struiver, M., and P. J. Reimer. 1993. Extended 14C Database and Revised CALIB 3.0 14C Age Calibration Program. *Radiocarbon* 35:215-230.

Taylor, W. W. 1948. *A Study of Archaeology*. American Anthropologist, Vol. 50, Pt. 2, Memoir No. 69. Menasha, Wisconsin.

Trigger, B. D. 1989. *A History of Archaeological Thought*. Cambridge University Press, Cambridge.

Versaggi, N. M. 1986. *Hunter to Farmer: 10,000 Years of Susquehanna Valley Prehistory*. Roberson Center for Arts and Sciences, Binghamton, New York.

Winter, J. 1971. A Summary of Owasco and Iroquois Maize Remains. *Pennsylvania Archaeologist* 41(3):1-11.

Yarnell, R. A. 1976. Early Plant Husbandry in Eastern North America. In *Cultural Change and Continuity: Essays in Honor of James Bennet Griffin*, edited by C. Cleland, pp. 265-274. Academic Press, New York.

—————. 1993. The Importance of Native Crops during the Late Archaic and Woodland Periods. In *Foraging and Farming in the Eastern Woodlands*, edited by C. Margaret Scarry, pp. 13-26. University of Florida Press, Gainesville.

# CHAPTER 5

# CORNCOBS AND BUTTERCUPS: PLANT REMAINS FROM THE GOLDKREST SITE

Tonya B. Largy, Lucianne Lavin, Marina E. Mozzi, and Kathleen Furgerson

The Goldkrest site is located on Kuyper Island in the floodplain of the Hudson River in the Town of East Greenbush, Rensselaer County, New York (Figure 5.1). In the seventeenth and eighteenth centuries, Kuyper Island was a discrete island adjacent to the larger Papscanee Island. The two islands were separated by the Kuyper Kill (Dunn 1994:28; Huey 1993:Figure 1). Today, Kuyper Island is attached to Papscanee, no longer an island but part of the mainland.

The site was discovered in May 1993, during investigation of a natural gas transmission pipeline corridor. Data recovery was conducted in Autumn, 1993, by a multidisciplinary team of researchers. Excavation at the Goldkrest site unearthed a buried living floor (Stratum III) radio-carbon-dated to the Late Woodland (A.D. 1000 to Contact) and early Historic (A.D. 1500 to 1600) periods. Associated with it were hearths and pit features, numerous post molds forming rectangular and oval patterns representing community structures, and biological remains such as charred plant parts, calcined bone, and shell (Lavin et al. 1996, 1997).

A small Middle Woodland (A.D. 1 to 1000) occupation was uncovered in the lower portion of Stratum IV, three feet below the Late Woodland-early Historic component. It contained few artifacts, one unidentifiable seed part, and two possible charred *Chenopodium* sp. or *Amaranthus* sp. seeds. The Middle Woodland component's irrelevance to archaeobotany precludes its discussion in this chapter.

Goldkrest is the first undisturbed major Late Woodland and early Historic Native American habitation site discovered in the upper Hudson valley. Additionally, it is the first site in the upper valley (and the second site within the entire length of its eastern side) to contain evidence of pole-frame community structures, including a longhouse. Significantly, Goldkrest is

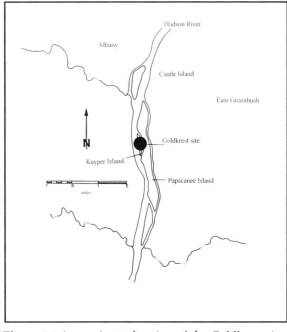

**Figure 5.1** Approximate location of the Goldkrest site in the Hudson River Valley. Map adapted from Huey (1993: Figure 1).

located in the heart of Mahikan tribal territory (Lavin et al. 1997, Vol. I). A mighty nation respected by both the Dutch and the English in the seventeenth and eighteenth centuries, the Mahikan once controlled huge land tracts on both sides of the upper and middle Hudson valley from Pine Plains, the Roeliff Jansen Kill on the south to Lake Champlain on the north, and as far east as the Housatonic River valley in what is now west-central Massachusetts and northwestern Connecticut (Dunn 1994). Except for scanty information derived from early European documents, relatively little is known about the early history of this once powerful Algonquian-speaking population.

Other Native American archaeological sites on the west bank of the Hudson have uncertain historic affiliations because at various points in time they were controlled by the Mohawk

Iroquois as well as the Mahikans. Goldkrest's association with the Mahikan cultural group, however, is undisputed (Dunn 1994:45-62). Consequently, archaeological investigations at Goldkrest are unearthing invaluable information on the lifeways of late prehistoric and early historic Mahikan people. Specifically, botanical remains from the site provide a window into the economy, medical herbalism, extractive technology, and settlement system of a fifteenth- to seventeenth-century Mahikan community.

## CHRONOLOGY

As noted above, the Late Woodland/early Historic occupations at Goldkrest were located in a buried living floor extending from Stratum III to the top of Stratum IV. Five features from the interface of these two strata were analyzed for this chapter. Three of these (Post Mold 3 in Excavation Unit 118, Post Mold 3 in Excavation Unit 127, and Red Stain A in Excavation Unit 127) were associated with the floor of a rectangular longhouse (Structure B) located in Locus 1 in the northern portion of the site (Figure 5.2). A date of $1090 \pm 90$ B.P. (Beta-70836; uncalibrated) was obtained on wood charcoal from Feature 22, a central post within the structure. However, this date likely is invalid since the feature had exhibited extensive rodent disturbance. A second date of $340 \pm 50$ B.P. (GX-22663-AMS, $^{13}$C-corrected) on wood charcoal from Red Stain A most probably dates the construction of the building.

An early Historic hearth (Feature 59) associated with Stratum III was discovered during monitoring at approximately S15E0. It lies within Locus 1 some distance from Structure B. It is not assumed to be associated with that structure at this stage of analysis. Its radiocarbon date of $350 \pm 50$ B.P. (Beta-76846; uncalibrated) identifies it as an early Historic feature. Its calibrated (Stuiver and Reimer 1993) date at $1\sigma$ is A.D. 1472-1641, however, which suggests it may have been a Late Woodland or Historic feature. Two sheet-brass fragments, which support an early Historic context, were recovered along with charred plant remains.

A concentrated deposit of shell remains (Feature 41) was recovered from the Late Woodland/early Historic levels at the interface of Strata III and IV in Locus 3 at the southern end of the site.

## ANALYTICAL METHODS

Flotation was carried out using a machine modeled after that used by Struever (1968). The contents of all cultural features were floated, and 50 percent of each sample was sorted by Archaeological Research Specialists (ARS) staff under low magnification using a stereomicroscope. Preliminary analysis of recovered botanical materials was conducted by Kathleen Furgerson and Marina Mozzi (Furgerson 1994). Those botanical specimens deemed to have high research potential and significance were analyzed further by Tonya Largy.

All specimens were examined under magnifications of 5X to 300X. All specimens (except seeds) were weighed to within 0.01 g. Individual specimens were manipulated with "feather-light" forceps to protect these fragile materials from breakage. Specimens were resorted into classes such as seed, nutshell, wood, and other plant parts. Uncharred seeds, discussed below, were identified without recording frequency (total numbers), but a representative sample of each taxon was saved. Wood fragments were only incidental in the samples submitted for analysis, and the request for analysis did not include identification of charred wood.

Taxa were identified to family, genus, and species using manuals (Martin and Barkley 1961; Montgomery 1978) and reference collections, including Largy's personal collection of charred seeds and nutshell supplemented by herbarium collections housed in the Morrill Science Center at the University of Massachusetts, Amherst. Identification of all species was made to the nearest taxonomic level possible using the described methods. All taxonomic nomenclature follows *Gray's Manual of Botany*, 8th edition (Fernald 1973 [1950]).

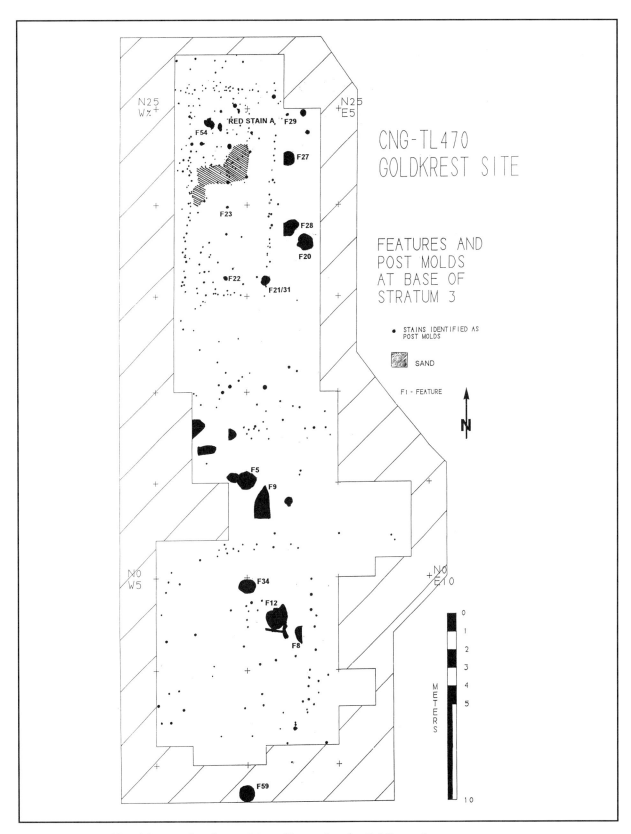

**Figure 5.2** Postmold and feature distribution Map of Locus 1 at the Goldkrest site.

**Table 5.1. pH Values for Selected Features at the Goldkrest Site.**

| Feature | Inventory Number | pH Value |
| --- | --- | --- |
| Feature 59 | Flot. No. 216 | 6.7 |
| Post Mold 3, EU 127 | S.S. No. 89 | 6.9 |
| Red Stain A, EU 127 | Flot. No. 173 | 6.9 |

## PRESERVATION AND RECOVERY

### Preservation

Preservation bias is a factor in the recovery of aboriginal plant remains from archaeological sites. In northern temperate latitudes with acidic soils such as are often found in New York and New England, plant remains are limited generally to the more structurally robust plant parts that preserve well when charred, unless unusual conditions are present. Goldkrest plant remains are limited to charred seeds, nutshell, maize (*Zea mays*) cob fragments, miscellaneous fragments of stems/roots, and very small fragments of unidentified plant material.

Soil pH values from both column and feature soil samples are close to neutral, ranging from 6.37 to 7.66. The literature on soil chemistry suggests that pH values are affected by a number of variables. For example, pH values measured in the laboratory may be different from measurements taken in the field due to the added absorption of carbon dioxide when soil samples are allowed to equilibrate with the atmosphere, a standard procedure (Coleman and Mehlich 1957:79). Table 5.1 lists the pH values for three of the five features submitted for analysis.

Another factor which contributed to the preservation of organics at the Goldkrest Site, and one which must not be underestimated during this analysis, is that of alluvial deposition. Frequent flooding of the Hudson River during historic times effectively protected Goldkrest's fragile archaeological components, as well as the faunal and botanical remains they contain, from

oxidation. As such, a comparatively high preservation potential was anticipated prior to, and confirmed upon, excavation and analysis.

No pH value was obtained from Feature 41, described as a "shell concentration" (Furgerson 1994), but we assume it is within the neutral range due to the calcium carbonate in the shell. Non-calcined bone and shell are preserved at Goldkrest, although in varying degrees of degradation due to taphonomic processes (Dirrigl in Lavin et al. 1997).

Plants are more fragile than animal bone and shell, which have a different set of preservation biases (Pearsall 1989), and therefore they would not be expected to preserve as well in an uncharred state in this region under normal conditions, unless the site were waterlogged. Plant preservation from Strata III and IV at Goldkrest is comparable to other sites examined by Largy in Southern New England. The literature reflects the difficulty in interpreting uncharred seeds recovered by flotation. We follow Minnis (1981) in considering only charred remains as prehistoric unless there is a specific reason to believe otherwise. Because of the nature of this project, no off-site controls are available for comparison with samples recovered on-site.

### Recovery

Recovery bias may affect plant macrofossil data obtained by flotation. Recovery rates may be monitored by adding controls to the flotation process, such as distinctive exotic charred or uncharred seeds of a certain number. The rate at which these controls are recovered by flotation gives some idea of the percentage of archaeobotanical seeds being recovered, although an equal rate cannot be

**Table 5.2. Uncharred Seed Taxa Recovered from Selected Features at the Goldkrest Site.**

| Feature No. | Unit No. | Item No. | Flotation No. | Common Name | Scientific Name |
|---|---|---|---|---|---|
| 59 | S15E0 | 02 | 216, 218 | Common purslane | *Portulaca oleracea* |
| 59 | S15E0 | 02 | 216, 218 | Common elderberry | *Sambucus canadensis* |
| 59 | S15E0 | 02 | 216, 218 | Green amaranth/pigweed | *Amaranthus retroflexus* |
| 59 | S15E0 | 02 | 216, 218 | Goosefoot | *Chenopodium* sp. |
| 59 | S15E0 | 01 | 216, 218 | Pink Family | Caryophyllaceae |
| 59 | S15E0 | 02 | 216, 218 | Composite Family | Compositae |
| PM 3 | EU127 | 20 | SS 54 | Grass Family | Gramineae |
| PM 3 | EU127 | 20 | SS 54 | Chickweed | *Stellaria* sp. |
| PM 3 | EU127 | 20 | SS 54 | Wood-Sorrel | *Oxalis* sp. |
| PM 3 | EU127 | 20 | SS 54 | Common purslane | *Portulaca oleracea* |
| PM 3 | EU127 | 20 | SS 54 | Goosefoot | *Chenopodium* [*album*] |
| PM 3 | EU127 | 20 | SS 54 | Green amaranth/pigweed | *Amaranthus retroflexus* |

assumed. Although no controls were used during flotation, the uncharred seed data suggest the recovery rate was good (Table 5.2). One of the smallest (<1.0 mm) seeds in the flora of New England, common purslane (*Portulaca oleracea*), was recovered from both Feature 59 and Post Mold 3, Unit 127. Most of the remaining uncharred seed species measure approximately 1 mm in length/width. It is probable that a high percentage of preserved charred plant data was recovered from Goldkrest soil samples.

## RESULTS OF ANALYSIS

### Uncharred Seeds

Nine taxa were identified from two features, Feature 59 (a hearth) and Post Mold 3. These taxa, with common names, are listed in Table 5.2. Six were identified to genus/species, while three were identified only to family. *Portulaca oleracea* (common purslane); *Chenopodium* sp. and *C. album* (goosefoot); *Amaranthus* cf. *retroflexus* (green amaranth or pigweed); *Stellaria* sp. (chickweed); *Oxalis* sp. (wood-sorrel); and families Caryophyllaceae (pink); Compositae (composite or daisy); and

Gramineae (grass) are herbaceous taxa while *Sambucus canadensis* (common elderberry) is a woody shrub. Common elderberry is found in moist soils along stream and riverbanks and other moist habitats. All other taxa are weedy species that invade disturbed habitats such as gardens, roadsides, and clearings. Many of the identified taxa are native to northeastern North America, while at least one, *C. album*, was introduced from the Old World.

There are no clear guidelines to the interpretation of uncharred seeds, as stated above. There often is no undisputed indication of contemporaneity with a prehistoric occupation, and the problem is compounded when more recently dated sites, such as Goldkrest, are under consideration. However, it is significant that insect body parts are present in the same samples. Extensive experience in analyzing archaeobotanical samples from sites in Southern New England leads us to conclude that there is a significant correlation between the presence of numerous taxa of uncharred seeds and insect body parts in the same sample.

Insect remains in an archaeological site may be interpreted in several ways. Dirrigl and Greenberg (1995) have discussed the usefulness of examining the role of insect remains in site interpretations. Elias (1994) has summarized many Quaternary fossil insect studies from North America and Canada. He has stated, "Insect exoskeletons are found chiefly in anoxic sediments that contain abundant organic detritus. Insects decompose rapidly in heavily oxidized sediments" (Elias 1994:18). Therefore, the long-term preservation of insect chitin from late Holocene archaeological contexts in very recent alluvial sediments, such as Goldkrest, is unknown for northeastern North America.

Little is known, too, about microhabitat segregation of insects (i.e., the vertical distribution of their living areas beneath the soil). Different insect species live in different microhabitats during various stages of their development, making it difficult to determine their microhabitat for each stage (Stefan Cover, personal communication). Direct dating of the insect remains from deeper contexts would address the issue of contemporaneity with cultural materials of a certain age in contexts other than human burials. (See Dirrigl and Greenberg 1995 for a discussion of insects associated with human burials).

Insect remains also may provide evidence of bioturbation. One unpublished example is Largy's identification of nutlets of *Crataegus Phaenopyrum* (Washington Thorn) from a prehistoric feature on Liberty Island in New York harbor. This commonly planted ornamental species of hawthorn has not ranged historically in that area; rather, it is native to regions much further south and west. These nutlets were present in flotation samples from all levels of the feature, which underlay a thick shell midden deposit and two strata of historic fill. Largy interpreted their presence as intrusions resulting from earthworm activity in the shell layer above, which she observed while samples were being collected from the feature. Following this, we argue that the uncharred seed from Goldkrest likely are intrusive and have no cultural association.

## Charred Seeds

Eight taxa were identified among 368 seeds from four features at the Goldkrest site. These taxa, with common names listed in Table 5.3, are summarized in Table 5.4.

Seven taxa native to Southern New England and one cultigen are included. Five seeds remain unidentified since no diagnostic landmarks are preserved. In addition, six specimens either are questionable as seed, incomplete, fragmentary, or lack their testa (outer seed coat), which precludes identification. Several are identified with the designation "cf.", meaning they "compare with" that taxon, but the specimen may be incomplete or somewhat distorted, preventing a definite identification.

Feature 59, an early Historic rock hearth feature dated to $350 \pm 50$ B.P., yielded 361 (98 percent) of the total number of charred seeds and 6 of the identified taxa (*Ranunculus* sp; *Rubus* sp.; *Sambucus canadensis*; cf. *Chenopodium* sp.; *Zea mays*; and Paniceae). From the features associated with the longhouse floor, three taxa (*Zea mays*; Polygonaceae/Cyperaceae; and cf. *Vitis* sp.) were identified from Post Mold 3, EU 127; one taxon (*Zea mays*) from Post Mold 3, EU 118; and one taxon (*Zea mays*) from Red Stain A, EU 127. No identified taxa were recovered from Feature 41.

All identified taxa, except maize, are native to northeastern North America, and all have economic uses as food or medicine, or ritual purpose (Moerman 1986; Tantaquidgeon 1972; Waugh 1973). However, most of the wild taxa also may be classified as ruderals, early succession "weedy" species that invade disturbed soils such as clearings and gardens. These taxa are commonly found in floodplain habitats. Common elderberry, the only shrub species represented, requires moist soils and grows in riparian habitats along stream banks, in swamps, and in wetlands.

*Ranunculus* sp. (buttercup) is the most frequently (317) recovered taxon (Figure 5.3). An additional 25 achenes distorted by the charring process came from the same sample and closely resemble this taxon. If both groups are combined, they represent 93 percent of the charred seed assemblage. The buttercup flower produces numerous fruits, technically referred to as ach-

**Table 5.3. Charred Seed Taxa Recovered from Selected Features at the Goldkrest Site.**

| Feature No. | Unit No. | Item No. | Flotation No. | Qty. | Common Name | Comments |
|---|---|---|---|---|---|---|
| 41 | | 18 | 160 | 1 | | Seed? |
| 59 | S15E0 | 07 | 216, 218 | 1 | | Seed endosperm |
| 59 | S15E0 | 07 | 216, 218 | 5 | | Unidentified Seed (no landmarks) |
| 59 | S15E0 | 07 | 216, 218 | 1 | | Incomplete seed |
| 59 | S15E0 | 07 | 216, 218 | 1 | | Incomplete seed |
| 59 | S15E0 | 07 | 216, 218 | 1 | Millet | Tribe Paniceae |
| 59 | S15E0 | 07 | 216, 218 | 2 | Common elderberry | *Sambucus canadensis* |
| 59 | S15E0 | 07 | 216, 218 | 3 | Bramble/Berries | *Rubus* sp. |
| 59 | S15E0 | 07 | 216, 218 | 9 | cf. Goosefoot | cf. *Chenopodium* |
| 59 | S15E0 | 07 | 216, 218 | 25+ | cf. Buttercup | cf. *Ranunculus* |
| 59 | S15E0 | 07 | 216, 218 | 317 | Buttercup | *Ranunculus* sp. |
| 59 | S15E0 | 07 | 216, 218 | 4 | Maize? | *Zea mays* kernel? frags |
| PM3 | EU127 | 15 | SS 52 | 1 | cf. Maize | cf. *Zea mays* seed frag |
| PM3 | EU127 | 14 | | 1 | Maize? | Poss. *Zea mays* |
| PM3 | EU127 | 14 | | 1 | Maize | *Zea mays* |
| PM3 | EU127 | 21 | SS 54 | 1 | | Seed? frag |
| PM3 | EU127 | 21 | SS 54 | 1 | cf. Grape | cf. *Vitis* sp. |
| PM3 | EU127 | 21 | SS 54 | 1 | Buckwheat/Sedge Family | Polygonaceae/Cyperaceae |
| PM3 | EU127 | 19 | SS 89 | 1 | Maize | *Zea mays* kernel |
| Red Stain A | EU127 | 07 | 177 | 1 | Maize | *Zea mays* kernel |

**Table 5.4. Summary of Charred Seed Taxa Recovered from Selected Features at the Goldkrest Site.**

| Plant Type | Genus/Species | Count | Common Name |
|---|---|---|---|
| Woody Shrub | *Sambucus canadensis* | 2 | Common elderberry |
| Woody Vine | *Rubus* sp. | 3 | Bramble/berries |
| Herbaceous | *Ranunculus* sp. | 317+ | Buttercup |
| Herbaceous | cf. *Chenopodium* sp. | 9 | Goosefoot |
| Herbaceous | cf. *Vitis* sp. | 2 | Grape |
| Herbaceous | Family Polygonaceae/Cyperaceae | 1 | Buckwheat Family/Sedge Family |
| Herbaceous | Gramineae, Tribe Paniceae | 1 | Grass Family, Millet Tribe |
| Cultigen | *Zea mays* | 3+5? | Maize |

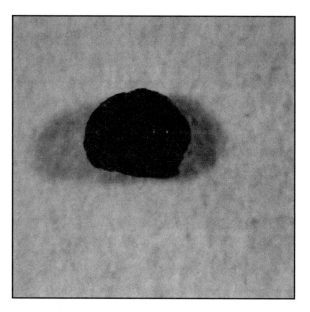

**Figure 5.3.** Sample of Charred *Ranunculus* Seeds recovered from Feature 59.

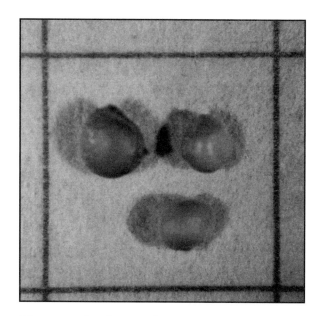

**Figure 5.4.** Modern uncharred *Ranunculus abortivus* Seeds for comparison (grid=5mm).

enes, clustered in a "head." These achenes, each consisting of a kernel (the true seed) inside the thin, dry fruit coat (pericarp), may number 30 or more per flower. Among the various species, uncharred achenes range from approximately 1 mm to 3.5 mm in size. This is the most unusual taxon identified at Goldkrest and may be a first for Southern New England. One achene has been reported by Asch Sidell (this volume) from a site in Maine. To our knowledge, there has been no other published identification.

The genus *Ranunculus* includes a number of species native to the Northeast. Six native species of buttercup are listed as growing in eastern New York within the geographic range of the Goldkrest site (NYFA 1990). None is edible, since they contain "acrid-narcotic poisons" (Fernald 1973 [1950]:642). Fernald and Kinsey (1958:202-203) discussed emergency food uses for two species, *R. bulbosus* and *R. scleratus*, but these are naturalized from Europe and Asia (Fernald 1973 [1950]). Several scholars (Arnason et al. 1981; Duke 1986; Herrick and Snow 1995; Moerman 1986) have listed numerous medicinal uses for plants of this genus by many native groups, including the Iroquois who used *R. abortivus* (Figure 5.4) against

witchcraft, for counteracting "poison another has given you" (Herrick and Snow 1995:88). Possibly, this plant was considered as powerful medicine because it possesses a hook-like structure, one of the features which the Iroquois associated with "love and/or basket (witching) medicines" (Herrick and Snow 1995:90). *R. abortivus* is also included among the group of plants "thought to be effective in curing or preventing certain severe, English-named diseases" (Herrick and Snow 1995:90-91).

*Ranunculus* was used to treat ills ranging from toothache to venereal disease. All methods, save one, given by early twentieth-century Iroquois informants, involve crushing or steeping roots and drinking or applying the liquid to the affected area. According to Herrick and Snow (1995:124), Cayuga informant David Jack related to F. W. Waugh that the method for treating venereal disease was to "dry and cut up 4 plants and boil them down a little in 3 qt. water and drink often until quantity is gone." The time of year for collecting the plant was not specified, so it is unclear whether the seeds themselves were an integral part of the process. If treatment was administered in the spring, the seeds would have been available for collection, as well.

Significantly, this taxon was found in Feature 59, the same feature that produced the two European sheet-brass fragments and a radiocarbon date of A.D. 1600. The frequency of *Ranunculus* achenes in the rock hearth suggests it is not an accidental inclusion. Assuming that the presence of this species represents intentional use, some medicinal or ritual (charm) purpose likely accounts for its presence in the hearth.

*Chenopodium* sp. has been recovered frequently from archaeological sites in eastern North America (George and Dewar, this volume). This prolific seed-producer colonizes disturbed ground and is commonly found in gardens and larger agricultural fields. *Chenopodium* likely was an important high-carbohydrate food resource for aboriginal foragers (Fritz 1990:403; Smith 1995). Reduction in testa (seed-coat) thickness of seeds recovered from sites in the midwestern United States shows that *Chenopodium berlandieri* ssp. *jonesianum* was domesticated between 3,500 and 3,400 B.P. (Smith 1992:108). There is no published evidence as yet for domestication of this taxon in New England (George and Dewar, this volume). When charred *Chenopodium* sp. is recovered, frequently its condition is very fragile, as was the case for the nine Feature 59 specimens, which fell apart during examination. Seeds of *Chenopodium* sp. from the Burnham-Shepard site in South Windsor, Connecticut, were well preserved. A small sample examined by Bruce Smith was found not to be domesticated (Bendremer et al. 1991). Subsequently, the entire sample was examined by George and Dewar. They concluded that a number of specimens "exhibit variability in some characters that have been used to identify cultivated and feral status in the Midcontinent" (George and Dewar, this volume).

*Sambucus canadensis*, common elderberry, produces a small purple-black berry borne in large panicles. Both flowers and fruits are edible. The fruits ripen in very late summer and early fall. The Mohegan of Connecticut used both flowers and fruit in various medicinal remedies (Tantaquidgeon 1977:75). Waugh (1916:127) included elderberry in his list of "principal varieties" of berries used by the Iroquois. Aranson et al. (1981:2198) listed it among foods high in crude fiber.

*Rubus* sp. is another commonly eaten berry, usually borne on canes or long stems with prickles and found in a variety of soils. The genus includes blackberry, black raspberry, and red raspberry. Dewberry, another species in the genus, grows on vines that form mats and run along the ground in dry, sandy soils. All species require sunlight to produce a good crop of fruit and often colonize disturbed areas, clearings and the edges of woods and thickets. The berries ripen in July and August.

The Mohegan used juice of *R. hispidus* (blackberry) as a cure for dysentery (Tantaquidgeon 1977:75). It is also eaten extensively by birds and small mammals. Largy once observed in the field small mammal droppings with more than a dozen nutlets of *Rubus*, sp. There are many such circumstances for the accidental deposition of this species (as with many others) on archaeological sites. *Rubus* nutlets are dense-walled, which contributes to excellent preservation, and it is one of the most commonly preserved charred taxa from sites in the Northeast.

One seed, identified as belonging to either of two families (Polygonaceae or Cyperaceae), from Post Mold 3, Unit 127, lacks certain landmarks for definite identification to family. Seeds of both families bear many morphological similarities and are difficult to separate unless these landmarks are preserved after charring. Both families are prolific producers of edible seeds. Species of both families are found in a variety of soils, including wet and dry, and both often colonize disturbed habitats.

Preliminary interpretations of the Goldkrest site describing flotation methodologies and tentative results have been published elsewhere (Lavin et al. 1996:125). Subsequent analyses have shown certain of the tentative identifications to be incorrect. The *Portulaca oleracea* (purslane) seed was uncharred rather than charred. The seed thought to have been Caprifoliaceae or *Celtis* sp. (viburnum or hackberry) does not resemble these taxa and the specimen remains unidentified at this writing.

## Cultigens

*Zea mays* (maize) is represented by kernels (Figure 5.5), cupules, and glumes. Two definite and 6

**Table 5.5. Distribution of Maize Kernels and Cob Fragments Recovered from Selected Features at the Goldkrest Site.**

| Feature | Count | Kernels Item No. | Wt. | Description | Cob Fragments Count | Item No. | Wt. |
|---|---|---|---|---|---|---|---|
| 59 | 4 [a] | 5 | 0.05 | Cupule fragment | 1 | 1 | 0.01 |
| | – | – | – | Cupule | 12 | 1 | 0.10 |
| | – | – | – | Paired cupule | 13 | 4 | 0.65 |
| Post Mold 3. | 1 [a] | 14 | 0.02 | – | – | – | – |
| Unit 118 | 1 | 14 | 0.02 | – | – | – | – |
| | 1 [b] | 15 | <0.01 | – | – | – | – |
| Post Mold 3 | – | – | – | Glume fragment | 2 | 19 | 0.01 |
| Unit 127 | | | | | | | |
| Red Stain A | 1 | 9 | 0.13 | – | – | – | – |

*Notes*

[a] Identification uncertain.

[b] cf. *Zea mays*

probable kernels, 26 cupules, and 2 glume fragments were found in 4 of the 5 features analyzed (Table 5.5). Morphologically, the kernels appear to be those of Northern Flint maize, being wider that they are deep (Figure 5.6).

Preservation of maize kernels and cobs apparently differs depending on which part of the maize plant is charred. An informal experiment to carbonize an ear of maize in Largy's wood stove resulted in complete combustion of the entire cob while the charred kernels were preserved among the ashes. This same result was obtained by Mozzi with a class of Connecticut schoolchildren conducting ethnoarchaeological experiments. However, at Goldkrest, fewer kernels than cob fragments were recovered. Cassedy and Webb (this volume) report the recovery of similar ratios of maize kernels to cob fragments from Late Woodland sites in the eastern Hudson River valley. Adding to the mystery is the discovery of maize parts in features such as post molds, which are not directly associated with food preparation and consumption and (assuming the community structures had been constructed prior to harvesting) not open during such procedures. This suggests that maize was originally present in greater abundance than indicated by the actual recovered quantity. One possible explanation for this is that the inhabitants of Goldkrest were shucking the cobs and transporting the majority of kernels for future consumption at another encampment within the group's settlement system such as the main village or a winter hamlet. Goldkrest has been interpreted as a seasonal summer-fall hamlet.

Bendremer and Dewar (1994:372) summarized Late and Final Woodland sites with cultigens in New England and eastern New York known before Cassedy and Webb's results were disseminated. Their map of sites west of the Hudson River shows only two sites, Getman and Nahrwold, on two tributaries in the general vicinity of Albany, New York. Goldkrest makes important additions to the sparse data recovered so far in this region.

Maize had medicinal and industrial uses among the Mohegan of Connecticut. Dried cobs were boiled, and the liquid was used as a wash to cure the toxic effects of poison ivy (*Rhus toxicodendron*) (Tantaquidgeon 1977:77). Cobs were also used in games and to make dolls for children, while the husks were used to make baskets, as well as dolls (Tantaquidgeon 1977:80).

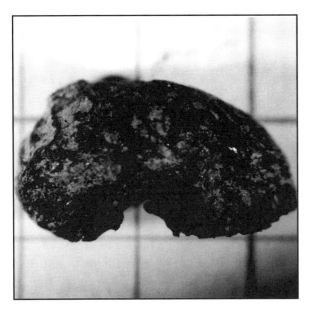

**Figure 5.5.** Maize kernal recovered from red stain A (grid=5mm).

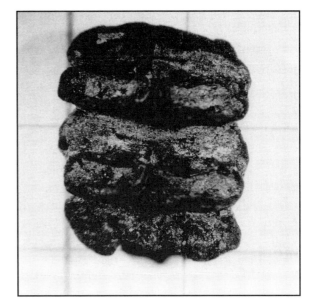

**Figure 5.6.** Paired cupules of maize recovered from Feature 59 (grid=5mm).

Little (1994; Little and Schoeninger 1995) has been working to establish a database of radiocarbon ages and $^{13}C$ values for maize in the Northeast. At her suggestion, a single charred maize kernel from Red Stain A, Unit 127, was submitted for AMS radiocarbon dating and isotope measurement to Geochron Labs., Inc., Cambridge, Massachusetts. A small wood charcoal sample, also from Red Stain A, Unit 127, was submitted for AMS dating for comparison (see Appendix I). The reported date for the kernel is 380 ± 50 B.P. ($^{13}C$-corrected; GX-22651-AMS). The date reported for the wood charcoal is 340 ± 50 B.P. ($^{13}C$-corrected; GX-22663-AMS). Little has reported that the two dates are likely to be nearly synchronous (Appendix I).

**Nutshell**

A total of 260 *Juglans cinerea* (butternut) shell fragments (9.31 g) was recovered from three features, (Feature 59, Post Mold 3 in Unit 118, and Post Mold 3 in Unit 127). Feature 59 yielded 90 percent of this sample. Post Mold 3 in Unit 118 produced 3 percent, and Post Mold 3 in Unit 127 produced 7 percent of the total. Note that this chapter does not include discussion of the 406 additional fragments of butternut from Goldkrest Features 12, 12A, 22,

23, 26, 27, 37, 43, 49, 54, 55, Post Mold 12, Post Mold 16, and three samples within Unit N10W4, identified by Furgerson (1994) during the earlier stage of analysis. Furgerson also reported 77 fragments of hickory (*Carya* sp.) from Features 22 and 26. No hickory nutshell was present in the five features analyzed by Largy.

Charred nutshell of any species may become incorporated in archaeological sediments in numerous ways. It may be indicative of cultural use for food, medicine, dye, or smudging to discourage insects. Non-cultural agents may include rodents, natural deposition from nearby trees, or the results of predation by other animals. Since nutshell is composed of dense plant tissue, it preserves well and can be charred as a result of a natural fire. However, when large numbers of nutshells are recovered from features and in the absence of off-site samples for comparison, we assume their presence indicates cultural use.

Butternut (*Juglans cinerea*) grows in bottomlands, on floodplains, and in mixed deciduous forests. Hickory (*Carya* sp.) grows in a variety of soil types and elevations. Both butternut and hickory ripen and are available through the fall. However, neither species produces a consistent crop annually. Both may be eaten fresh or stored for later use. Certainly butternut, also known as white walnut, would have been an important dietary component of aboriginal people. It contains exceptional amounts of iron, exceeding 6.5 mg/g, as well as protein and "significant quantities of oil" (Aranson et al. 1981:2197-2198).

Waugh documented butternut as one of the nut species used by modern Iroquois in a variety of ways (Waugh 1916:122-124). He stated that "the gathering of nuts was usually left to the women and children, who gathered the harvest after the frosts had brought it down. The hickory nut seems to have been the most widely esteemed" (Waugh 1916:122). In a small settlement such as Goldkrest, the presence of nutshell may represent women's and children's activities. He writes "nut-cracking outfits, consisting of a couple of rounded stones with pitted centres, were used in removing the shells. Many of the older people still remember these and a few specimens are occasionally found" (Waugh 1916:123). Native peoples boiled cracked hickory, walnuts, and "several others" to extract oil and to separate shells from nutmeat.

During boiling, shells fall to the bottom, nutmeats rise just above the shell, and oil rises to the surface where it is skimmed off and placed in a separate container (Fernald and Kinsey 1958:148). After skimming the nutmeats, these were mixed with other foods or crushed and added to maize soup (Waugh 1916:124). Nutmeat oil had numerous uses besides food. Waugh (1916:124) wrote, "It was often added to the mush used by the False-Face Societies. Nutmeat oil also was used formerly (like sunflower oil) for the hair, either alone or mixed with bear's grease." According to Lafitau (cited in Waugh 1916:124), the mixture was used as protection against mosquitos.

Talalay et al. (1984) suggested that butternuts were processed by cracking and extracting the meats by hand as described by Waugh rather than by boiling. Experiments show that boiling crushed walnuts (*Juglans nigra*) with shell density similar to butternut results in sinking of both shell and nutmeats to the bottom of the pot, unless the nuts were kept very dry for at least several months (Talalay et al. 1984:354). Their experiments further showed that during extended boil-

ing, walnut hull fragments dissolve and quickly contaminate the nutmeats and oil, rendering them "unpalatable, if not inedible" (Talalay et al. 1984:354).

Late Woodland/early Historic stone-filled hearths discovered on the site contained nutshells and numerous charcoal and reddened earth and stone indicative of very intense firing. Several explanations exist to explain the presence of butternut shell in Goldkrest's hearths. One possible scenario is that the butternuts were first dried out by heating in the fires, then crushed and boiled in water as mentioned above. Other explanations include nut roasting and processing, and the incorporation of the sharp butternut shell fragments into the fire for use as fuel.

## SUMMARY AND CONCLUSION

As the first intact Late Woodland and early Historic settlement investigated in the upper Hudson valley, Goldkrest offers the first opportunity for the archaeobotanical study of a Mahikan site. No other habitation sites with undisputed Mahikan affiliation have been excavated to date.

No written ethnobotany exists for the Mahikan people. In fact, few written ethnobotanies for northeastern Native Americans exist for the early Historic period other than general observations of early explorers and Jesuit missionaries.

The archaeobotanical data help to define early Mahikan diet, use of herbal medicine, and settlement patterning. The lithic, ceramic, and feature data suggest the Goldkrest site was an unfortified hamlet recurrently occupied by family groups over hundreds of years. Faunal analyses conducted by Dirrigl (Lavin et al. 1997, vols. I and IIIa) suggest the Goldkrest occupants fished, collected fresh-water shellfish, and hunted terrestrial mammals, all within the floodplain area. The archaeobotanical analysis expands the economic picture by demonstrating that the Mahikans also collected locally available wild plant resources and grew maize. The seasonal availability of several species allows us to establish the seasons of site occupation as mid-summer to early fall. The recovery of both maize kernels and cob fragments suggest that the planting fields may have been nearby. The discovery of a possible hoe fragment supports this theory (Lavin et al. 1997:60), as does documentary information. Seventeenth-century Dutch records note that land on the river in East Greenbush and Papscanee Island were cleared Indian fields prior to their purchase by the Dutch in the early 1600s (Dunn 1994:225-226). Goldkrest also allows a glimpse of how plants were used in ways other than subsistence.

Feature 59 represents the first occurrence of an obviously poisonous species found in great numbers in a context which may be interpreted as ritual or ceremonial. The recovery of Euro-American trade goods in the form of brass fragments from the same feature that yielded evidence of a plant species possibly used as a charm to ward off European disease is, perhaps, an omen of hard times to come.

## ACKNOWLEDGEMENTS

The authors would like to acknowledge the following individuals for their assistance during the various stages of research and publication of this article. Two peer reviewers provided insightful questions and comments that served to enhance this manuscript. In particular, Gayle Fritz's comments and suggested revisions were invaluable. Elizabeth Little provided the appendix entitled, "Maize Ages and Isotope Values at the Goldkrest Site." Paul Huey, of the New York State Office of Parks, Recreation and Historic Preservation Bureau of Historic Sites, graciously allowed the adaptation of a figure from his 1993 publication for this volume. Archaeological Research Specialists staff members Michael Bourassa, Brent Wimmer, Christopher Lowe, William Roche, and S. Douglas Dumas assisted during the flotation and sorting of Goldkrest's feature matrices. Stephen Cover of the Entomology Department, Harvard University Museums of Natural History, clarified insect microhabitat, and Karen Searcy, University of Massachusetts (Amherst) Herbarium Director, facilitated our use of those collections. And lastly, John Hart of the New York State Museum and chair of the New York Natural History Conference IV, tirelessly served as this volume's editor. His perseverance and patience have been most appreciated.

## APPENDIX I: MAIZE AGE AND ISOTOPE VALUES AT THE GOLDKREST SITE

Elizabeth A. Little

### Background

Archaeological finds of maize kernels in the Northeast have been, until recently, few and far between. In case their one or two kernels might provide genetic or other information, archaeologists on the coast have been averse to sacrificing these kernels to radiocarbon-dating procedures. Instead, we have been dating charcoal "associated" with maize kernels since William Ritchie's time (1969; see Bendremer and Dewar 1994; Hart, this volume). Now that Accelerator Mass Spectrometry (AMS) dating is available and well tested (Creel and Long 1986; Hedges and Gowlett 1986), single kernels can be dated. It is more costly than the $^{14}$C-decay counting method, but it requires only one kernel and gives greater accuracy than the method using radiocarbon activity measurements.

Comparisons between "associated" charcoal and AMS maize ages in Illinois by Conard et al. (1984) suggest that many charcoal dates may not apply to the "associated" maize kernels. Some reasons suggested for this poor association are that:

(1) The wood used in a particular fire may have been old when it died (see Schiffer 1986), may have stood dead for many years before falling, or may have been drifting from one river or coastal shore to another over a long period of time.

(2) The feature or site may have been disturbed at any time by the activities of animals or people, or by trees toppling. Thus, young maize might have been introduced into an old feature, or, alternatively, very old charcoal could have come from an old forest fire or an early component of the site.

In summary, maize ages should be evaluated by comparing AMS ages of kernels with "associated" charcoal ages until we understand our site and feature chronology better than we do at present.

Along with $^{14}$C aging, the lab can measure $\delta^{13}$C and $\delta^{15}$N isotope values for a kernel. The $\delta^{13}$C values provide a correction for fractionation in maize up to 200 years (Hall 1967). They are also valuable for diet studies in the Northeast (Little and Schoeninger 1995) and can provide data on the changes in $\delta^{13}$C values of the atmosphere (Marino and McElroy 1991). $\delta^{15}$N values can provide information on the use of fertilizer by prehistoric people (DeNiro and Epstein 1981). However, since the nitrogen appears to have been destroyed by charring in the one northeastern archaeological kernel analyzed so far (Strauss 1994), in this instance we only plan a test to confirm the negative results.

**Goldcrest Maize Kernel and Wood Charcoal**
One nearly whole kernel, identified by Tonya Largy as typical maize with skin striations, was selected for $^{14}$C aging, $\delta^{13}$C and $\delta^{13}$N measurements at Geochron Labs, Inc., Cambridge. The sample is illustrated in Figure 5.5. Its provenience is Item No. 9, Red Stain A, E1/2, Unit 127, N23W2; Light Fraction of Flotation No. 177. A small sample of wood charcoal from the same Red Stain A, Unit 127, was also selected for aging and $\delta^{13}$C measurement. Both samples were associated with the longhouse with an estimated age of less than 1000 years. Because of the very small sizes of both samples, both were aged by the AMS method.

**Results**
For the charred maize kernel from the Goldkrest Site, Item No. 9, Unit 127, Geochron Labs reported the AMS radiocarbon age, GX-22651-AMS as 380 ± 50 $^{14}$C yrs B.P., $\delta^{13}$C-corrected for fractionation. The value of $\delta^{13}$C is -9.8‰. There was no nitrogen in the sample (NR-82895) for measurement of $\delta^{15}$N.

For the Goldkrest small wood charcoal sample from Red Stain A, Unit 127, Geochron Labs reported the AMS radiocarbon age, GX-22663-AMS, as 340 ± 50 $^{14}$C yrs B.P., $\delta^{13}$C-corrected for fractionation. The value of $\delta^{13}$C is -26.7‰.

**Discussion**
These two $\delta^{13}$C-corrected radiocarbon ages may be calibrated by Stuiver and Reimer's (1993) 20-year CALIB 3.03 program. The ages, now cal dates A.D., with the intercepts in parentheses and the ± 1-σ range (67 percent probability) on the left and right, become:

Maize: cal A.D. 1448 (1483) 1631, and
Charcoal: cal A.D. 1477 (1520, 1569, 1627) 1644
For ± 2σ, or 95 percent probability, the ranges are:
Maize: cal A.D. 1435-1648, and
Charcoal: cal A.D. 1445-1660

Because of the large overlap in age ranges, the two dates are likely to be fairly close in time (Long and Rippeteau 1974).

## SUMMARY

The radiocarbon ages and $\delta^{13}$C values for associated maize and charcoal are valuable early contributions to a maize radiocarbon and stable isotope database for the Northeast. There are no surprises here. The lack of nitrogen in charred maize suggests that for the measurement of $\delta^{15}$N in maize, uncharred kernels or cobs would be valuable to test.

## REFERENCES CITED

Aranson, T., R. J. Hebda, and T. Johns. 1981. Use of Plants for Food and Medicine by Native Peoples of Eastern Canada. *Canadian Journal of Botany* 59:2189-2325.

Bendremer, J. C. M., and R.E. Dewar. 1994. The Advent of Prehistoric Maize in New England. In *Corn and Culture in the Prehistoric New World*, edited by S. Johannessen and C. A. Hastorf, pp. 369-393. Westview Press, Boulder.

Bendremer, J. C. M., E. A. Kellogg, and T. B. Largy. 1991. A Grass-Lined Maize Storage Pit and Early Maize Horticulture in Central Connecticut. *North American Archaeologist* 12:325-350.

Coleman, N. T., and A. Mehlich. 1957. The Chemistry of Soil pH. In *Soil: The Yearbook of Agriculture*, pp. 72-79. United States Department of Agriculture, Washington, D.C.

Conard, N., David L. Asch, N. B. Asch, D. Elmore, H. Gove, M. Rubin, J. A. Brown, M. D. Wiant, K. B. Farnsworth, and T. G. Cook. 1984. Accelerator Radiocarbon Dating of Evidence for Prehistoric Horticulture in Illinois. *Nature* 308:443-446.

Creel, D., and A. Long. 1986. Radiocarbon Dating of Corn. *American Antiquity* 51:826-837.

DeNiro, M. J., and S. Epstein. 1981. Influence of Diet on the Distribution of Nitrogen Isotopes in Animals. *Geochimica et Cosmochimica Acta* 45:341-351.

Dirrigl, F. J., Jr., and B. Greenberg. 1995. The Utility of Insect Remains to Assessing Human Burials: A Connecticut Case Study. *Archaeology of Eastern North America* 23:1-7.

Duke, J. A. 1986. *Handbook of Northeastern Indian Medicinal Plants*. Quarterman Publications, Inc., Lincoln, Massachusetts.

Dunn, S. W. 1994. *The Mohicans and Their Land 1609-1730*. Purple Mountain Press, Fleishmanns, New York.

Elias, S. A. 1994. *Quaternary Insects and Their Environments*. Smithsonian Institution Press, Washington, D.C.

Fernald, M. L. 1973. [1950] *Gray's Manual of Botany*. 8th edition. Corrections supplied by R. C. Collins. Dioscorides Press, Portland, Oregon.

Fernald, M. L., and A. C. Kinsey. 1958. *Edible Wild Plants of Eastern North America*. Harper and Row, New York.

Fritz, G. J. 1990. Multiple Pathways to Farming in Precontact Eastern North America. *Journal of World Prehistory* 4:387-435.

Furgerson, K. 1994. Archaeobotanical Remains from the Goldkrest Site: Preliminary Results. Paper presented at the November Meeting of the Eastern States Archaeological Federation, Albany, New York.

Hall, R. 1967. Those Late Corn Dates: Isotopic Fractionation as a Source of Error in Carbon-14 Dates. *Michigan Archaeology* 13(4):171-180.

Hedges, R. E. M., and J. A. J. Gowlett. 1986. Radiocarbon Dating by Accelerator Mass Spectrometry. *Scientific American* (January): 100-107.

Herrick, J. W., and D. R. Snow. 1995. *Iroquois Medical Botany*. Syracuse University Press, Syracuse, New York.

Huey, P. R. 1993. The Mahicans, the Dutch, and the Schodack Islands in the 17th and 18th Centuries. In *Northeast Historical Archaeology, From Prehistory to the Present: Studies in Northeastern Archaeology in Honor of Bert Salwen*. Northeast Historical Archaeology pp. 21-22, 96-118.

Lavin, L., M. E. Mozzi, J. W. Bouchard, and K. Hartgen. 1996. The Goldkrest Site: An Undisturbed, Multi-Component Woodland Site in the Heart of Mahican Territory. *Journal of Mid-Atlantic Archaeology* 12:113-129.

Lavin, L., M. Mozzi, K. Furgerson, S. D. Dumas, T. Largy, F. J. Dirrigl, Jr., J.W. Bouchard, A. Krievs, and D. Mackey. 1997. *Stage III Archaeological Investigations: The Goldkrest Site, CNG TL-470, East Greenbush, New York.* 4 vols. Report submitted to the CNG Transmission Corporation, Clarksburg, West Virginia. On file at the New York State Office of Parks, Recreation, and Historic Preservation, Peebles Island, New York.

Little, E. A. 1994. Radiocarbon Ages of Shell and Charcoal in a Pit Feature at Myrick's Pond, Brewster, MA. *Bulletin of the Massachusetts Archaeological Society* 55:74-77.

Little, E. A., and M. J. Schoeninger. 1995. The Late Woodland Diet on Nantucket Island and the Problem of Maize in Coastal New England. *American Antiquity* 60:351-368.

Long, A., and B. Rippeteau. 1974. Testing Contemporaneity and Averaging Radio-carbon Dates. *American Antiquity* 39:205-215.

Marino, B. D., and M. B. McElroy. 1991. Isotopic Composition of Atmospheric $CO_2$ Inferred from Carbon in C4 Plant Cellulose. *Nature* 349:127-131.

Martin, A. C., and W. D. Barkley. 1961. *Seed Identification Manual*. University of California Press, Berkley.

Minnis, P. 1981. Seeds in Archaeological Sites: Sources and Some Interpretive Problems. *American Antiquity* 46:145-152.

Moerman, D. E. 1986. *Medicinal Plants of Native America*. 2 vols. Technical Reports No. 19, Research Reports in Ethnobotany Contribution 2. Museum of Anthropology, University of Michigan, Ann Arbor.

Montgomery, F. H. 1977. *Seeds and Fruits of Plants of Eastern Canada and Northeastern United States*. University of Toronto Press, Toronto.

New York Flora Association (NYFA). 1990. *Atlas of New York State Flora*. New York State Museum Institute, Albany.

Pearsall, D. M. 1989. *Paleoethnobotany: A Handbook of Procedures*. Academic Press, New York.

Ritchie, W. A. 1969. *The Archaeology of New York State*. Revised edition. Natural History Press, Garden City.

Schiffer, M. 1986. Radiocarbon Dating and the "Old Wood" Problem: The Case of the Hohokam Chronology. *Journal of Archaeological Science* 13:13.

Smith, B. D. 1992. Prehistoric Plant Husbandry in Eastern North America. In *The Origins of Agriculture: An International Perspective*, edited by C. W. Cowan and P. J. Watson, pp. 101-119. Smithsonian Institution Press, Washington, D.C.

—————. 1995. *The Emergence of Agriculture*. Scientific American Library, New York.

Struiver, S. 1968. Flotation Techniques for the Recovery of Small-Scale Archaeological Remains. *American Antiquity* 33:353-362.

Struiver, M., and P. J. Reimer. 1993. High-Precision Bidecadal Calibration of the Radiocarbon Time Scale, 500-2500 B.C. *Radiocarbon* 35:25-33.

Straus, A.E. 1994. *Intensive Archaeological Survey and Excavation of a Prehistoric Shell Pit Feature at Houselot 37, Bates Lane in Brewster, Massachusetts*. Report submitted to Massachusetts Historical Commission, Boston.

Talalay, L., D. R. Keller, and P. J. Munson. 1984. Hickory Nuts, Walnuts, Butternuts, and Hazelnuts: Observations and Experiments Relevant to Their Aboriginal Exploitation in Eastern North America. In *Experiments and Observations on Aboriginal Wild Plant Food Utilization in Eastern North America*, edited by P. J. Munson, pp. 338-359. Prehistory Research Series 6(2). Indiana Historical Society, Indianapolis.

Tantaquidgeon, G. 1977. *Folk Medicine of the Delaware and Related Algonkian Indians*. Pennsylvania Historical and Museum Commission, Anthropology Series, No. 3. Harrisburg.

Waugh, F. W. 1916. *Iroquois Foods and Food Preparation*. Geological Survey Memoir 86, Anthropological Series No. 12, Ottawa. (Facsimile edition published by National Museums of Canada in 1973).

# CHAPTER 6

# NEW DATA ON THE CHRONOLOGY OF MAIZE HORTICULTURE IN EASTERN NEW YORK AND SOUTHERN NEW ENGLAND

Daniel Cassedy and Paul Webb

## INTRODUCTION

Over two decades ago, Ritchie and Funk (1973:356) suggested that maize (*Zea mays*) horticulture likely constituted an important aspect of the subsistence economy of the late Middle Woodland Hunter's Home phase, although at the time, they had little conclusive evidence to support this assertion. Throughout the 1970s and 1980s, a radiocarbon determination of A.D. 1070 from the Roundtop site in Endicott, New York, was believed to be the oldest known date associated with maize in the Northeast. Recently, Hart's (this volume) reexamination of the Roundtop collection has determined that the maize from Feature 35 actually dates to no earlier than the end of the thirteenth century A.D.

The accumulation of multiple radiocarbon dates from excavations in the Susquehanna and Hudson valleys of central and eastern New York since 1990 strongly suggests that maize was cultivated in this region starting ca. A.D. 800. In combination with data from Ontario (Crawford and Smith 1996), Pennsylvania (Hart and Asch Sidell 1996), and New England (Bendremer and Dewar 1994), this clearly suggests that Native Americans in the Northeast were participating in the overall eastern expansion of maize horticulture that has been documented for the last two centuries of the first millennium A.D.

Excavations for the Iroquois Pipeline Project in 1991 and 1992 provided some of the first systematic information about the occurrence and dating of maize horticulture in eastern New York and southwestern Connecticut (Cassedy et al. 1993; Millis et al. 1993). An extensive program of soil sample flotation recovered archaeobotanical remains from numerous archaeological sites along the 370-mi pipeline right-of-way, and charred

maize was recovered from five of these sites. Two of the five (154A-7-1 and 230-3-1) dated to the Late Prehistoric period (ca. A.D. 1400-1600), and maize in these contexts is neither unusual nor unexpected. At the other three sites, the maize is from radiocarbon-dated contexts that are earlier than most known regional contexts. One of the three sites is located in the eastern Hudson valley on the Roeliff Jansen Kill, and the other two sites are located in Connecticut on the lower Housatonic River near Long Island Sound (Figure 6.1). This article discusses how data from these three sites relate to existing ideas concerning the timing of the introduction of tropical cultigens to the region.

The sites are referred to by their project site numbers, which are 211-1-1, 294A-AF2-1 and 294A-25-2. Garrow and Associates' Iroquois Pipeline studies employed a systematic program of soil sample processing using water flotation equipment. Both an automated flotation system (adapted from Pearsall 1989:52-66) and a manual flotation system were utilized to process the thousands of liters of soil recovered during the data recovery excavations. Generally, 100 percent of the feature fill was floated for all cultural features. Heavy fractions were manually sorted by lab staff, and light fractions were sorted and identified by the archaeobotanical consultants. Nancy Asch Sidell (1992a) was the consultant for the sites discussed here.

Charcoal larger than 2 mm was sorted using a binocular microscope at 7X magnification and evaluated quantitatively by counting fragments. In samples with more than about 500 fragments >2 mm, each sample was divided using a riffle sampler to produce a subsample of 400-600 pieces for quantitative analysis. The remainder of the >2 mm charcoal was scanned to obtain an exact count of rare categories; seeds and cultivated plant remains were removed and counted. Charcoal smaller than 0.5 mm was not systematically exam-

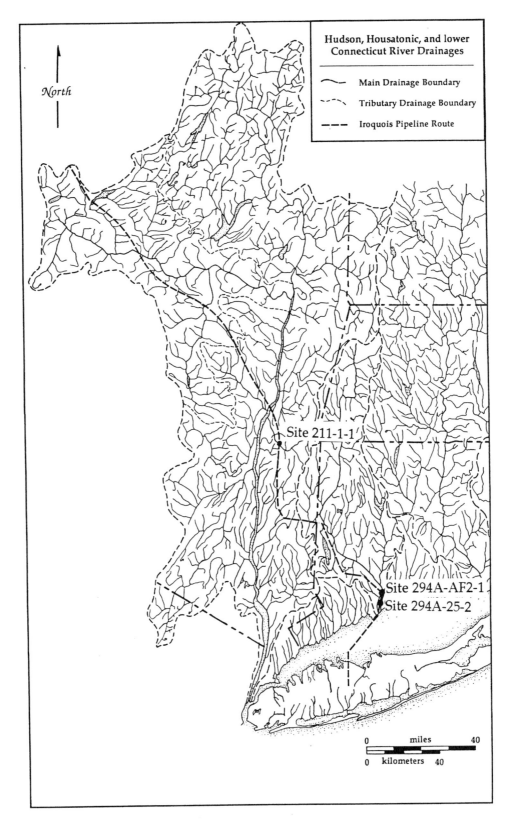

**Figure 6.1.** Location of Sites 211-1, 294A-AF2-1, and 294A-25-2.

*Cassedy and Webb*

ined because this size fraction rarely yields identifiable remains. From counts of the charcoal >2 mm, the occurrence of charcoal types by weight can be calculated. Testing by the Center for American Archeology Archaeobotanical Laboratory for sites in Illinois has shown that the method can give results closely comparable to complete sorting and weighing of samples. Full details on the flotation program and the archaeobotanical analyses are provided in the contract reports (Cassedy et al. 1993).

## SITE SUMMARIES

### Site 211-1-1

Site 211-1-1 is an extensive Woodland to Contact period site situated in a broad floodplain on the Roeliff Jansen Kill in southwestern Columbia County, New York. Located at a river-crossing staging area for the pipeline, the data recovery investigations consisted of hand excavation of 238 m$^2$ of deposits and mechanized stripping of a 7,000-m$^2$ area. The combined data from all phases of investigation suggest that this site represents several overlapping occupations that took place between the Early Woodland and Contact periods. The most intensive occupation appears to have occurred during the late Middle Woodland (ca. A.D. 600-1000) and late Late Woodland-Contact period (ca. A.D. 1300-1750).

The 43 features located within the right-of-way include a variety of hearths, posts, pits, and midden deposits. No evidence of structures was located, although several postholes may represent racks or an above-ground storage facility. The identified features apparently represent the periphery of the main occupation, which appears to be situated west and north of the study area. In general, the deposits excavated are believed to represent short-term activities such as food processing and cooking, tool manufacture and refurbishment, and refuse disposal.

The investigations yielded considerable data concerning late Middle Woodland through Late Woodland period material culture and subsistence practices. Thirty-two maize fragments were recovered from 8 separate features, including 25 cupules, 5 kernels, 1 glume, and 1 embryo.

Data on the chronological associations and contexts of the maize remains are provided in Table 6.1. During the initial data recovery analysis, three features containing maize produced radiocarbon dates on associated wood charcoal. Of particular interest, two of these features produced uncalibrated mean dates older than A.D. 1000 (Feature 44, A.D. 850 ± 70; Feature 32, A.D. 900 ± 60). The third dated feature with maize was assigned to the Contact period (Feature 43, A.D. 1710 ± 50). Three other features containing maize (Features 30B, 30C, and 33) were provisionally dated to before A.D. 1000 based on their proximity to the early dated features. The remaining two features with maize also contained ceramics. Feature 9 contained ceramics assigned to the late Late Woodland-Contact period, and Feature 15 could date anytime from the late Middle Woodland to the Contact period.

The two early dates of A.D. 850 ± 70 (Feature 44) and A.D. 900 ± 60 (Feature 32) were obtained in 1992 on charcoal associated with the maize in the features. In 1995, in conjunction with additional research undertaken for an overall technical synthesis of the pipeline research, we ran three AMS dates directly on maize kernels from these two features and from one of the nearby features (Feature 33) that was suspected to be early based on spatial association. The AMS dating results are as follows:

Feature 32 was a shallow, midden-filled depression or pit. The wood charcoal produced a date of A.D. 900 ± 60 and the maize kernel produced a date of A.D. 900 ± 50. These two agree almost perfectly.

Feature 33 was a cluster of oxidized soil patches and was a probable hearth remnant. There were no associated artifacts, just charred wood and charred maize. The wood was not dated, but the AMS date on maize is A.D. 1100 ± 60.

Feature 44 was a large hearth that produced lithic debitage, fire-cracked rock,

**Table 6.1. Maize Remains and Associated Radiocarbon Dates from Iroquois Pipeline Sites 211-1-1, 294A-F2-1, and 294A-25-2.**

| Provenience | Feature Type | Lab Number (all Beta) | Radiocarbon Determination Y.B.P. ± 1σ[a] | 13C-Corrected Age Y.B.P. ± 1σ[a] | 13C-Corrected Calendar Date | 13C-Corrected 2σ Date Range | Calibrated Two-Sigma Date Range[b] | Directly Associated Diagnostic Artifacts | Maize Remains |
|---|---|---|---|---|---|---|---|---|---|
| 211-1-1 F.9 | Midden | NA | NA | NA | NA | NA | NA | ILW-Contact Sherds | 1 Cupule |
| 211-1-1 F.15 | Pit | NA | NA | NA | NA | NA | NA | Levanna Proj. Points | 1 Cupule, 1 Glume, 1 Embryo |
| 211-1-1 F.30B | Post | NA | NA | NA | NA | NA | NA | None | 1 Cupule |
| 211-1-1 F.30C | Post | NA | NA | NA | NA | NA | NA | None | 2 Cupules |
| 211-1-1 F.32 | Midden | 53451 / 84969 | 1090±60 / 810±50 | 1050±60 / 1050±50 | A.D. 900 / A.D. 900 | A.D. 780-1020 / A.D. 800-1000. | A.D. 783-1152 / A.D. 890-1040 | None | 3 Cupules |
| 211-1-1 F.33 | Hearth(s) | 84970 | 590±60 | 850±60 | A.D. 1100 | A.D. 980-1220 | A.D. 1035-1260 | None | 4 Kernels |
| 211-1-1 F.43 | Midden | 53238 | 250±50 | 240±560 | A.D. 1710 | A.D. 1610-1810 | A.D. 1560-1955 | ILW-Contact sherds | 15 Cupules, 1 Kernel |
| 211-1-1 F.44 | Hearth | 53452 / 84971 | 1130±70 / 170±50 | 1100±70 / 390±50 | A.D. 850 / A.D. 1560 | A.D. 710-990 / A.D. 1460-1660 | A.D. 770-1147 / A.D. 1430-1645 | None | 1 Cupule |
| 294A-AF2-1 F.3a | Hearth? | NA | NA | NA | NA | NA | NA | MW-LW sherd | 2 Cupules |
| 294A-AF2-1 F.4 | Rock Conc. | NA | NA | NA | NA | NA | NA | Unidentified sherds | 1 Cupule |
| 294A-AF2-1 F.10 | Pit | 50787 / 50788 | 430±70 / 440±80 | 440±70 / 430±80 | A.D. 1510 / A.D. 1520 | A.D. 1370-1650 / A.D. 1360-1680 | A.D. 1329-1640 / A.D. 1327-1650 | Final Wood. Sherds | 39 Cupules, 10 Glumes, 9 Kernels |
| 294A-AF2-1 F13 | Rock Conc. | NA | NA | NA | NA | NA | NA | Unidentified sherds | 1 Glume |
| 294A-AF2-1 F16 | Hearth | NA | NA | NA | NA | NA | NA | Unidentified sherds | 1 Cupule |
| 294A-AF2-1 F18 | Hearth | NA | NA | NA | NA | NA | NA | LW-FW sherds | 1 Glume |
| 294A-AF2-1 F20 | Rock Conc. | NA | NA | NA | NA | NA | NA | Unidentified sherds | 1 Cupule |
| 294A-25-2 F.5 | Pit | 49944 | 230±60 | NA | A.D. 1720[c] | A.D. 1600-1840 | A.D. 1484-1955 | EW or eMW sherds | 1 Kernel |
| 294A-25-2 F.6a | Pit | 84972 | 50±60 | 310±60 | A.D. 1640 | A.D. 1520-1760 | A.D. 1450-1950 | eMW sherds | 3 Kernels |
| 294A-25-2 F.8 | Pit | 50789 | 560±70 | 550±70 | A.D. 1400 | A.D. 1260-1540 | A.D. 1280-1450 | eMW sherds | 2 Cupules, 1 Glume |
| 294A-25-2 F.9 | Pit | 52920 / 84973 | 730±50 / 470±60 | 710±50 / 690±60 | A.D. 1240 / A.D. 1260 | A.D. 1140-1340 / A.D. 1140-1380 | A.D. 1220-1389 / A.D. 1245-1405 | IEW, eMW sherds | 4 Cupules |
| 294A-25-2 F.13a | Pit | NA | NA | NA | NA | NA | NA | Unidentified sherds | 1 Cupule |
| 294A-25-2 F.14 | Pit | NA | NA | NA | NA | NA | NA | Unidentified sherds | 2 Kernels |

*Notes*
[a] Based on half-life of 5,568 years
[b] Based on Stuiver and Reimer (1993) CALIB rev. 3.03 program with ATM10.14C data base.

charred wood and nutshell, and charred maize. The wood charcoal was dated at A.D. 850 ± 70, but the AMS date on the maize is much more recent at A.D. 1560 ± 50.

As with many archaeological issues, the dating results are mixed, but there is now reasonable evidence to suggest that maize was present at Site 211-1-1 in the century or two before A.D. 1000. At two standard deviations, the three oldest dates cover uncalibrated spans of A.D. 710-990, A.D. 780-1020, and A.D. 800-1000. Calibration shifts these ranges to A.D. 770-1147, A.D. 783-1152, and A.D. 890-1040.

Most of the maize from early contexts at site 211-1-1 was recovered from a complex of features that may represent an above-ground storage or processing facility. These include Features 30A-30F, 33, 34, and 44, all located within a 3-m-x-4-m area of the site. These nine features include four posts, two shallow pits, and three apparent hearths. Four of these nine features, including two of the posts, produced charred maize, and one of the nine (Feature 44) produced the radiocarbon date of A.D. 850 ± 70. Maize was also recovered in Feature 32, a nearby midden deposit radiocarbon dated to A.D. 900 ± 50.

At least five of the group of nine features appear to have been functionally related, and these have been designated the Feature 30 complex (Figure 6.2). Four posts (Features 30B-30E) were arranged in a rough square measuring from 60 to 80 cm on a side, and probably formed either the support posts for a small platform or possibly a set of racks. A shallow basin designated Feature 30A was mainly contained within the outline made by the four posts, but extended outside the outline to the northeast. A second basin, Feature 30F, was located less than 40 cm north of the northern edge of Feature 30A. The functional relationship between these pits and the post pattern is unclear. Neither appears large enough to have represented a storage facility. Given their proximity to the posts, they may represent processing pits that were used in association with the platform or racks.

The relative abundance of maize in the area of the Feature 30 complex suggests it might have been a location at which maize was processed or stored, and it is tempting to hypothesize that some or all of the features in this area were associated with maize preparation or use. In particular, the post pattern making up part of Feature 30 could conceivably represent the foundation of a small granary. The storage of maize in such above-ground facilities is attested to ethnographically in the Middle Atlantic region (Hudson 1990:144-146), and such an explanation has been invoked previously to account for the lack of evidence for maize storage facilities at other sites in the Northeast at which maize was utilized (Ritchie and Funk 1973:252).

## Sites 294A-AF2-1 and 294A-25-2

These two sites are both located on the east bank of the river in Milford, Connecticut. Site AF2-1 is furthest upstream and is located at the pipeline's river crossing 9 mi from Long Island Sound. Site 25-2 is a mile downstream from AF2-1. Both sites were excavated using a combination of hand-dug units and mechanically assisted plow-zone stripping. Systematic excavation units were used to identify topsoil depths and activity loci, and to obtain a sample of artifacts from within the plow zone. A backhoe with a smooth bucket was then used to remove the plow zone and to expose cultural features.

Site AF2-1 was located at the staging area for construction of the pipeline across the Housatonic River. An area of 722 m$^2$ was stripped and excavated at this site, and 38 prehistoric features were documented. In contrast, Site 25-2 was intercepted by the standard 23-m pipeline right-of-way, and data recovery excavations of 825 m$^2$ were distributed along a relatively narrow corridor at the western edge of the known site. Nineteen prehistoric features were excavated at Site 25-2.

At AF2-1, the feature sample was dominated by clusters of fire-cracked rock and shallow hearth remnants, while Site 25-2 contained pits almost exclusively. Both sites produced charred nutshells and maize, but the pits at 25-2 held numerous mollusk shell fragments, which also preserved animal and fish bones better than at AF2-1.

Six features from Site 25-2 yielded a total of

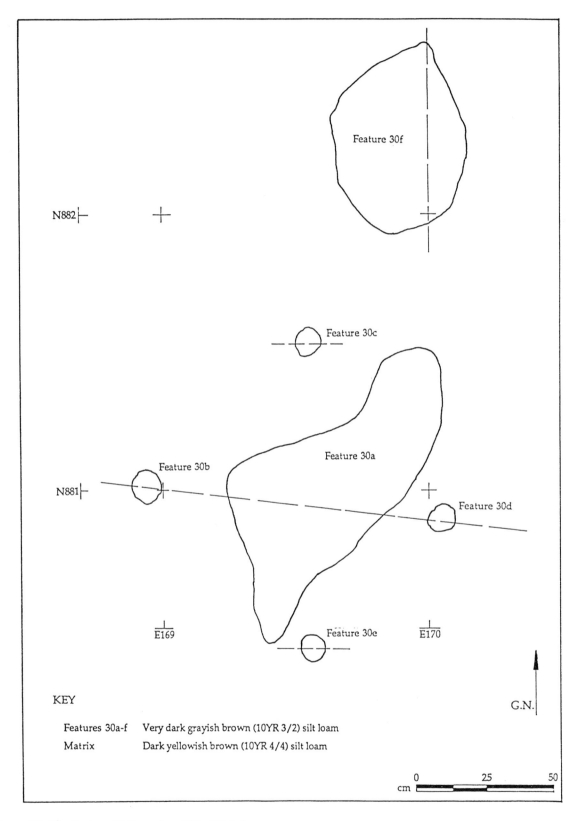

**Figure 6.2.** The Feature 30 Complex at Site 211-1-1.

14 fragments of carbonized maize, which included fragments of seven cupules, one glume, and one kernel (see Table 6.1). Maize was present in four pits and two midden-filled basins, and four of these six features yielded five radiocarbon dates. Feature 5 produced a wood charcoal date of A.D. 1720 ± 60, while Feature 8 produced a wood charcoal date of A.D. 1390 ± 70. We dated both wood charcoal and charred maize from Feature 9, and the two dates of A.D. 1240 ± 50 and A.D. 1260 ± 60 agree quite nicely. Feature 6A contained sherds that appear to be early Middle Woodland types, but an AMS date on charred maize is at A.D. 1640 ± 60. We have interpreted the sherds as fill admixture from an earlier component.

Seven features from Site AF2-1 yielded a total of 65 fragments of carbonized maize, which included fragments of 44 cupules, 12 glumes, and 9 kernels (see Table 6.1). Maize was present in three hearths, three rock concentrations, and one pit. The lone pit, Feature 10, produced 90 percent of the maize recovered from the site, and wood charcoal from that feature yielded overlapping radiocarbon dates of A.D. 1510 ± 70 and A.D. 1520 ± 80. The six undated features with maize all contained aboriginal pottery. Four had unidentifiable sherds, but the other two produced Late Woodland ceramic types.

## DISCUSSION

### Chronology

Smith (1992:110) has suggested that "the earliest convincing macrobotanical evidence recovered to date for the presence of maize in the Eastern Woodlands are carbonized kernel fragments from the Icehouse Bottom site in the Little Tennessee River valley of eastern Tennessee." This site has yielded a direct accelerator date of A.D. 175 ± 100, and the Edwin Harness site in Ohio has produced direct AMS dates of A.D. 220 ± 85 and A.D. 230 ± 105 on maize kernels (Ford 1987; Riley et al 1994).

Despite these early dates, maize did not become common in the Eastern Woodlands until approximately 600 years later. Smith (1992:111) has noted that there is a "seemingly abrupt and widespread appearance of maize in the archaeo-logical record of the Midwest and Southeast at A.D. 800-900," and "agricultural economies domi-nated by corn had been established over a broad area of the eastern United States by A.D. 1150."

Until recently, there was a perceived time lag in the introduction of maize to the Northeast. This was due not only to a lack of evidence for early maize, but also a general perception that the Northeast has been a marginal region both in terms of cultural developments and in terms of a climate suitable for the cultivation of tropical cultigens. In the past five to ten years, sufficient northeastern dates have been obtained to push the introduction of maize back several more centuries. These dates suggest that the ca. A.D. 800 expansion of maize identified by Smith reached well into the Northeast close to the limits of climatic suitability (Crawford and Smith 1996; Demeritt 1991).

Table 6.2 provides a listing of most of the published dates associated with maize in the northeastern U.S. Most of the dates on this list are taken from Bendremer and Dewar (1994), who summarized the published and unpublished dates available as of 1991. Their list includes several dates at or near A.D. 1000, including dates of A.D. 1060 and 1020 from Smithfield Beach on the Delaware River, A.D. 1010 from the Boland site near Binghamton, New York, and A.D. 890 for a single fragment of probable maize from the Selden Island site in Connecticut. Bendremer and Dewar also included a date of A.D. 1000 from the Bowman's Brook site on Long Island, and a date of A.D. 1070 from Calf Island in Massachusetts. However, in her original report on the Bowman's Brook date, Ceci (1990) considered it unreliable,[1] and Luedtke also believes the Calf Island date may be too old (Luedtke, personal communica-tion 1993). Table 6.2 also includes AMS dates pub-lished by Snow (1995) for the Turnbull site, and four new dates on samples from Roundtop just obtained by Hart (this volume). In addition to Bendremer et al.'s data, Blake and Cutler (1983) reported a date of A.D. 920 ± 80 for maize from the Gnagey site in Pennsylvania.

The three oldest dates that we obtained from Iroquois Project Site 211-1-1 join the Selden Island sample as the first New York or New England mean dates at or before A.D. 900. Soon

**Table 6.2. Radiocarbon Dates Associated with Maize in the Northeast** [a]

| Site | Drainage | Date BP | ± | −2 σ | Uncalibrated Date A.D. | +2 σ | −2 σ | Calibrated [b] Date A.D. | +2 σ |
|---|---|---|---|---|---|---|---|---|---|
| 211-1-1 (44) | Hudson | 1100 | 70 | 710 | 850 | 990 | 770 | 915 | 1147 |
| Sheldon Island S. | Lower CT | 1060 | 70 | 750 | 890 | 1030 | 779 | 985 | 1154 |
| 211-1-1 (32) AMS | Hudson | 1050 | 50 | 800 | 900 | 1000 | 890 | 1000 | 1040 |
| 211-1-1 (32) | Hudson | 1050 | 60 | 780 | 900 | 1020 | 783 | 990 | 1152 |
| Binghamton | Susquehanna | 1000 | 70 | 810 | 950 | 1090 | 890 | 1008 | 1207 |
| Boland | Susquehanna | 940 | 80 | 850 | 1010 | 1170 | 904 | 1142 | 1260 |
| Smithfield Beach | Upper Delaware | 930 | 80 | 860 | 1020 | 1180 | 980 | 1119 | 1260 |
| Smithfield Beach | Upper Delaware | 890 | 60 | 940 | 1060 | 1180 | 1000 | 1158 | 1260 |
| Fortin | Susquehanna | 870 | 75 | 930 | 1080 | 1230 | 1000 | 1174 | 1280 |
| Skitchewaug | Upper CT | 850 | 50 | 1000 | 1100 | 1200 | 1030 | 1196 | 1280 |
| 211-1-1 (33) AMS | Hudson | 850 | 60 | 980 | 1100 | 1220 | 1035 | 1215 | 1260 |
| Mago Point | Lower CT | 840 | 80 | 950 | 1110 | 1270 | 1002 | 1212 | 1280 |
| Highland | LI Sound | 835 | 120 | 875 | 1115 | 1355 | 980 | 1214 | 1391 |
| Skitchewaug | Upper CT | 830 | 60 | 1000 | 1120 | 1240 | 1030 | 1215 | 1280 |
| Roundtop (235) AMS | Susquehanna | 830 | 60 | 1000 | 1120 | 1240 | 1030 | 1215 | 1280 |
| Hornblower II | LI Sound | 790 | 80 | 1000 | 1160 | 1320 | 1030 | 1257 | 1386 |
| Morgan | Middle CT | 780 | 70 | 1030 | 1170 | 1310 | 1041 | 1259 | 1383 |
| Morgan | Middle CT | 780 | 90 | 990 | 1170 | 1350 | 1030 | 1259 | 1390 |
| World's End | Eastern MA | 765 | 70 | 1045 | 1185 | 1325 | 1069 | 1262 | 1387 |
| Skitchewaug | Upper CT | 760 | 50 | 1090 | 1190 | 1290 | 1163 | 1263 | 1300 |
| Skitchewaug | Upper CT | 750 | 110 | 980 | 1200 | 1420 | 1020 | 1268 | 1410 |
| Malluzo | Eastern MA | 735 | 80 | 1055 | 1215 | 1375 | 1132 | 1227 | 1394 |
| Skitchewaug | Upper CT | 730 | 80 | 1060 | 1220 | 1380 | 1160 | 1278 | 1396 |
| Highland | LI Sound | 730 | 115 | 990 | 1220 | 1450 | 1030 | 1278 | 1420 |
| Medwin Knoll II | Upper Delaware | 720 | 50 | 1130 | 1230 | 1330 | 1220 | 1279 | 1388 |
| 25-2 (9) | Housatonic | 710 | 50 | 1140 | 1240 | 1340 | 1220 | 1280 | 1389 |
| 25-2 (9) AMS | Housatonic | 690 | 60 | 1140 | 1260 | 1380 | 1245 | 1295 | 1405 |
| Binghamton | Susquehanna | 680 | 50 | 1170 | 1270 | 1370 | 1258 | 1282 | 1394 |
| Roundtop (35) AMS | Susquehanna | 675 | 55 | 1165 | 1275 | 1385 | 1264 | 1299 | 1404 |
| Smithfield Beach | Upper Delaware | 670 | 70 | 1140 | 1280 | 1420 | 1220 | 1283 | 1410 |
| Roundtop (35) AMS | Susquehanna | 670 | 55 | 1170 | 1280 | 1390 | 1268 | 1300 | 1406 |
| Roundtop (35) AMS | Susquehanna | 658 | 48 | 1196 | 1292 | 1388 | 1279 | 1303 | 1405 |
| Nahrwold I | Hudson | 640 | 95 | 1120 | 1310 | 1500 | 1210 | 1373 | 1440 |
| Morgan | Middle CT | 630 | 70 | 1180 | 1320 | 1460 | 1260 | 1371 | 1430 |
| Medwin North | Upper Delaware | 630 | 105 | 1110 | 1320 | 1530 | 1210 | 1371 | 1440 |

# Table 6.2. Continued

| Site | Region | | | | | | | | |
|---|---|---|---|---|---|---|---|---|---|
| Burnham-Shepard | Middle CT | 630 | 70 | 1180 | 1320 | 1460 | 1260 | 1371 | 1430 |
| Burnham-Shepard | Middle CT | 620 | 70 | 1190 | 1330 | 1470 | 1260 | 1369 | 1430 |
| Bowman's Brook | LI Sound | 610 | 60 | 1220 | 1340 | 1460 | 1280 | 1367 | 1388 |
| Burnham-Shepard | Middle CT | 600 | 80 | 1190 | 1350 | 1510 | 1260 | 1363 | 1440 |
| Smithfield Beach | Upper Delaware | 590 | 60 | 1240 | 1360 | 1480 | 1280 | 1350 | 1430 |
| Smithfield Beach | Upper Delaware | 590 | 100 | 1160 | 1360 | 1560 | 1260 | 1350 | 1460 |
| Morgan | Middle CT | 590 | 70 | 1220 | 1360 | 1500 | 1280 | 1350 | 1440 |
| Pleasant Hill | LI Sound | 565 | 90 | 1205 | 1385 | 1565 | 1265 | 1341 | 1470 |
| Sebonac | LI Sound | 555 | 85 | 1225 | 1395 | 1565 | 1280 | 1336 | 1470 |
| Getman | Hudson | 552 | 150 | 1098 | 1398 | 1698 | 1193 | 1407 | 1650 |
| Medwin North | Upper Delaware | 550 | 135 | 1130 | 1400 | 1670 | 1220 | 1407 | 1640 |
| Burnham-Shepard | Middle CT | 550 | 60 | 1280 | 1400 | 1520 | 1280 | 1407 | 1440 |
| 25-2(8) | Housatonic | 550 | 70 | 1260 | 1400 | 1540 | 1280 | 1407 | 1450 |
| Donahue | Champlain | 510 | 115 | 1210 | 1440 | 1670 | 1280 | 1418 | 1640 |
| Calf Island | Eastern MA | 510 | 145 | 1150 | 1440 | 1730 | 1228 | 1418 | 1660 |
| Nahrwold I | Hudson | 500 | 80 | 1290 | 1450 | 1610 | 1280 | 1422 | 1620 |
| Early Fall | Saco | 460 | 60 | 1370 | 1490 | 1610 | 1328 | 1435 | 1621 |
| 6-HT-116 | Middle CT | 460 | 100 | 1290 | 1490 | 1690 | 1280 | 1435 | 1650 |
| 6-HT-116 | Middle CT | 445 | 90 | 1325 | 1505 | 1685 | 1304 | 1438 | 1650 |
| Roundtop (440) AMS | Susquehanna | 440 | 45 | 1420 | 1510 | 1600 | 1396 | 1439 | 1570 |
| AF2-1 (10) | Housatonic | 440 | 70 | 1370 | 1510 | 1650 | 1329 | 1439 | 1640 |
| Turnbull | Hudson | 435 | 50 | 1415 | 1515 | 1615 | 1412 | 1440 | 1510 |
| AF2-1 (10) | Housatonic | 430 | 80 | 1360 | 1520 | 1680 | 1327 | 1441 | 1650 |
| Burnham-Shepard | Middle CT | 420 | 80 | 1370 | 1530 | 1690 | 1329 | 1443 | 1650 |
| Calf Island | Eastern MA | 410 | 100 | 1340 | 1540 | 1740 | 1320 | 1446 | 1660 |
| Smithfield Beach | Upper Delaware | 400 | 70 | 1410 | 1550 | 1690 | 1410 | 1450 | 1650 |
| 211-1-1 (44) AMS | Hudson | 390 | 50 | 1460 | 1560 | 1660 | 1430 | 1475 | 1645 |
| Turnbull | Hudson | 360 | 40 | 1510 | 1590 | 1670 | 1408 | 1490 | 1770 |
| Barlow Pond | LI Sound | 355 | 205 | 1185 | 1595 | 2005 | 1260 | 1492 | 1955 |
| Smithfield Beach | Upper Delaware | 330 | 60 | 1500 | 1620 | 1740 | 1440 | 1590 | 1660 |
| Roundtop (35) | Susquehanna | 330 | 45 | 1530 | 1620 | 1710 | 1452 | 1558 | 1660 |
| 25-2 (6A) AMS | Housatonic | 310 | 60 | 1520 | 1640 | 1760 | 1450 | 1640 | 1950 |
| Donahue | Champlain | 250 | 115 | 1470 | 1700 | 1930 | 1430 | 1650 | 1950 |
| 211-1-1 (43) | Hudson | 240 | 50 | 1610 | 1710 | 1810 | 1560 | 1653 | 1955 |
| 25-2 (5) | Housatonic | 230 | 60 | 1600 | 1720 | 1840 | 1494 | 1656 | 1955 |

*Notes*

a Dates derived from Bendremer and Dewar (1994), Hart (this volume), Snow (1995), Wurst and Versaggi (1993), and Iroquois Pipeline Project data.

b Based on Stuiver and Reimer (1993) CALIB rev. 3.03 program using the ATM10.14C database.

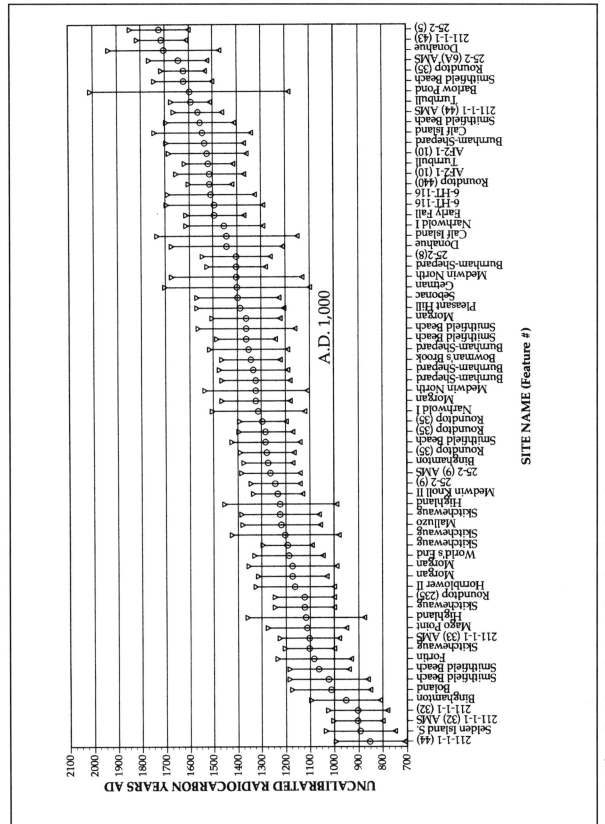

**Figure 6.3.** Chronological Distribution of Uncalibrated Radiocarbon Dates.

after the Site 211-1-1 analysis, excavations in Binghamton, New York, by the Public Archaeology Facility of SUNY Binghamton also uncovered evidence of maize predating A.D. 1000. A feature from the Binghamton Mall site at the confluence of the Susquehanna and Chenango rivers returned a mean date of A.D. 950. Another carbon sample associated with maize was dated several centuries earlier, but the context and integrity of that date are not clear (Wurst and Versaggi 1993).

When first reported in conference papers and contract reports, the early dates from Site 211-1-1 and the Binghamton Mall site were also believed to have a possible analog at the Turnbull site on the Mohawk River, where maize kernels were excavated in the early 1950s (Ritchie et al. 1953). The Turnbull site had been dated by stylistic analogy to ca. A.D. 900, but Funk (1976:296) noted that the maize association was not considered completely secure due to the nature of the excavation and the presence of a minor Late Woodland component at the site. During his reanalysis of Mohawk valley collections, Snow (1995:65) ran two AMS assays on maize kernels from Turnbull, but these returned dates in the late fifteenth century.

Evidence for earlier maize has continued to accumulate in the 1990s as Crawford and Smith (1996) have recently reported multiple direct AMS dates on maize from Ontario in the A.D. 600 to A.D. 1000 range. Based on their recovery of multiple maize fragments from several sites in Ontario, they have concluded that "Princess Point people were at least incipient horticulturalists by A.D. 800, ... and as early as the sixth century" (Crawford and Smith 1996:787). Hart and Asch Sidell (1996) have reported maize from multiple radiocarbon-dated Clemson's Island contexts ranging from about A.D. 700 to A.D. 1000 at the Memorial Park site on the West Branch of the Susquehanna in Lock Haven, Pennsylvania.

Figure 6.3 illustrates the chronological distribution of the uncalibrated northeastern radiocarbon dates associated with maize. At two standard deviations below the mean, fifteen of the dates could predate A.D. 1000. Of course many could also post-date A.D. 1000, but based on the combined distributions, the data suggest to us that the perceived time lag in the introduction of maize to the Northeast is diminishing rapidly.

Focusing on the Long Island region, a number of researchers have suggested that maize cultivation was not common in Southern New England until after A.D. 1500 (Ceci 1982; Lavin 1988:113; McBride and Dewar 1987:305). The Iroquois Project data from the lower Housatonic valley also indicate that the use of maize occurred earlier than previously thought. Fourteen radiocarbon dates associated with maize are now available for the coastal region extending from the Hudson River to Martha's Vineyard, including five dates from our two Iroquois Pipeline sites on the lower Housatonic River. Notably, 10 of the 14 mean dates in this sample are older than A.D. 1500.

## Subsistence Patterns

While the frequencies of maize remains at the Iroquois project sites are not high, the presence of cob fragments at all three sites indicates that the maize was probably grown and processed at the sites or nearby. If the maize was obtained as a trade item or used as travel food, the maize would have been processed first to remove the bulky cobs.

Maize horticulture in the Northeast is generally thought to have included the growing of *Cucurbita pepo* (squash, pumpkin) and beans (*Phaseolus vulgaris*) among the maize plants. However, *Cucurbita* rind and seeds were not found at any of our project sites, and only a small number of questionable bean fragments were found. This is not that surprising, given the fact that remains of *Cucurbita* and beans are usually rare even at sites with ethnohistorical documentation of their use (Asch and Asch 1975; Asch Sidell 1992b). The scarcity of these two cultigens in the samples does not necessarily document lack of use but may relate to number and size of samples examined.

Although maize appears as early as A.D. 200 in parts of the East, Smith (1992:110) has suggested that between ca. A.D. 200 and 800, maize played a relatively minor role in eastern plant husbandry systems. He has noted that during this period when maize was still a relatively minor factor, the evidence suggests an intensification of the use of indigenous cultigens such as chenopodium (*Chenopodium berlandieri*) and knotweed (*Polygonum erectum*). "Along with the introduced tropical cultigens, a wide variety of indigenous food crops continued under cultivation in many areas (sumpweed, sunflower, knotweed, chenopod, maygrass, and little barley)" (Smith 1992:113). In this context, evidence for the use of indigenous crops in the Northeast is now beginning to appear, including the discovery of little barley (*Hordium pusillum*) at the Binghamton Mall and Memorial Park sites (Hart and Asch Sidell 1996; Wurst and Versaggi 1993), sunflower (*Helianthus annus*) at the Burnham-Shepard site (Bendremer et al. 1991), and chenopodium at numerous northeastern locations (George and Dewar, this volume).

Although agricultural economies dominated by maize had been established over a broad area of the eastern United States by A.D. 1150, this was not a uniform adaptation. Different regions exhibited variations in the type of maize grown, as well as in the importance of maize relative to indigenous cultigens and other food resources. Despite the widespread acceptance of maize in the Northeast, this region was not a major participant in "the rapid and widespread emergence of 'Mississippian' ranked societies based on maize dominated agriculture" (Smith 1992:113).

Additional data from our Iroquois Pipeline sites (Cassedy 1996) confirm previous interpretations that the subsistence system of Middle to Late Woodland people in the Northeast included a substantial focus on hunting terrestrial animals and migratory fowl, fishing, shellfish collecting (where available), and gathering of wild plants (McBride 1984:325). The subsistence data from Iroquois project sites indicate that, in the lower Housatonic valley, maize was somewhat more common in the Late Woodland period than Lavin (1988b) and others have suggested for the coastal Long Island region.

Maize was relatively common at both of our Iroquois project sites on the lower Housatonic, and was found in both cob and kernel fragments. A total of 13 different features produced 79 fragments of carbonized maize. Although the absolute quantities of maize recovered from our

Housatonic River sites are not large relative to amounts recovered from some of the major inland sites, these samples are still larger than most sites previously reported for the Long Island Sound area.[2] For long stretches of coastline, maize horticulture may not have been, in fact, a particularly viable subsistence strategy. However, the people living near the mouths of major rivers had more options. Rather than being restricted to either a coastal or an inland subsistence regime, the inhabitants of areas such as the lower Housatonic River valley enjoyed the best of both settings, with easy access to both marine resources and produce from gardens in the fertile river floodplain.

## SUMMARY

These new data strengthen Snow's (1980:282) assertion that maize horticulture was introduced to the Northeast by the Middle Woodland period. Although the relative importance of maize during this time period remains to be demonstrated, it should be noted that over twenty five years ago Ritchie and Funk (1973:356) predicted that future excavations would support their assertion that maize horticulture constituted an important aspect of the economy of the late Middle Woodland Hunter's Home phase.

The Iroquois Pipeline data add to an emerging picture of maize cultivation in the Susquehanna and Hudson drainages of central and eastern New York during the last few centuries of the first millennium. This span of time has been traditionally designated by archaeologists as the latter portion of the Middle Woodland period. Given the accumulating evidence of early horticulture and village life in the Susquehanna and Hudson drainages ca. A.D. 750-1000, we should probably include these components with the beginning of the Late Woodland rather than the end of the Middle Woodland.

Snow (1996:793) has noted, "There are [now] at least four radiocarbon dates from Owasco occupations [in south-central New York] that calibrate to earlier than A.D. 900 (Funk 1993:158-171; Wurst and Versaggi 1993)." Snow (1996:794) further noted that the original authors have rejected four such dates that calibrate to the seventh and eighth centuries A.D., but that we should perhaps not be so quick to discount them. McBride's (1984) chronology for the lower Connecticut River valley recognizes the earlier termination of Middle Woodland manifestations, and in the upper Delaware, Fischler and French (1991) defined a "terminal Middle Woodland" phase that ended at A.D. 900.

For Ontario, researchers have recently concluded that "Princess Point is not, in fact, a Middle Woodland culture at all, but should be considered to be early Late Woodland, or at least 'Transitional' Woodland" (Crawford and Smith 1996:789). We suggest that a division between Middle and Late Woodland at about A.D. 800-900 correlates with the widespread appearance of maize throughout much of the eastern United States and is a better interpretation of the archaeological record.

This increasing evidence for earlier maize cultivation in the Northeast is undoubtedly the result of the increasing roles of flotation and archaeobotanical analysis in modern archaeology (cf. Hart and Asch Sidell 1997). As Fritz (1990:411) has predicted, "researchers across much of eastern North America should not be surprised by the occurrence of maize in samples immediately preceding 1,000 B.P. in quantities just above the level of archaeological visibility." In this context, the low densities of maize remains in the features at Site 211-1-1 should be reemphasized. The maize density of 0.012 fragments per liter in the early features indicates that only slightly more than one maize fragment was recovered for every 100 liters of floated and analyzed fill.

Although many of the early dates are based on associated wood charcoal samples rather than on charred maize fragments themselves, direct AMS dating is now being used more frequently. Although not 100 percent conclusive, AMS dating has corroborated previous indications and clarified earlier misassociations (Hart, this volume; Snow 1995). It is clear that systematic flotation processing, professional archaeobotanical analyses, and direct AMS dating can provide data to support a more detailed analysis of Northeast subsistence patterns now than was available even a decade ago.

## ACKNOWLEDGEMENTS

This article presents information compiled through the efforts of a number of researchers. Our flotation program was guided by Kathy Furgerson and Marina Mozzi, who were responsible for processing thousands of liters of soil from dozens of sites. Nancy Asch Sidell identified the maize remains and prepared an internal report that formed the core of our descriptive text on the archaeobotanical samples. All research was funded by the Iroquois Gas Transmission System, L.P., Shelton, Connecticut.

## END NOTES

1. The date of A.D. 1000 ± 70 was obtained from wood charcoal from Burial 1. Carbonized maize from that same feature was directly dated by the AMS method at A.D. 1340 ± 60, and Ceci (1990:9) suggested that this is evidence of older firewood in a younger feature.

2. The Tubbs Site in Niantic, Connecticut produced at least 45 kernels and 2 cobs but has not been dated (Bendremer and Dewar 1993). Most other Long Island Sound sites have produced only a few fragments. Interestingly, the only other regional site with reports of substantial quantities of maize is located near the mouth of the Housatonic River in Milford, about 8 mi downstream from our pipeline project sites. This is the so-called Indian River site, which Rogers (1943) reported to have produced "two quarts" of maize.

## REFERENCES CITED

Asch, D. A., and N. B. Asch. 1975. Plant Remains from the Zimmerman Site–Grid A: A Quantitative Perspective. In *The Zimmerman Site: Further Excavations at the Grand Village of the Kaskaskia*, by M. K. Brown, pp. 116-120. Reports of Investigations No. 32. Illinois State Museum, Springfield.

Asch Sidell, N. 1992a. Archaeobotany of Sites 294A-25-2 and 294A-AF2-1 in the Housatonic River Valley. Submitted to Garrow and Associates, Inc. Copies available from Garrow and Associates, Inc., Raleigh, North Carolina.

—————. 1992b *Plant Use by Norridgewock Indians: A Comparison of the Historic and Archaeological Records.* Submitted to the University of Maine at Farmington, Archaeological Research Center. Copies available from the Maine State Historic Preservation Commission.

Bendremer, J. C. M., E. Kellogg, and T. B. Largy. 1991. A Grass-Lined Storage Pit and Early Maize Horticulture in Central Connecticut. *North American Archaeologist* 12:325-349.

Bendremer, J. C. M., and R. E. Dewar. 1994. The Advent of Maize Horticulture in New England. In *Corn and Culture in the Prehistoric New World,* edited by S. Johannessen and C. A. Hastorf, pp. 369-393. Westview Press, Boulder.

Blake, L. W., and H. C. Cutler. 1983. Plant Remains from the Gnagey Site (36SO55). *Pennsylvania Archaeologist* 53(4):83-88.

Cassedy, D. 1996. *From the Erie Canal to Long Island Sound: Technical Synthesis of the Iroquois Pipeline Project, 1989-1993.* Garrow and Associates, Inc., Atlanta. Submitted to Iroquois Gas Transmission System, L.P., Shelton, Connecticut. Copies available from the New York State Office of Parks, Recreation, and Historic Preservation.

Cassedy, D., P. Webb, A. Dowd, J. Jones, C. Cobb, R. S. Dillon, M. Rheinbold, and T. Millis. 1993. *Iroquois Gas Transmission System Phase III Archaeological Data Recovery Report, Volume 2: The Hudson Valley Region.* Garrow and Associates, Inc., Atlanta. Submitted to Iroquois Gas Transmission System, L.P., Shelton, Connecticut. Copies available from the New York State Office of Parks, Recreation, and Historic Preservation.

Ceci, L. 1982. Method and Theory in Coastal New York Archaeology: Paradigms of Settlement Pattern. *North American Archaeologist* 3:5-36.

—————. 1990 Radiocarbon Dating "Village Sites" in Coastal New York: Settlement Pattern Change in the Middle to Late Woodland. *Man in the Northeast* 39:1-28.

Crawford, G., and D. Smith. 1996. Migration in Prehistory: Princess Point and the Northern Iroquoian Case. *American Antiquity* 61:782-790.

Demeritt, D. 1991. Agriculture, Climate, and Cultural Adaptation in the Prehistoric Northeast. *Archaeology of Eastern North America* 19:183-202.

Fischler, B. and J. French. 1991. The Middle to Late Woodland Transition in the Upper Delaware Valley, New Information from the Smithfield Beach Site (36MR5). In *The People of the Minisik,* edited by D.G. Orr and D.V. Campana, pp. 145-174. National Park Service, Mid-Atlantic Region, Philadelphia.

Ford, R.I. 1987. Dating Early Maize in the Eastern United States. Paper presented at the Tenth Ethnobotany Meetings, Gainesville, FLorida.

Fritz, G. J. 1990. Multiple Pathways to Farming in Precontact Eastern North America. *Journal of World Prehistory* 4:387-435.

Funk, R. E. 1976. *Some Recent Contributions to Hudson Valley Prehistory.* New York State Museum Memoir 22. New York State Museum, Albany.

—————. 1993. *Archaeological Investigations in the Upper Susquehanna Valley, New York State.* Persimmon Press, Buffalo.

Hart, J. P., and N. Asch Sidell. 1996. Prehistoric Agricultural Systems in the West Branch of the Susquehanna River Basin, A.D. 800 to A.D. 1350. *Northeast Anthropology* 52:1-30.

—————. 1997. Additional Evidence for Early Cucurbit Use in the Northern Eastern Woodlands East of the Allegheny Front. *American Antiquity* 62:523-537.

Heckenberger, M. J., J. B. Petersen, and N. Asch Sidell. 1992. Early Evidence of Maize Agriculture in the Connecticut River Valley of Vermont. *Archaeology of Eastern North America* 20:125-149.

Hudson, C. 1990. *The Juan Pardo Expeditions.* Smithsonian Institution Press, Washington, D.C.

Lavin, L. 1988. Coastal Adaptation in Southern New England and Southern New York. *Archaeology of Eastern North America* 16:101-120.

McBride, K. 1984. *Prehistory of the Lower Connecticut River Valley*. Unpublished Ph.D. dissertation, Department of Anthropology, University of Connecticut, Storrs.

McBride, K., and R. Dewar. 1981. Prehistoric Settlement in the Lower Connecticut River Valley. *Man in the Northeast* 22:37-66.

—————. 1987. Agriculture and Cultural Evolution: Causes and Effects in the Lower Connecticut River Valley. In *Emergent Horticultural Economies of the Eastern Woodlands*, edited by W. F. Keegan, pp. 305-328. Center for Archaeological Investi-gations, Occasional Papers No. 7. Southern Illinois University at Carbondale.

Millis, T., D. Cassedy, H. Millis, P. Webb, and N. Asch Sidell. 1993. *Iroquois Gas Transmission System Phase III Archaeological Data Recovery Report, Volume 3: The Connecticut Sites.* Garrow and Associates, Inc., Atlanta. Submitted to Iroquois Gas Transmission System, L. P., Shelton, Connecticut.

Pearsall, D. M. 1989. *Paleoethnobotany: A Handbook of Procedures.* Academic Press, New York.

Riley, T. J., G. R. Walz, C. J. Bareis, A. C. Fortier, and K. E. Parker. 1994. Accelerator Mass Spectrometry (AMS) Dates Confirm Early *Zea mays* in the Mississippi River Valley. *American Antiquity* 59:490-498.

Ritchie, W. A., D. Lenig, and P.S. Miller, 1953. *An Early Owasco Sequence in Eastern New York.* New York State Museum Circular 32. Albany.

Ritchie, W. A., and R. E. Funk. 1973. *Aboriginal Settlement Patterns in the Northeast.* Memoir 20, New York Museum and Science Service. The University of the State of New York, Albany.

Rogers, E. H. 1943. The Indian River Village Site. *Bulletin of the Archaeological Society of Connecticut* 15:7-78.

Smith, B. 1992. Prehistoric Plant Husbandry in Eastern North America. In *The Origins of Agriculture: An International Perspective*, edited by C. W. Cowan and P. J. Watson, pp. 101-119. Smithsonian Institution Press, Washington, D.C.

Snow, D. R. 1980. *The Archaeology of New England.* Academic Press, New York.

—————. 1995. Mohawk Valley Archaeology: The Sites. *Occasional Papers in Anthropology* 23. Matson Museum of Anthropology, The Pennsylvania State University, University Park, Pennsylvania.

—————. 1996. More on Migration in Prehistory: Accommodating New Evidence in the Northern Iroquoian Case. *American Antiquity* 61:791-796.

Stuiver, M., and P. J. Reimer. 1993. Extended $^{14}C$ Database and Revised CALIB 3.0 $^{14}C$ Age Calibration Program. *Radiocarbon* 35:215-230.

Wurst, L., and N. Versaggi. 1993. *Under the Asphalt: The Archaeology of the Binghamton Mall Project.* Public Archaeology Facility, State University of New York at Binghamton. Submitted to the City of Binghamton Urban Renewal Agency. Copies available at the New York State Office of Parks, Recreation, and Historic Preservation.

# CHAPTER 7

# PREHISTORIC USE OF PLANT FOODS ON LONG ISLAND AND BLOCK ISLAND SOUNDS

David J. Bernstein

Over the last two decades, the subject of the use of plant foods by pre-contact native peoples on the coast of Long Island and Block Island sounds has generated much discussion (Ceci 1979-80; Silver 1980). In the years since this debate was initiated, substantial new data on the exploitation of botanical resources, and subsistence practices in general, have been obtained. The goal of this paper is to summarize and synthesize the archaeobotanical record from the region and offer some preliminary statements regarding the use of plant foods during the last four or five thousand years prior to the European arrival (Table 7.1). This is the most recent installment in my effort to reconstruct and understand long-term trends in Native American subsistence and settlement on the coast of New York and Southern New England (Bernstein 1992, 1993b).

The archaeobotanical records from a number of subregions are summarized below. Reconstructing the exploitation of plants (wild and domesticated) in this part of eastern North America is not easy. As my colleagues working with plant assemblages from other parts of the world are quick to point out, northeastern coastal samples are often terribly small and fragmented. There is also the danger that some of the charred plant remains may not represent the actual consumption of a particular species. For example, some of the seeds may have made their way into hearths and other features with fuel. However, despite these problems, the regional database is now of sufficient quality to support some general statements regarding subsistence practices.

I have personal familiarity only with some of the Narragansett Bay and Long Island samples. All other information is drawn from publications, dissertations, cultural resource management reports, and personal communications. Undoubtedly, there are other unpublished data (especially from the Connecticut coast) relevant to this synthesis that I

did not have available when writing this chapter. It is also important to remember that the assemblages from the different sites are not necessarily comparable. Sample sizes and reporting formats vary from site to site, as do methods of recovery and analysis. For example, the reason that only charred nutshells (and no seeds) were recovered at most of the Long Island sites excavated prior to 1975 (e.g., Wading River, Cusano, Shoreham, Stony Brook, and Englebright) is probably that these sites were dug before the common use of flotation. In some cases no screening (dry or wet) whatsoever was employed. Nutshells are readily identifiable and are large in comparison to other types of archaeological floral remains. Therefore, they are often noted by excavators even when they are not quantified. I have included only charred botanical remains in the following analysis.

## NON-AGRARIAN PLANTS

The overwhelming majority of edible plants represented at coastal sites in Southern New England and New York are from non-cultivated species (Tables 7.2-7.5). As discussed below, the situation at interior riverine sites is somewhat different, but here also the remains of wild plants are much more common than domesticates. Unlike in the Midcontinent, no native cultigens have yet been identified at coastal sites. Plants such as *Chenopodium*, known to have been widely cultivated in the North American interior (Smith 1989), are commonly identified in samples from coastal sites, but they do not appear to be cultigens (see George and Dewar this volume for a fuller discussion of *Chenopodium* at New England sites).

### Long Island
Non-agrarian charred plant remains have been reported for eight prehistoric sites on Long Island, all but one of which (MPM Farm) are on the north

**Table 7.1. Prehistoric Chronology for Long Island and Southern New England.**

| Period | Approximate Dates |
|---|---|
| Late Woodland | A.D. 1000-1500 |
| Middle Woodland | A.D. 0-1000 |
| Early Woodland | 700 B.C.-A.D. 0 |
| | |
| Terminal Archaic | 1,000-700 B.C. |
| Late Archaic | 4,000-1,000 B.C. |
| Middle Archaic | 6,000-4,000 B.C. |
| Early Archaic | 8,000-6,000 B.C. |
| | |
| Paleoindian | 10,500-8,000 B.C. |

**Table 7.2. Taxonomic List of Plants Represented at Archaeological Sites Discussed in Text.**

| Taxonomic Name | Common Name |
|---|---|
| *Amaranthus* sp. | pigweed |
| *Carya* sp. | hickory |
| *Chenopodium* sp. | goosefoot, lamb's quarters |
| *Corylus* sp. | hazelnut |
| *Cornus canadensis* | bunchberry |
| *Crataegus* sp. | hawthorn |
| *Cyperus* sp. | sedge |
| *Galium* sp. | bedstraw, cleavers |
| *Gaylussacia* sp. | huckleberry, dangleberry |
| *Hordeum* sp. | foxtail or little barley |
| *Impatiens* sp. | jewelweed |
| *Juglans* sp. | walnut, butternut |
| *Mitchella repens* | partridgeberry |
| *Phytolacca* sp. | pokeweed |
| *Polygonatum commutatum* | Solomon's seal |
| *Polygonum* sp. | knotweed, smartweed |
| *Prunus* sp. | plum, wild cherry |
| *Quercus* sp. | oak (acorn) |
| *Rhus* sp. | sumac |
| *Rubus* sp. | blackberry, raspberry |
| *Sambucus* sp. | elderberry |
| *Scirpus* sp. | bulrush |
| *Solanum* sp. | nightshade |
| *Tilia* sp. | basswood |
| *Vaccinium* sp. | blueberry |
| *Vitis* sp. | wild grape |
| *Zea mays* | maize |
| *Zizania aquatica* | wild rice |

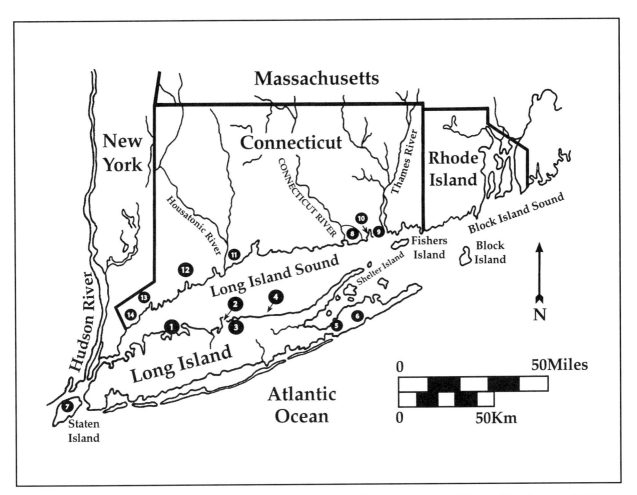

**Figure 7.1.** Map of Long Island and Block Island Sound region showing locations discussed in the text. (1) Henry Lloyd Manor; (2) Stony Brook and Engelbright; (3) Pipestave Hollow; (4) Wading River, Shoreham and Cusano; (5) Sebonac; (6) MPM Farm; (7) Bowmans Brook; (8) 75-1, 75-7, 105-3, Bliss-Howard, Griffin, Broeder Point, Ames, Leffingwell Pond, Heflon, Arbucci, Klinck, Funnell, Griswold Point, Chadwick, Great Island, Gladeview; (9) Mamacoke Cove; (10) Mago Point; (11) 294A-25-2 and 294-AF2-1; (12) Bear Rock Shelter, D'aulaire Shelter, Perkin-Elmer Shelter, Sasqua Hill, Spruce Swamp; (13) Highland; (14) Cobb Island Drive.

shore (Figure 7.1). Only two sites (Henry Lloyd Manor and MPM Farm) yielded materials other than nutshell. The lack of seeds reported from Long Island sites is puzzling. For sites excavated more than 25 years ago, one would assume that seeds were not recovered because flotation was not employed. However, seeds are also absent at many sites where extensive programs of flotation were undertaken (Bernstein 1993a; Bernstein et al. 1993; Gwynne 1982). In fact, some of the sites on the north shore have yielded virtually no carbonized plant remains, aside from wood charcoal, even though hundreds of liters of soil from

hearths, middens, and other features were processed (Bernstein 1993a; Bernstein et al. 1993). This may reflect poor preservation, absence of behaviors that lead to the discard and deposition of plant remains, or sampling problems.

The single site yielding a good sample of plant remains is Henry Lloyd Manor (Silver 1991). This is a multicomponent shell-bearing site dating from the Late Archaic to the Late Woodland, with the Middle Woodland occupation being the most extensive and best studied. All of the other Long Island sites shown in Tables 7.3-7.5 are also coastal occupations with shell middens. Among these is

# Table 7.3. Frequency of Nutshell at Coastal Sites.

| Site | Period | *Carya* sp. | *Quercus* sp. | *Juglans* sp. | *Corylus* sp. | Unidentified nut | References |
|---|---|---|---|---|---|---|---|
| **Long Island** | | | | | | | |
| Henry Lloyd Manor | Late Woodland | c | p | c | – | – | Silver 1991 |
| | Middle Woodland | d | p | d | – | – | |
| Wading River | Late Archaic | p | – | – | – | – | Wyatt 1977 |
| Cusano | Woodland | p | – | – | – | – | Wyatt 1977 |
| Shoreham | Late Archaic | p | – | – | – | – | Wyatt 1977 |
| Stony Brook | Terminal Archaic | p | – | – | – | – | Ritchie 1959 |
| Englebright | Late Woodland | p | – | – | – | – | Gramly and Gwynne 1979 |
| Pipestave Hollow | Late Woodland | p | – | – | – | – | Gwynne 1979, 1982 |
| MPM Farm | Late Woodland | p | – | – | – | – | Bernstein et al. 1996 |
| **Shelter Island** | | | | | | | |
| Sungic Midden | Middle-Late Woodland | – | b | – | – | p | Lightfoot et al. 1987 |
| Kettle Hole | Woodland | – | b | – | – | b | Lightfoot et al. 1987 |
| Sanwald | Late Archaic | – | – | – | – | – | Lightfoot et al. 1987 |
| Smith | Late Archaic-Woodland | p | – | – | – | – | Latham 1957 |
| **Fishers Island** | | | | | | | |
| Barlow Pond | Late Woodland | a | – | – | – | – | Funk and Pfeiffer 1988, 1992-93 |
| | Late Archaic | – | – | p | – | – | |
| Cant | Early-Middle Woodland | p | p | – | – | – | Funk and Pfeiffer 1988, 1992-93 |
| Flounder In North | Late Woodland | p | – | – | – | – | Funk and Pfeiffer 1988, 1992-93 |
| Sharp | Terminal Archaic-Late Woodland | – | – | – | – | p | Funk and Pfeiffer 1988, 1992-93 |
| Turtle Pond #2 | Woodland | p | – | – | – | p | Funk and Pfeiffer 1988, 1992-93 |
| | Late Archaic | p | – | – | – | – | |
| Two Springs | Terminal Archaic | – | – | – | – | p | Funk and Pfeiffer 1988, 1992-93 |
| | Late Archaic | a | – | – | – | – | |
| **Block Island** | | | | | | | |
| RI1428 | Early Woodland | p | – | – | – | – | Jaworski 1990 |
| **Coastal Connecticut** | | | | | | | |
| Southwest Coast | | | | | | | |
| Cobb Island Drive | Woodland | d | – | b | – | – | Pappalardo 1994 |

**Table 7.3. Continued**

| Site | Time Period | | | | | Reference |
|------|-------------|---|---|---|---|-----------|
| **Lower Connecticut River Valley** | | | | | | |
| Great Island | Early Woodland | p | – | – | – | Pfeiffer 1992 |
| | Terminal Archaic | p | – | – | p | |
| Griffin | Terminal Archaic | p | p | – | – | Pfeiffer 1980 |
| 75-1 | Late Woodland | p | p | – | – | McBride 1984 |
| 75-7 | Late Woodland | – | – | – | – | McBride 1984 |
| 105-3 | Late Woodland | p | – | – | – | McBride 1984 |
| Bliss-Howard | Late Archaic | p | p | p | – | Pfeiffer 1984 |
| Ames | Terminal Archaic | p | p | – | – | Pfeiffer 1992 |
| | Late Archaic | p | – | – | – | |
| Leffingwell Pond | Late Archaic | p | – | – | – | Pfeiffer 1992 |
| Heflon | Late Archaic | p | – | – | – | Pfeiffer 1992 |
| Arbucci | Late Archaic | p | – | – | – | Pfeiffer 1992 |
| Klinck | Terminal Archaic | p | – | – | – | Pfeiffer 1992 |
| | Late Archaic | p | – | – | – | |
| Funnell | Terminal Archaic | p | – | p | – | Pfeiffer 1992 |
| Gladeview | Early Woodland | p | – | – | – | Pfeiffer 1992 |
| | Terminal Archaic | p | – | – | – | |
| Broeder Point | Early Woodland | p | p | – | – | Pfeiffer 1992 |
| | Late Archaic | p | – | – | – | |
| Griswold Point | Late Archaic | p | p | p | – | Pfeiffer 1992 |
| Chadwick | Late Archaic | p | – | – | – | Pfeiffer 1992 |
| **Lower Housatonic River Valley** | | | | | | |
| 294A-25-2 | Late Woodland | d | c | – | – | Millis et al. 1995 |
| | Middle Woodland | d | b | c | – | |
| | Early Woodland | b | a | – | – | |
| 294A-AF2-1 | Late Woodland | c | b | b | – | Millis et al. 1995 |
| | Woodland | c | b | – | – | |
| | Early-Middle Woodland | c | – | – | – | |
| | Early Woodland | c | – | – | – | |
| | Terminal Archaic-Early Woodland | c | b | b | – | |
| | Terminal Archaic | d | c | c | – | |
| **Lower Norwalk Drainage** | | | | | | |
| Bear Rock Shelter | Late Archaic | p | – | – | – | Wiegand 1983 |
| D'aulaire Shelter | Woodland | p | – | – | – | Wiegand 1983 |
| Perkin-Elmer Shelter | Woodland | p | p | – | – | Wiegand 1983 |
| | Late Archaic | p | – | – | – | |

**Table 7.3. Continued**

| Site | Period | Carya sp. | Quercus sp. | Juglans sp. | Corylus sp. | Unidentified nut | References |
|---|---|---|---|---|---|---|---|
| **Lower Thames River** | | | | | | | |
| Mamacoke Cove | Middle-Late Woodland | – | a | – | – | – | Juli 1992 |
| **Niantic Bay** | | | | | | | |
| Mago Point | Late Woodland | p | p | – | – | – | McBride and Dewar 1987 |
| **Narragansett Bay** | | | | | | | |
| Greenwich Cove | Late Woodland | b | – | – | – | – | Bernstein 1992 |
| | Middle Woodland | – | a | – | – | – | |
| | Early Woodland | c | – | – | – | – | |
| | Terminal Archaic | b | b | – | – | – | |
| Joyner | Late Woodland | b | – | – | – | – | Holt 1990 |
| | Early Woodland | c | – | – | – | – | |
| | Late Archaic | c | – | – | – | – | |
| RI670 | Middle Woodland | b | b | – | c | – | Morenon et al. 1986 |
| | Early Woodland | c | b | – | c | – | |
| | Late Archaic | d | – | – | – | – | |
| RI667 | Late Woodland | c | a | – | d | – | Morenon et al. 1986 |
| | Middle Woodland | b | – | – | b | – | |
| | Early Woodland | c | a | – | a | – | |
| Providence Cove | Late Woodland | p | – | – | – | – | Artemel et al. 1984 |
| Campbell | Late Woodland | a | – | – | – | – | Cox and Thorbahn 1981 |
| | Middle Woodland | – | – | – | b | – | |
| Hoskins Park | Late Woodland | c | a | – | – | – | Largy 1990; Leveillee and Van Coughyen 1990 |
| Lambert Farm | Late Archaic | c | a | – | – | – | Kerber et al. 1989; Largy 1989 |
| | Late Woodland | b | – | – | – | – | |
| Peckham | Late Woodland | c | b | – | b | c | Allan Leveillee, personal communication 1995 |

*Key*
a 1 specimen
b 2-10 specimens
c 11-99 specimens
d 100 or more specimens
p present, quantity not provided

**Table 7.4. Frequency of Fruit Remains at Coastal Sites.**

| Site | Period | Rubus sp. | Vitis sp. | Prunus sp. | Gaylussacia sp. | Sambucus sp. | Cornus canadensis | Vaccinium sp. | Mitchella repens | Crataegus sp. | References |
|---|---|---|---|---|---|---|---|---|---|---|---|
| **Long Island** | | | | | | | | | | | |
| Henry Lloyd Manor | Late Woodland | a | – | – | – | – | – | – | – | – | Silver 1991 |
| | Middle Woodland | b | a | – | – | – | – | – | – | – | |
| MPM Farm | Late Woodland | – | – | – | – | – | – | c | – | – | Bernstein et al. 1996 |
| **Shelter Island** | | | | | | | | | | | |
| Sungic Midden | Middle–Late Woodland | – | – | a | – | – | – | – | – | – | Lightfoot et al. 1987 |
| Sanwald | Late Archaic | – | – | b | – | – | – | – | – | – | Lightfoot et al. 1987 |
| Laspia | Late Woodland | – | b | – | – | – | – | – | – | – | Lightfoot et al. 1987 |
| **Fishers Island** | | | | | | | | | | | |
| Turtle Pond #2 | Woodland | – | p | – | – | – | – | – | – | – | Funk and Pfeiffer 1988, 1992–93 |
| **Block Island** | | | | | | | | | | | |
| RI1428 | Early Woodland | p | – | – | – | – | – | – | – | – | Jaworski 1990 |
| **Coastal Connecticut** | | | | | | | | | | | |
| Lower Connecticut River Valley | | | | | | | | | | | |
| 75-1 | Late Woodland | p | – | – | – | – | – | – | – | – | McBride 1984 |
| 105-3 | Late Woodland | – | – | p | – | – | – | – | – | – | McBride 1984 |
| Lower Housatonic River Valley | | | | | | | | | | | |
| 294A-25-2 | Late Woodland | a | – | – | a | – | – | – | – | – | Millis et al. 1995 |
| | Middle Woodland | b | – | – | – | – | – | – | – | – | |
| | Early Woodland | b | – | – | – | – | – | – | – | – | |
| Lower Norwalk Drainage | | | | | | | | | | | |
| Sasqua Hill | Woodland | – | p | – | – | – | p | – | – | p | Powell 1981 |
| Niantic Bay | | | | | | | | | | | |
| Mago Point | Late Woodland | p | – | – | – | p | – | – | – | – | McBride and Dewar 1987 |
| **Narragansett Bay** | | | | | | | | | | | |
| Joyner | Late Archaic | – | b | – | – | – | – | – | – | – | Holt 1990 |
| RI670 | Middle Woodland | – | – | – | – | – | – | – | a | – | Morenon et al. 1986 |
| RI667 | Late Woodland | – | – | a | – | – | – | – | – | – | Morenon et al. 1986 |
| Providence Cove | Late Woodland | p | p | – | – | – | – | – | – | – | Artemel et al. 1984 |
| Peckham | Late Woodland | b | – | – | – | – | – | b | – | – | Allan Leveillee, personal communication 1995 |

Key
a  1 specimen   b  2–10 specimens   c  11–99 specimens   p  present, quantity not provided

# Table 7.5. Seeds, Grains, Roots, Tubers, and Other Plants at Coastal Sites.

| Site | Period | Chenopodium sp. | Amaranthus sp. | Polygonum sp. | Phytolacca sp. | Rhus sp. | Hordeum sp. | Solanum sp. | Cyperus sp. | Galium sp. | Tilia sp. | Impatiens sp. | Scirpus sp. | Polygonatum commutatum | Zea mays | Zizania aquatica | References |
|---|---|---|---|---|---|---|---|---|---|---|---|---|---|---|---|---|---|
| **Long Island** | | | | | | | | | | | | | | | | | |
| Henry Lloyd Manor | Late Woodland | b | – | a | b | a | a | – | – | – | – | – | – | – | – | – | Silver 1991 |
| | Middle Woodland | c | a | a | – | a | a | a | – | – | – | – | – | – | c | – | |
| Sebonac | Late Woodland | – | – | – | – | – | – | – | – | – | – | – | – | – | c | – | Ceci 1990; Harrington 1902, 1903, 1924 |
| **Staten Island** | | | | | | | | | | | | | | | | | |
| Bowmans Brook | | – | – | – | – | – | – | – | – | – | – | – | – | – | p | – | Ceci 1990; Skinner 1897, 1903, 1909a, 1909b, 1924 |
| **Shelter Island** | | | | | | | | | | | | | | | | | |
| Kettle Hole | Woodland | – | – | b | – | – | – | – | – | – | – | – | – | – | – | – | Lightfoot et al. 1987 |
| Sanwald | Late Archaic | – | – | b | – | – | – | – | – | – | – | – | – | – | – | – | Lightfoot et al. 1987 |
| **Fishers Island** | | | | | | | | | | | | | | | | | |
| Hawks Nest Point | | l- | – | – | – | – | – | – | – | – | – | – | – | – | a | – | Funk and Pfeiffer 1988, 1992-93 |
| Flounder In North | | – | – | – | – | – | – | – | – | – | – | – | – | – | a | – | Funk and Pfeiffer 1988, 1992-93 |
| Sharp | | – | – | – | – | – | – | – | – | – | – | – | – | – | p | – | Funk and Pfeiffer 1988, 1992-93 |
| Turtle Pond #2 | | – | – | – | – | – | – | – | – | – | – | – | – | – | p | – | Funk and Pfeiffer 1988, 1992-93 |
| Barlow Pond | | – | – | – | – | – | – | – | – | – | – | – | – | – | b | – | Funk and Pfeiffer 1988, 1992-93 |
| **Coastal Connecticut** | | | | | | | | | | | | | | | | | |
| Southwest Coast | | | | | | | | | | | | | | | | | |
| Highland | Late Woodland | – | – | – | – | – | – | – | – | – | – | – | – | – | b | – | Bendremer 1993 |

**Table 7.5. Continued**

| Site | Period | 1 | 2 | 3 | 4 | 5 | 6 | 7 | 8 | 9 | 10 | 11 | 12 | Reference |
|---|---|---|---|---|---|---|---|---|---|---|---|---|---|---|
| *Lower Connecticut River Valley* | | | | | | | | | | | | | | |
| Griffin | Terminal Archaic | p | – | – | – | – | – | – | – | – | – | – | – | Pfeiffer 1980 |
| 75-7 | Late Woodland | – | – | – | – | – | – | – | p | – | – | – | – | McBride 1984 |
| 105-3 | Late Woodland | – | – | – | – | – | – | – | p | – | – | – | – | McBride 1984 |
| Bliss-Howard | Late Archaic | p | – | – | – | – | – | – | – | – | – | – | – | Pfeiffer 1984 |
| *Lower Housatonic River Valley* | | | | | | | | | | | | | | |
| 294A-25-2 | Middle Woodland | – | – | – | – | – | – | – | – | – | – | b | – | Millis et al. 1995 |
|  | Late Woodland | a | b | c | – | a | – | – | – | – | – | b | – | Millis et al. 1995 |
| 294A-AF2-1 | Late Woodland | – | – | – | – | – | – | – | – | – | – | a | – | Millis et al. 1995 |
| *Lower Norwalk Drainage* | | | | | | | | | | | | | | |
| Sasqua Hill | Woodland | p | – | – | p | – | – | – | – | – | – | – | – | Powell 1981 |
| Spruce Swamp | ? | – | p | – | – | – | – | – | – | – | – | – | – | Powell 1981 |
| *Lower Thames River* | | | | | | | | | | | | | | |
| Mamacoke Cove | Middle-Late Woodland | – | – | – | c | – | – | – | – | – | – | – | – | Juli 1992 |
| *Niantic Bay* | | | | | | | | | | | | | | |
| Mago Point | Late Woodland | – | p | p | p | p | p | p | – | – | – | – | – | McBride and Dewar 1987 |
| *Narragansett Bay* | | | | | | | | | | | | | | |
| Joyner | Late Woodland | – | – | b | b | – | – | – | a | – | – | – | – | Holt 1990 |
|  | Early Woodland | – | b | – | b | – | – | – | – | – | – | – | – | |
|  | Late Archaic | a | a | – | c | – | – | – | – | – | – | – | – | |
| RI667 | Late Woodland | – | – | – | – | – | – | – | – | – | a | – | – | Morenon et al. 1986 |
| Providence Cove | Late Woodland | – | – | – | – | – | – | – | p | p | a | – | – | Artemel et al. 1984 |
| Campbell | Late Woodland | a | – | – | – | a | b | – | – | – | – | – | – | Cox and Thorbahn 1981 |
|  | Middle Woodland | a | – | – | a | b | b | – | – | – | – | b | – | |
| Peckham | Late Woodland | c | c | – | – | b | b | b | – | – | – | a | – | Allan Leveillee, personal communication 1995 |

*Key*

a   1 specimen

b   2-10 specimens

c   11-99 specimens

p   present, quantity not provided

MPM Farm (Bernstein et al. 1996), where nearly 300 liters of soil from a large clay-lined pit were floated. Included in the pit fill were fish bones, shells (oyster [*Crassostrea virginica*] is the most abundant), cord-wrapped-stick-impressed and brushed pottery, a fragment of steatite, a small number of lithic tools and debitage, and carbonized remains of hickory nut and blueberry (Patricia Crawford, personal communication 1996). Two radiocarbon dates were obtained on wood charcoal from the feature: $880 \pm 70$ B.P. (Beta-93015; $\delta^{13}C = -26.5‰$, calibrated $2\sigma$-range = A.D. 1025 to 1290) and $780 \pm 70$ B.P (Beta-93016; $\delta^{13}C = -26.0‰$, calibrated $2\sigma$-range = A.D. 1170-1315 and A.D. 1345-1390).

**Shelter Island**

Five sites on Shelter Island (Figure 7.1) yielded carbonized plant remains. The Smith site was excavated by an avocational archaeologist who noted finding charred nutshells in hearth features (Latham 1957). The other four sites were studied in the course of a large-scale (survey and testing on 825 ha) research program conducted in the southeastern portion of the island (Lightfoot et al. 1987). Flotation samples were systematically collected and processed from each site. According to Lightfoot et al. (1987:122-124), plant food remains were found primarily at three types of sites (cf. Thomas 1983): residential bases that are thought to have been the "hubs" of the Woodland settlement system; field camps where various extractive activities took place; and plant-procurement locations where wild plants were harvested and possibly processed. The latter are characterized by a low diversity of artifacts, few lithic remains, comparatively large numbers of ceramics, and relatively abundant (by local standards) plant remains. No remains of domesticated plants were found at any of the Shelter Island sites.

**Fishers and Block Islands**

Fishers Island is located approximately 4 km off the south coast of Connecticut (Figure 7.1). Over the last decade, Funk and Pfeiffer (1988, 1992-93) have conducted a large-scale investigation of the island's archaeology and paleoecology. They have studied 27 prehistoric sites, six of which yielded charred botanical remains (Tables 7.3 and 7.4). As discussed further below, small quantities of maize were found at five of the Fishers Island sites. The earliest radiocarbon date for any of the sites is 5,295 B.P. $\pm 180$ (uncalibrated) from Turtle Pond #2 (Funk and Pfeiffer 1992-93:21). Prior to the Late Woodland (ca. A.D. 1000), sites were very small, rarely exceeding 400m$^2$. During the Late Woodland, sites became bigger and more numerous on Fishers Island. As of this writing, the floral materials have not been quantified, so it is premature to speculate on the relative importance of the different plant foods represented in the Fishers Island sites (John Pfeiffer, personal communication 1995).

Block Island (Figure 7.1), off the coast of Rhode Island, has yielded well-preserved archaeological faunal collections (Bellantoni 1987), but unfortunately archaeobotanical remains from the island are not as abundant as the zooarchaeological materials. In her synthesis of research at the Early Woodland Site RI1428 conducted by the University of Connecticut under the direction of Kevin McBride, Jaworski (1990) noted that raspberry and hickory are represented and that no cultigens were recovered.

**Coastal Connecticut**

Coastal Connecticut is the best known archaeologically of all the areas treated in this paper (Figure 7.1). The lower Connecticut River valley, in particular, has been intensively studied (Bendremer 1993, this volume; McBride 1984; Pagoulatos 1986; Pfeiffer 1992). For purposes of this paper, I am treating only the coastal zone in the southern part of the state (within 25 km of Long Island Sound). However, it should be noted that many sites in the interior reaches of the Connecticut River Valley have yielded rich assemblages of domesticated and wild botanical remains, some of which are comparable in quality to those from the American Midcontinent (Bendremer, this volume; Lavin 1988b; McBride 1978). At least one of the interior sites, Woodchuck Knoll, has strong evidence for the systematic storage of *Chenopodium* (George and Dewar, this volume; McBride 1978).

Numerous botanical assemblages have also been excavated at sites outside the Connecticut

River valley. Powell (1981) has published a summary of the plant assemblages from four of the Connecticut sites, two of which are coastal (Spruce Swamp and Sasqua Hill). They are both in the lower Norwalk Drainage. Wiegand (1983) has described a series of rockshelters throughout the southwestern part of the state that have yielded well-preserved faunal and floral subsistence remains recovered via flotation. On the southeast coast, Mago Point (McBride and Dewar 1987) and Mamacoke Cove (Juli 1992) have produced the best studied botanical assemblages.

## Narragansett Bay
Narragansett Bay is the easternmost region considered in this paper (Figure 7.2). Botanical remains from nine Narragansett Bay sites are itemized in Tables 7.3-7.5. All the assemblages were recovered via flotation. Eight of the sites (excluding Peckham Farm) are described in Bernstein (1992). The Peckham Farm data are provided by Leveillee (personal communication 1995).

## CULTIGENS

In recent years, several researchers have reviewed the evidence for prehistoric agriculture (primarily maize) on the coast of Southern New England and New York (Bendremer 1993, this volume; Bendremer and Dewar 1994; Bernstein 1992; Ceci 1990; George and Bendremer 1995; McBride and Dewar 1987) and elsewhere in the Northeast (Demeritt 1991; Heckenberger et al. 1992). In this discussion, consistently the most interesting question has been whether or not coastal Algonquins were raising and consuming maize in significant quantities prior to the initial European arrival, usually placed at A.D. 1524. For now, the archaeological evidence suggests that the answer to this question is no. The presence of maize, or any other cultigens, at sites in the region, especially those in coastal New York, is very limited, although until many more late (post-A.D. 1000) prehistoric sites are excavated, the issue remains unresolved.

Ceci (1979-80, 1982, 1990) summarized the evidence for cultivation in coastal New York, noting that the available data indicate this to have been a marginal activity at best. Of critical importance is her finding that much of the archaeologically recovered maize in the region is from post-contact, not prehistoric, components. The only maize from coastal New York that can be confidently dated to before the European arrival comes from the following sites.

## Bowmans Brook
Bowmans Brook is a large, multicomponent site on Staten Island containing both historic and prehistoric materials (Ceci 1979-80, 1990) that was initially excavated nearly a hundred years ago (Skinner 1897, 1903, 1909a, 1909b, 1924). A sample of maize from Bowmans Brook recovered by an avocational archaeologist in 1961 was radiocarbon dated by Ceci (1990) to A.D. 1340 (corrected for fractionation). The calibrated ($2\sigma$) date (cf. Klein et al. 1982) is A.D. 1270-1410.

## Sebonac
Sebonac, on the south fork of Long Island (Figure 7.1), was excavated by Harrington (1902, 1903, 1924). The maize came from a refuse pit that yielded "35 tiny kernel/cob fragments" (Ceci 1990:2). Ceci (1990) obtained an AMS date of A.D. 1395 (calibrated $2\sigma$ range A.D. 1260-1485) from a sample of the maize (Ceci 1990). Other materials from Sebonac, including sturgeon bone, marine shell, and wood charcoal, have also been radiocarbon dated to before the European arrival. A piece of whale bone from Sebonac has a calibrated date range of A.D. 1420-1950.

## Fishers Island
The Fishers Island sites excavated by Funk and Pfeiffer (1988, 1992-93) are discussed above. Six of the 27 sites they have studied yielded charred botanical remains (Tables 7.3 and 7.4). Five of these (Hawks Nest Point, Flounder In North, Sharp, Turtle Pond #2, and Barlow Pond) yielded maize kernels in addition to wild plants. At Hawks Nest Point, a single charred maize kernel was recovered in a pit feature that also yielded Late Woodland artifacts (Windsor pottery and Levanna-style projectile points) and a variety of other subsistence remains. A radiocarbon date of A.D. 275 ± 90 B.P. obtained on charcoal from the

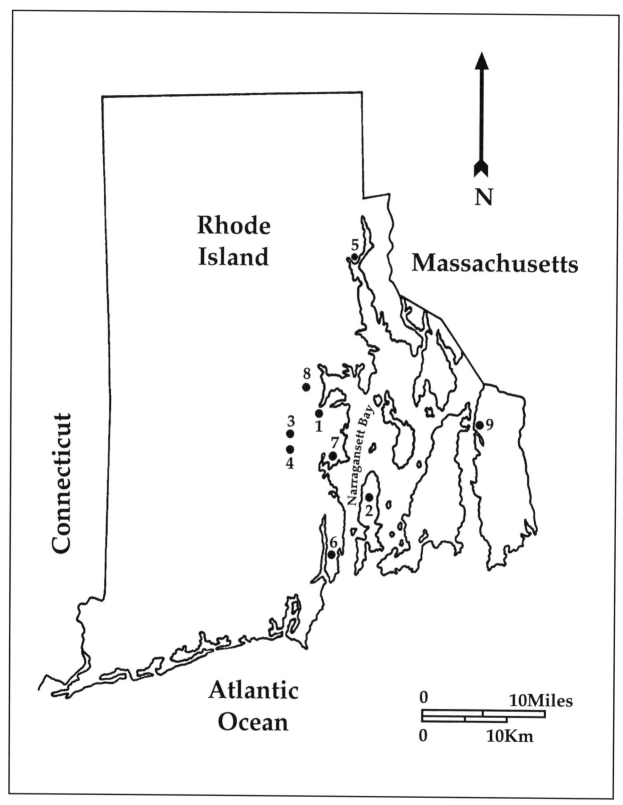

**Figure 7.2.** Map of Narragansett Bay showing locations discussed in the text. (1) Greenwich Cove; (2) Joyner; (3) RI670; (4) RI667; (5) Providence Cove Lands; (6) Campbell; (7) Hoskins park; (8) Lambert Farm; (9) Peckham Farm.

feature is considered by the excavators to be "too old for the associated Late Woodland artifacts" (Funk and Pfeiffer 1992-93:17). The Barlow Pond site yielded five charred maize kernels in association with a charred hickory nut (Funk and Pfeiffer 1992-93:22). At Flounder In North, a single maize kernel was found, along with hickory nuts and small fragments of calcined bone in a feature dated to A.D. 1095 ± 125 (Funk and Pfeiffer 1992-93:25). Maize was also found in refuse deposits at Turtle Pond #2 and Sharp.

**Coastal Connecticut**

Tentative evidence suggests that growing maize may have been somewhat more important on the south coast of Connecticut, especially along the river valleys, but again, until more data are available, this issue cannot be completely settled. As is the case for the islands, some scattered evidence for maize has been found in coastal Connecticut. A single maize kernel was found in a shell midden at the Mago Point site on Niantic Bay (McBride and Dewar 1987). It is associated with abundant and diverse wild plant remains, as well as an even more varied faunal assemblage. The best sample of maize from this region was recovered from two sites (294A-25-2 and 294-AF2-1) on the east bank of the Housatonic River (Cassedy, this volume; Millis et al. 1995). However, even here, wild plants dominate in the pre-contact assemblages. Finally, the Highland site in Rowayton, Connecticut, has yielded four fragments of maize with two associated Late Woodland radiocarbon dates (Bendremer 1993 citing a personal communication with Wiegand).

## DISCUSSION

The coastal assemblages considered for this paper contain a minimum of 28 potential plant foods (Table 7.2). Maize is the only certain domesticate, although Millis et al. (1995) have suggested the possibility of the presence of bean (*Phaseolus vulgaris*) at their lower Housatonic River sites. At least four genera of nuts were consumed (Table 7.3). Nine genera of fruits are present (Table 7.4), as are at least eight plants yielding edible seeds or grains (*Chenopodium, Amaranthus, Polygonum, Rhus, Hordeum, Solanum, Zea, Zizania*) (Table 7.5). Six have edible roots, tubers, or shoots (*Phytolacca, Cyperus, Galium, Impatiens, Scirpus, Polygonatum*), although in some cases they also produce edible seeds or fruits. *Tilia* yields both edible flowers and sap (Densmore 1974; Elias and Dykeman 1990).

Although quantitative data for charred plant remains are extremely difficult to interpret (Hillman 1989:218), cumulatively, the samples from the coastal sites discussed here suggest that beginning with the Late Archaic a few foods (especially hickory nut, acorn, and *Chenopodium*) were very important, while a large number of plants made a lesser dietary contribution (Tables 7.3-7.5). Nuts, especially hickory, are the most widely distributed of any of the plant groups (Table 7.3). With few exceptions, at sites where botanical materials are preserved, nuts make up the majority of the recovered remains. Of the 59 sites inventoried, 47 yielded hickory remains in 70 out of 87 components. Specialized features for processing and storing hickory nuts have been identified at a number of the sites in Southern New England, including RI670 (Figure 7.2) (Morenon et al. 1986). Chestnut (*Castanea dentata*), a food resource often mentioned in the historical literature (Salwen 1978), and one represented in the pre-contact pollen record (Gaudreau 1988), is not reported from any of the sites. Bendremer (1993:150) has attributed the archaeological scarcity of chestnut to its thin shell.

*Chenopodium* may have been the most important of the seed foods. It is represented at eight of the coastal sites in 10 components, although at only two (Henry Lloyd Manor and Peckham) were more than 10 charred seeds recovered (Table 7.5). As discussed above, there is evidence for the large-scale collection, processing, and storage of *Chenopodium* at interior riverine sites (George and Dewar, this volume; McBride 1978, 1984). However, similar evidence is so far lacking for the coast. Initially exploited in its wild state, *Chenopodium* was brought under cultivation in much of the eastern half of the continent between 250 B.C. and A.D. 200 (Smith 1989). Domesticated *Chenopodium* has been recently reported from early Late Prehistoric contexts on the West Branch of the Susquehanna River basin (Hart and Asch Sidell 1996). At this point, the status of the Long Island and Block Island sound specimens is not known. *Rhus* (sumac) and *Polygonum* (knotweed/smartweed) are also relatively abundant, although like *Chenopodium*, their absolute frequencies are still low. At the Joyner site on Narragansett Bay, 67 charred *Rhus* seeds were recovered from 15 features (Holt 1990:14). Thirty-seven were found in and adjacent to a shell midden at the Mamacoke Cove site on Niantic Bay. Despite its relative abundance, *Rhus* may not have made a major dietary contribution because both its seeds and berries are quite small (Asch et al. 1972:18; Watson 1969:44). Munson (1984:469) noted that ethnohistorical sources frequently state that in addition to being eaten, sumac seeds were often used to make beverages. Its medicinal properties are also well known (Densmore 1974; Hostek 1983). Some species of *Polygonum* yield large quantities of edible seeds, and like *Chenopodium*, it may have been cultivated prehistorically.

Nine genera of fruits are present in the botanical assemblages (Table 7.4). *Rubus* (blackberry/raspberry) is the most abundant as represented by charred seeds; the other eight are present in only very small numbers.

The archaeological evidence is consistent with historic accounts of Native American plant consumption in that both sets of data emphasize the broad range of species that were exploited for food. The historic documents indicate that no less than two dozen genera of non-domesticated plants were regularly used, and that some of the plants were of great importance in the early years of contact (Denton 1845; Gookin 1792 [1674]; Johnson 1959 [1654]; Josselyn 1988 [1674]; Van der Donck 1968 [1656]; Williams 1827 [1643]; Wood 1977 [1634]). Among the more important plants during this period were nuts (hickory, chestnut, walnut, and acorn) and fruits (e.g., plums, strawberries, raspberries, blackberries, blueberries, and grapes). Roots and tubers are also discussed in the historical sources (e.g., groundnut [*Apios americana*] and Jerusalem artichoke [*Helianthus tuberosus*])(Strong 1997; Warner 1972).

Probably the most vexing issue still confronting researchers working on the coast of New York and Southern New England is the role of cultigens in the prehistoric subsistence economy. For decades, it has been assumed that sometime after A.D. 1000 the inhabitants of the coast became actively involved in raising tropical cultigens, especially maize (Ritchie 1969; Salwen 1975; Smith 1950; Snow 1980). This belief has a long history, despite the relative lack of direct evidence for agriculture from coastal archaeological sites. With the accumulation of new data on late prehistoric subsistence patterns from both interior and coastal New England and New York, a different pattern is emerging. As recently noted by a number of researchers (Bendremer, this volume; Bendremer and Dewar 1994; Bernstein 1993b; Ceci 1990; Heckenberger et al. 1992; Lavin 1988a), it now seems that plant domestication, especially that involving tropical species, was a much more important enterprise in the interior river valleys of the Northeast than it was along the coast. Further, it appears that the growing of maize was a late development on the coast, and one which probably had a negligible impact on overall lifeways (Bendremer et al. 1991; Bragdon 1996; Ceci 1990; McBride and Dewar 1987). The limited work that has been done on reconstructing diet with carbon and nitrogen stable isotope analyses has also indicated that maize had a limited, if any, role in the prehistoric diet. Bridges (1994:15), for example, has analyzed human skeletal samples from Staten Island, New York (Figure 7.1), and concludes that her results indicate that there was "a diet based on a mixture of marine and terrestrial resources, but one which included no maize."

This is not to say that maize was not grown and consumed on the coast–it surely was–only that it was probably not a central feature of the coastal economy. Quite possibly, its symbolic and social importance outweighed its dietary significance. Even after the introduction of maize, coastal societies continued to exploit a broad range of resources, as they had done for thousands of years. This pattern is reflected in archaeological assemblages from throughout the region and is a particularly pronounced in the faunal remains from coastal sites (Bernstein 1993a,

1993b; Funk and Pfeiffer 1992-93; McBride and Dewar 1987; Ritchie 1959; Silver 1991). For millennia, coastal economies seem to have been relatively stable. Diversification in the use of resources was emphasized, and long-established patterns were seemingly not interrupted by developments occurring to the west.

## ACKNOWLEDGEMENTS

I am grateful to a number of my colleagues for their generosity. Patricia Crawford has advised me on numerous archaeobotanical matters over the past two years and analyzed the flotation samples from MPM Farm. This paper would not have been possible without her guidance. Daniel Cassedy, David George, John Hart, Cheryl Holt, Jordan Kerber, Tonya Largy, Lucianne Lavin, Allan Leveillee, Daria E. Merwin, E. Pierre Morenon, Michael Pappalardo, John Pfeiffer, Paul A. Robinson, John Strong, Ernest Wiegand, and Richard Yarnell have all been more than willing to share their data and comments. Catherine Dowling produced the figures for this paper, and William Ward assisted with the tables.

## REFERENCES CITED

Artemel, J. G., E. J. Flanagan, E. Crowell, and L. Akerson. 1984. *Providence Cove Lands Phase III Report*. Report prepared by De Leuw, Cather/Parsons for the Federal Railroad Administration Northeast Corridor Project.

Asch, N. B., R. I. Ford, and D. L. Asch. 1972. *Paleoethnobotany of the Koster Site: The Archaic Horizons*. Report of Investigations No. 24. Illinois State Museum, Springfield.

Bellantoni, N. 1987. *Faunal Resource Availability and Prehistoric Cultural Selection on Block Island, Rhode Island*. Unpublished Ph.D. dissertation, Department of Anthropology, University of Connecticut, Storrs.

Bendremer, J. C. M. 1993. *Late Woodland Settlement and Subsistence in Eastern Connecticut*. Unpublished Ph.D. dissertation, Department of Anthropology, University of Connecticut, Storrs.

Bendremer, J. C. M., and R. E. Dewar. 1994. The Advent of Prehistoric Maize in New England. In *Corn and Culture in the Prehistoric New World*, edited by S. Johannessen and C. A. Hastorf, pp. 369-393. Westview Press, Boulder.

Bendremer, J., E. Kellogg, and T. B. Largy. 1991. A Grass-Lined Storage Pit and Early Maize Horticulture in Central Connecticut. *North American Archaeologist* 12:325-349.

Bernstein, D. J. 1992. Prehistoric Use of Plant Foods in the Narragansett Bay Region. *Man in the Northeast* 44:1-13.

—————. 1993a. *Archaeological Data Recovery at the Van der Kolk Site, Mount Sinai, Town of Brookhaven, Suffolk County, New York*. Institute for Long Island Archaeology. Copies available from the Institute for Long Island Archaeology, State University of New York at Stony Brook.

—————. 1993b. *Prehistoric Subsistence on the Southern New England Coast: The Record from Narragansett Bay*. Academic Press, San Diego.

Bernstein, D. J., M. J. Lenardi, and D. E. Merwin. 1993. *Archaeological Investigations at Eagles Nest, Mount Sinai, Town of Brookhaven, Suffolk County, New York*. Institute for Long Island Archaeology. Copies available from the Institute for Long Island Archaeology, State University of New York at Stony Brook.

Bernstein, D.J., D. E. Merwin, and M.J. Lenardi. 1996. *A Stage II Archaeological Evaluation of the MPM Farm Corporation Property, Southampton, New York*. Institute for Long Island Archaeology. Copies available from the Institute for Long Island Archaeology, State University of New York at Stony Brook.

Bragdon, K. J. 1996. *Native People of Southern New England, 1500-1650*. University of Oklahoma Press, Norman.

Bridges, P. S. 1994. Prehistoric Diet and Health in a Coastal New York Skeletal Sample. *Northeast Anthropology* 48:13-23.

Ceci, L. 1979-80. Maize Cultivation in Coastal New York: The Archaeological, Agronomical, and Documentary Evidence. *North American Archaeologist* 1:45-73.

———. 1982. Method and Theory in Coastal New York Archaeology: Paradigms of Settlement Pattern. *North American Archaeologist* 3:5-36.

———. 1990. Radiocarbon Dating "Village Sites" in Coastal New York: Settlement Pattern Change in the Middle to Late Woodland. *Man in the Northeast* 39:1-28.

Cox, D. C., and P. F. Thorbahn. 1981. *Prehistoric Archaeological Investigations at Narragansett, Rhode Island: Campbell and Sprague I Sites.* Public Archaeology Laboratory, Brown University, Providence, Rhode Island.

Demeritt, D. 1991. Agriculture, Climate, and Cultural Adaptation in the Prehistoric Northeast. *Archaeology of Eastern North America* 19:183-202.

Densmore, F. 1974. *How Indians Use Wild Plants for Food, Medicine and Crafts.* Dover, New York.

Denton, D. 1845 [1670]. *A Brief Description of New York Formerly Called New Netherlands.* W. Gowans, New York.

Elias, T., and P. A. Dykeman. 1990. *Edible Wild Plants.* Sterling Publishing, New York.

Funk, R. E., and J. E. Pfeiffer. 1988. Archaeological and Paleoenvironmental Investigations on Fishers Island, New York: A Preliminary Report. *Bulletin of the Archaeological Society of Connecticut* 51:69-110.

———. 1992-93. Prehistoric Adaptations on Fishers Island, New York: A Progress Report. *Northeast Historical Archaeology* 21-22: 11-43.

Gaudreau, D. C. 1988. The Distribution of Late Quaternary Forest Regions in the Northeast: Pollen Data, Physiography, and the Prehistoric Record. In *Holocene Human Ecology in Northeastern North America,* edited by G. P. Nicholas, pp. 215-256. Plenum Press, New York.

George, D. R., and J. C. M. Bendremer. 1995. Late Woodland Subsistence and the Origins of Maize Horticulture in New England. Paper presented at the 60th Annual Meeting of the Society for American Archaeology, Minneapolis.

Gookin, D. 1792 [1674]. *Historical Collections of the Indians of New England.* Collections of the Massachusetts Historical Society. Belknap and Hall, Boston.

Gramly, R. M., and G. A. Gwynne. 1979. Two Late Woodland Sites on Long Island Sound. *Bulletin of the Massachusetts Archaeological Society* 40(1):5-19.

Gwynne, G. A. 1979. Prehistoric Archaeology at Mt. Sinai Harbor, Suffolk County, New York. *Bulletin and Journal of the New York State Archaeological Association* 77:14-25.

———. 1982. *The Late Archaic Archaeology of Mount Sinai Harbor, New York: Human Ecology, Economy and Residence Patterns on the Southern New England Coast.* Unpublished Ph.D. dissertation, Department of Anthropology, State University of New York at Stony Brook.

Harrington, M. R. 1902. Exploration of an Ancient Village Site at Shinnecock Hills, L.I. Ms. on file, Museum of the American Indian-Heye Foundation, New York.

———. 1903. Shinnecock Notes. *Journal of American Folklore* 16(60): 37-39.

———. 1924. An Ancient Village Site of the Shinnecock Indians. *Anthropological Papers of the American Museum of Natural History* 22:227-283.

Hart, J. P., and N. Asch Sidell. 1996. Prehistoric Agricultural Systems in the West Branch of the Susquehanna River Basin, A.D. 800 to A.D. 1350. *Northeast Anthropology* 52:1-30.

Heckenberger, M. J., J. B. Petersen, and N. Asch Sidell. 1992. Early Evidence of Maize Agriculture in the Connecticut River Valley of Vermont. *Archaeology of Eastern North America* 20:125-149.

Hillman, G. C. 1989. Late Palaeolithic Plant Foods from Wadi Kubbaniya in Upper Egypt: Dietary Diversity, Infant Weaning, and Seasonality in a Riverine Environment. In *Foraging and Farming: The Evolution of Plant Exploitation,* edited by D. R. Harris and G. C. Hillman, pp. 207-239. Unwin Hyman, London.

Holt, C. A. 1990. Floral and Faunal Analyses, Joyner Site, RI 706. In *The Joyner Site: Late Archaic-Early Woodland Adaptations and Cultural Dynamics on Conanicut Island, Rhode Island,* edited by R. G. Kingsley and B. R. Roulette. Report prepared by John Milner Associates, West Chester Pennsylvania, for Rhode Island Department of Transportation.

Hostek, A. 1983. *Native and Near Native: An Introduction to Long Island Plants.* The Environmental Centers of Setauket-Smithtown, Inc., Smithtown.

Jaworski, C. 1990. Discovery on Block Island: 2,500-Year-Old Village Predates Agriculture. *Nor'Easter* 2(2):32-37.

Johnson, E. 1959 [1654]. *Johnson's Wonder-Working Providence, 1628-1651,* edited by J. Franklin Jameson. Barnes and Noble, New York.

Josselyn, J. 1988 [1674]. *John Josselyn, Colonial Traveler: A Critical Edition of an Account of Two Voyages to New England Made During the Years 1638 and 1663,* edited by P. J. Lindholdt. University Press of New England, Hanover.

Juli, H. D. 1992. *Archaeology in the Connecticut College Arboretum.* Connecticut College Arboretum Bulletin No. 33. Connecticut College, New London.

Kerber, J., A. D. Leveillee, and R. L. Greenspan. 1989. An Unusual Dog Burial Feature at the Lambert Farm Site, Warwick, Rhode Island: Preliminary Observations. *Archaeology of Eastern North America* 17:165-174.

Klein, J., J. C. Lerman, P. E. Damon, and E. K. Ralph. 1982. Calibration of Radiocarbon Dates. *Radiocarbon* 24: 103-150.

Largy, T. 1989. Analysis of Archaeobotanical Samples from the Hoskins Park Site, the Lambert Farm Site, and Cedar Swamp. Unpublished ms. on file at Public Archaeology Laboratory, Pawtucket, Rhode Island.

——————. 1990 Analysis of Botanical Samples-Hoskins Park, Phase III, North Kingstown, Rhode Island. Unpublished ms. on file at Public Archaeology Laboratory, Pawtucket, Rhode Island.

Latham, R. 1957. A Preliminary Report of the Smith Site, Shelter Island. *Bulletin of the New York State Archaeological Association* 11:1-17.

Lavin, L. 1988a. Coastal Adaptations in Southern New England and Southern New York. *Archaeology of Eastern North America* 16:101-120.

——————. 1988b. The Morgan Site, Rocky Hill, Connecticut: A Late Woodland Farming Community in the Connecticut River Valley. *Bulletin of the Archaeological Society of Connecticut* 51: 7-22.

Leveillee, A., and R. Van Coughyen. 1990. *The Hoskins Park and South Wind Sites: A Program of Data Recovery in Rhode Island's Coastal Zone.* Copies available from The Public Archaeology Laboratory, Pawtucket, Rhode Island.

Lightfoot, K. G., R. Kalin, and J. Moore. 1987. *Prehistoric Hunter-Gatherers of Shelter Island, New York: An Archaeological Study of the Mashomack Preserve.* Contributions of the University of California Archaeological Research Facility No. 46. Department of Anthropology, University of California, Berkeley.

McBride, K. A. 1978. Archaic Subsistence in the Lower Connecticut River Valley: Evidence from Woodchuck Knoll. *Man in the Northeast* 15/16:124-131.

——————. 1984. *Prehistory of the Lower Connecticut River Valley.* Unpublished Ph.D. dissertation, Department of Anthropology, University of Connecticut, Storrs.

McBride, K. A., and R. E. Dewar. 1987. Agriculture and Cultural Evolution: Causes and Effects in the Lower Connecticut River Valley. In *Emergent Horticultural Economies of the Eastern Woodlands,* edited by W. F. Keegan, pp. 305-328. Center for Archaeological Investigations, Occasional Papers No. 7. Southern Illinois University at Carbondale.

Millis, T., D. Cassedy, H. Millis, P. Webb, and N. A. Sidell. 1995. *Iroquois Gas Transmission System Phase III Archaeological Data Recovery Report, Volume 3, the Connecticut Sites.* Garrow and Associates, Atlanta. Report prepared for Iroquois Gas Transmission, L.P.

Morenon, E. P., P. Pearson, and P. McDowell. 1986. Environmental Diversity. In *Archaeological sites at an Ecotone: Route 4 Extension, East Greenwich and North Kingstown, Rhode Island.* Occasional Papers in Archaeology, No. 14. Public Archaeology Program, Rhode Island College, Providence.

Munson, P. J. 1984. Comments on Some Additional Species, With Summary of Seasonality. In *Experiments and Observations on Aboriginal Wild Plant Food Utilization in Eastern North America,* edited by P. J. Munson, pp. 459-473. Prehistory Research Series 6(2). Indiana Historical Society, Indianapolis.

Pagoulatos, P. 1986. *Terminal Archaic Settlement and Subsistence in the Connecticut River Valley.* Unpublished Ph.D. dissertation, Department of Anthropology, University of Connecticut, Storrs.

Pappalardo, A. M. 1994. *Final Report of the Archaeological Monitoring of the Cobb Island Drive, Lot 6 Site, Greenwich, Connecticut.* Report prepared for Joseph Deluca by Historical Perspectives, Westport, Connecticut.

Pfeiffer, J. E. 1980. The Griffin Site: A Susquehanna Cremation Burial in Southern Connecticut. *Man in the Northeast* 19:129-133.

—————. 1984. The Late and Terminal Archaic Periods of Connecticut Prehistory. *Archaeological Society of Connecticut Bulletin* 47:73-88.

—————. 1992. *Late and Terminal Archaic Cultural Adaptations of the Lowest Connecticut Valley.* Unpublished Ph.D. dissertation, Department of Anthropology, State University of New York at Albany.

Powell, B. W. 1981. Carbonized Seed Remains from Prehistoric Sites in Connecticut. *Man in the Northeast* 21:75-85.

Ritchie, W. A. 1959. *The Stony Brook Site and its Relation to Archaic and Transitional Cultures on Long Island.* New York State Museum and Science Service, Bulletin 372. The University of the State of New York, Albany.

—————. 1969. *The Archaeology of New York State.* Revised edition. Natural History Press, Garden City.

Salwen, B. 1975. Post-Glacial Environments and Cultural Change in the Hudson River Basin. *Man in the Northeast* 10:43-70.

—————. 1978. Indians of Southern New England and Long Island: Early Period. In *Northeast,* edited by Bruce G. Trigger, pp. 160-176. Handbook of North American Indians, Vol. 15, W.C. Sturtevant, general editor. Smithsonian Institution, Washington, D.C.

Silver, A. L. 1980. Comment of Maize Cultivation in Coastal New York. *North American Archaeologist* 2:117-130.

—————. 1991. *The Abbott Interaction Sphere: A Consideration of the Middle Woodland Period in Coastal New York and a Proposal for a Middle Woodland Exchange System.* Unpublished Ph.D. dissertation, Department of Anthropology, New York University, New York.

Skinner, A.B. 1897. Early Work at Burial Ridge, Tottenville. Unpublished ms. on file, Museum of the American Indian-Heye Foundation, New York.

—————. 1903. List of Indian of Indian Villages and Camp Sites on Staten Island. *Proceedings of the Natural Science Association of Staten Island* 8(22):59-61.

—————. 1909a. The Lenape Indians of Staten Island. In *The Indians of Greater New York and the Lower Hudson,* edited by C. Wissler, pp. 3-63. Anthropological Papers of the American Museum of Natural History 3. New York.

—————. 1909b. Archaeology of the New York Coastal Algonkin. In *The Indians of Greater New York and the Lower Hudson,* edited by C. Wissler, pp. 213-231. Anthropological Papers of the American Museum of Natural History 3. New York.

—————. 1924. The Passing of a Great Staten Island Indian Village Site. *Proceedings of the Staten Island Institute of Arts and Sciences* 3(1-4):70-81.

Smith, B. D. 1989. Origins of Agriculture in Eastern North America. *Science* 246:1566-1571.

Smith, C.S. 1950. *The Archaeology of Coastal New York.* Anthropological Papers of the American Museum of Natural History 43(2). New York.

Snow, D. R. 1980. *The Archaeology of New England.* Academic Press, New York.

Strong, J. A. 1997. *The Algonquian Peoples of Long Island from Earliest Times to 1700.* Heart of the Lakes Publishing, Interlaken, New York [in press].

Thomas, D. H. 1983. The Archaeology of the Monitor Valley 1. Epistemology. *Anthropological Papers of the American Museum of Natural History* 58:1-194.

Van der Donck, A. 1968 [1656]. *A Description of the New Netherlands,* edited T. F. O'Donnell. Syracuse University Press, Syracuse.

Warner, F. W. 1972. The Foods of the Connecticut Indians. *Bulletin of the Archaeological Society of Connecticut* 37:27-47.

Watson, P. J. 1969. *The Prehistory of Salts Cave, Kentucky.* Reports of Investigations No. 16. Illinois State Museum, Springfield.

Wiegand, E. A. 1983. *Rockshelters of Southwestern Connecticut: Their Prehistoric Occupation and Use.* Norwalk Community College, Norwalk.

Williams, R. 1827 [1643]. *A Key Into the Language of America.* Rhode Island Historical Society, Providence. [Originally published 1643 by Gregory Dexter, London.]

Wood, W. 1977 [1634]. *New England's Prospect,* edited by A. T. Vaughan University of Massachusetts Press, Amherst.

Wyatt, R. J. 1977. The Archaic on Long Island. *Annals of the New York Academy of Sciences* 288:400-410.

# CHAPTER 8

# *CHENOPODIUM* IN CONNECTICUT PREHISTORY: WILD, WEEDY, CULTIVATED, OR DOMESTICATED?

David R. George and Robert E. Dewar

## INTRODUCTION

*Chenopodium* has been established as a domesticated crop in the Midcontinent before the incorporation of maize and beans into prehistoric diets. Bruce Smith (1984, 1992), Gayle Fritz (1984), the Asches (1977), and others (Gremillion 1993, 1997; Wilson 1981) have documented morphological changes that mark domesticated forms, as well as other varieties that may represent weedy, and feral conspecific, sympatric populations (Fritz 1997). Morphological changes noted in domesticated *Chenopodium* include reduced testa thickness from between 40 and 80 mm to 20 mm or less, development of a truncate margin to accommodate a larger internal seed volume, and a shift from a reticulate to a smooth testa surface (Smith 1984; Smith and Funk 1985). AMS dates indicate that morphological changes in midcontinent *Chenopodium* populations occurred prior to approximately 3,000 B.P. (Fritz 1997; Fritz and Smith 1988; Gremillion 1997; Smith 1992; Smith and Cowan 1987).

Similar changes in *Chenopodium* assemblages from New England have yet to be identified. Archaeobotanical studies in New England have traditionally focused on the timing of the arrival of maize horticulture, thought to be the establishment of a farming economy (George 1997a, 1997b; George and Bendremer 1995). Nevertheless, in the 1960s, William Ritchie suggested that *Chenopodium* was important in Early Woodland period subsistence patterns, and even suggested that it might have been cultivated (Ritchie and Funk 1973), but little attention has been paid to this suggestion. To our knowledge, nowhere east of the Appalachians has any variety of *Chenopodium* been identified as a prehistoric cultivar.

Two archaeological sites situated on the western edge of the Appalachians and southwest of our study region that have yielded evidence of domesticated or potentially domesticated *Chenopodium* are the Memorial Park site in Clinton County, Pennsylvania (Hart and Asch Sidell 1996), and Site 36Ti58 in Tioga County, Pennsylvania (Gardner 1993). *Chenopodium* from the Memorial Park site dates to the Early and Late Clemson's Island occupations of the site, between approximately A.D. 750 and 1100. A total of 21 carbonized *Chenopodium* seeds were recovered. These seeds represent two types, including *Chenopodium berlandieri* spp. *jonesianum* and a second type that resembles the Mexican cultigen huazontle, a pale-seeded variety of *Chenopodium berlandieri* (Hart and Asch Sidell 1996:17).

At Site 36Ti58, a total of 121 carbonized *Chenopodium* seeds from the Clemson's Island occupation dating to between approximately A.D. 900 and 1300 were recovered. Although none of these seeds can be identified confidently as *Chenopodium berlandieri* ssp. *jonesianum*, some of them do have seed coats as thin as 30 μm, which is not typical for wild varieties (Gardner 1993). While the *Chenopodium* seeds at Site 36Ti58 cannot be definitely labelled as domesticated, according to Gardner they may represent a poorly managed crop that hybridized with local weed populations (Gardner 1993:6). The samples derived from these two sites are important, nevertheless, since they represent the only documented potentially domesticated *Chenopodium* in the northeastern United States.

It is our intention here to describe the preliminary results of an examination of the role of *Chenopodium* in Connecticut prehistory, including recent findings suggesting that the history of *Chenopodium* in this region may have a human, as well as natural, component. We will show that (1) *Chenopodium* was an important element of subsistence from the second millennium B.C. onward; (2) from its first archaeological appearance, it was associated with storage facilities and semi-permanent occupations; and (3) *Chenopodium* samples from Late Woodland period contexts display variations in morphological characters that have been used to identify the effects of domestication in Midcontinent contexts.

We stop short, however, of announcing *Chenopodium* from Connecticut as a prehistoric domesticate for four reasons. First, our samples are limited in number, and our analyses are ongoing. Second, we have yet to resolve fundamental problems of taxonomy. Third, reliable samples from pre-maize contexts are lacking. Finally, we recognize the complexity of *Chenopodium* taxonomy in the Midcontinent, and are mindful of the complications that paleoethnobotanists working there have elucidated (Asch and Asch 1977, 1985; Fritz 1986; Smith 1992; Smith and Funk 1985). It is possible that differences in geography and environment between New England and the Midcontinent will introduce further, as yet unidentified, variation. Thus, we foresee much more work before any confident assessment can be made of the prehistoric human use of and impact upon *Chenopodium* in Southern New England.

## CHENOPODIUM IN THE ARCHAEOLOGICAL RECORD OF CONNECTICUT

### The Late Archaic Period (6,000-3,700 B.P.)

While *Chenopodium* can obviously be seen as playing a major role in prehistoric diets and agricultural systems of the Midcontinent, its role in prehistoric Connecticut River valley economies is less clear. *Chenopodium* is common in archaeological deposits of the region and has been found in contexts that indicate that it was frequently exploited since at least the end of the Late Archaic period, 4,000 years ago. Two sites in particular show evidence of the harvesting and likely storage of *Chenopodium* during the Late Archaic period.

The Bliss-Howard site, a large Late Archaic base camp/cemetery dated to 4,775 ± 120 B.P. located in Old Lyme, Connecticut, has yielded the oldest sample of *Chenopodium* from the region (Figure 8.1). Excavations at the Bliss-Howard site revealed "oblong structures with compact living floors, storage pits, refuse pits, hearths, and work-

shops in addition to the burial area" (Pfeiffer 1984:76). Floral remains recovered from the site include hickory nuts (*Carya* sp.), acorn (*Quercus* sp.), walnut (*Juglans* sp.), and *Chenopodium*. Pfeiffer (1984) interpreted the storage facilities, house construction, and multiple, contemporaneous burials as evidence for a long-term, and perhaps even permanent, settlement. He suggested the economic focus of the site was on the gathering of plant (especially *Chenopodium* and nuts) and animal resources from the adjacent, but now inundated, Connecticut River floodplain.

Similarly, the Woodchuck Knoll site, located on the eastern floodplain of the Connecticut River in South Windsor, Connecticut, and dated to 3,690 ± 80 B.P., has also yielded *Chenopodium* (McBride 1978). This site is situated on a long, linear feature of the approximately 3-km-wide floodplain, and was the locale of probably hundreds of occupations during the Late Archaic period (Figure 8.1). Flotation of a series of features, including possible storage pits, yielded charred *Chenopodium*, hickory nut remains, and hazelnuts (*Corylus americana*).[1] McBride reported the recovery of 35 complete and 50 fragmentary *Chenopodium* seeds from flotation samples taken from six hearths. While not recovered in massive quantities, the association of these taxa is consistent among features, suggesting they were gathered and stored together. All three taxa are available in the immediate vicinity of the site, which is situated near littoral, upland, and floodplain resource zones.

Also recovered in three of the features with plant remains were fragmentary and carbonized granary weevils (*Sitophilus granarius*). The presence of the weevils validates the interpretation that grain storage was a recurrent activity at the site since *Sitophilus granarius* cannot fly and is therefore an obligate pest of stored grains (Levinson and Levinson 1994). It seems likely that *Chenopodium*, because of its small seed size (approximately 1-1.5 mm in diameter), however, would not have been an appropriate host for *Sitophilus* larval development. *Sitophilus granarius* larvae are approximately 2 mm long and attain a total body length of 3.5-5 mm at adulthood, thus making *Chenopodium* seeds too small for larval growth (Peter Clarke, Central Science Laboratory,

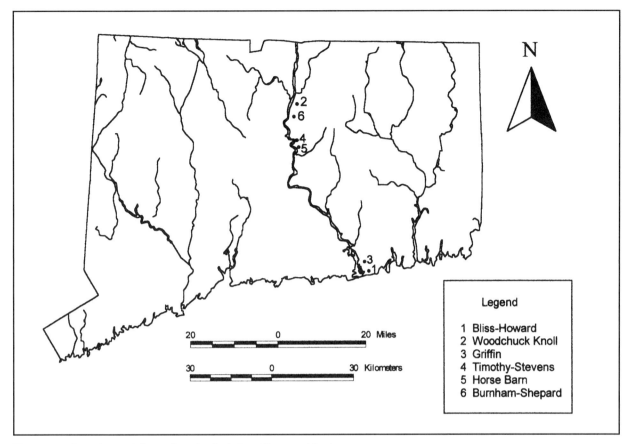

**Figure 8.1.** Locations of the archaeological sites discussed in the text.

York, UK, personal communication; Levinson and Levinson 1994). In addition, *Chenopodium* was likely parched by Native Americans prior to storage to prevent premature germination of stored seeds. It is unlikely that parched seeds would have been an attractive food source for *Sitpohilus granarius*, since the weevils require more than 10 percent water in their food source for normal growth (Levinson and Levinson 1994). Parched *Chenopodium* seeds probably would not have met these minimum moisture requirements. It is more likely that the weevils were exploiting other stored species. Howe (1965), for example, indicated that *Sitpohilus granarius* can reproduce effectively using stored acorns as a breeding environment. Clearly, the presence of the weevils indicates a storage context.

The Bliss-Howard and Woodchuck Knoll sites indicate that a broad-spectrum resource base was common during the Late Archaic period, with small-grain harvesting and storage being important to the subsistence economy. The increased numbers of plant-processing tools, storage facilities, and reuse of strategic locales argue for a cultural adaptation characterized by increasing length of occupation at base camps, an increased reliance on plant foods, and perhaps the formation and maintenance of territories. Similar conditions have been noted during the Late Archaic period in the Midcontinent, where it is clear that plant cultivation and domestication were already occurring.

### The Terminal Archaic Period (3,700-2,700 B.P.)

In the subsequent Terminal Archaic period, reports of *Chenopodium* are more frequent; it has been recovered from hearths, pits, and burials (Pagoulatos 1986; Pfeiffer 1983). Pfeiffer, in particular, has regarded *Chenopodium* as central to economic patterns of the Connecticut River valley during the Terminal Archaic period. He has, for example, recovered grave offerings of *Chenopodium*, *Amaranthus*, hickory nuts, hazelnuts, and acorns from cremation burials at the Griffin site dated to between 3,535 ± 140 B.P. and 2,985 ± 70 B.P. (Figure 8.1). The location of most Terminal Archaic base camps on river terraces above rivers has been traditionally interpreted as evidence of fishing camps (Cook 1976; Turnbaugh 1975). Pfeiffer (n.d.) has suggested that such locations were chosen to take advantage of floodplain resources by groups who were dependent on a specialized gathering strategy. In particular, he has identified *Chenopodium* as a key resource. "[T]hus, within the archaeological record one finds Chenopodium, the tools to process the plant material, and local availability that corresponds to the distribution of Broad Spear [Terminal Archaic] sites" (Pfeiffer n.d.:30).

Pagoulatos (1986, 1988) also has reported *Chenopodium* from the Timothy Stevens and Horse Barn sites located along the Connecticut River in Glastonbury, Connecticut (Figure 8.1). He has noted that these Terminal Archaic residential sites are situated on river terrace soils that have a high agricultural resource potential. While Pagoulatos has not argued that Terminal Archaic hunter/gatherers were cultivating plants, he has suggested that intensive harvesting of wild plant resources was likely, in particular *Chenopodium* harvesting (Pagoulatos 1988:81). We have yet to examine any of these, or the Late Archaic collections, so we do not know what species, let alone subspecies or variety, is represented at these sites. Further, with the exception of Woodchuck Knoll, numbers of recovered *Chenopodium* seeds have yet to be reported.

## Early and Middle Woodland (2,700 B.P.-A.D. 800)
We have yet to identify reliable Early or Middle Woodland *Chenopodium* samples from Southern New England. Ritchie suggested, however, a reliance on the storage of *Chenopodium* for his Middle Woodland Kipp Island phase sites in New York State. At the type site of the phase, he reported the recovery of *Chenopodium* from basin-shaped pits of a fairly large size (Ritchie and Funk 1973:161). He indicated that while the pits were likely used for the storage of nuts and seeds, the use of cultigens should not be ruled out (Ritchie and Funk 1973:161). We hope to be able to examine these samples, if they are still preserved, in the near future. The identification of domesticated *Chenopodium* from Early or Middle Woodland period components in Southern New England or New York State would prompt a revision of our current interpretations that the introduction of maize horticulture represents the initial transition to farming in the Northeast.

## Late Woodland Association with Maize, Beans, and Sunflower (A.D. 800-1500)
In Late Woodland period horticultural contexts in the Connecticut River valley, *Chenopodium* continues to be recovered archaeologically in hearth and storage-pit contexts. The best example is the Burnham-Shepard site on the floodplain of the Connecticut River, only 500 m south of the Woodchuck Knoll site (Figure 8.1). The site is situated on a low, remnant levee created by the meandering of the main river channel. Riverbank erosion has claimed a portion of the western extent of the site. Transect-interval sampling and block excavations, however, have indicated that the remaining site area covers some 1,000-1,500 m$^2$. Activities represented at the site include lithic reduction and maintenance, animal butchering and hide scraping, and plant processing. Feature types found at the site include hearths, storage pits, midden, burials, and numerous post molds that are remnants of house construction (Bendremer 1993). The archaeobotanical assemblage indicates that the site is without doubt the creation of farmers, and the context of the *Chenopodium* is unmistakable.

Jeffrey Bendremer, the excavator of the site, was able to clearly establish the form and function of storage pits at the site and recover a remarkable array of archaeobotanical samples, including nut, fruit, grass, tuber, and disturbed habitat species, as well as domesticates (Bendremer 1993; Bendremer et al. 1991). The functional context of the storage pits is clear and is best illustrated by

Feature 6, a deep storage pit in which a microstratigraphic record of multiple uses was preserved (see Figure 8.2). The pit was repeatedly burned out, lined with big blue-stem grass (*Andropogon gerardi*), and re-used. Ethnographically, this grass was in common use in the Midcontinent as a liner of storage pits, apparently for its qualities as a retardant to fungal development (Bendremer et al. 1991). Smith has also reported its use to line a storage pit containing *Chenopodium* at Ash Cave in Ohio during the Late Archaic period, approximately 3,500 years ago.

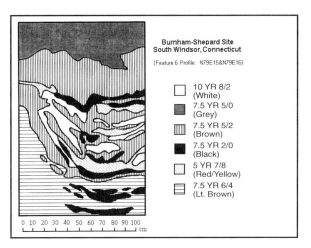

**Figure 8.2.** A profile of Feature 6 from the Burnham-Shepard Site (adapted from Bendremer 1993).

## BURNHAM-SHEPARD *CHENOPODIUM* SAMPLES

We examined the *Chenopodium* from three features (6, 8, and 17) from the Burnham-Shepard site. All three pits are interpreted as storage facilities, are elliptical in plan view, and are of varying depths. Feature 6 had a diameter of 1.5 m and a maximum depth of 1.1 m (Figure 8.2). While in use, the feature was lined with big blue-stem grass as evidenced by charred fragments recovered from the feature fill. In addition to *Chenopodium*, Feature 6 yielded the charred remains of walnut, hickory nuts, maize (*Zea mays*), and grasses.

Feature 8 at the Burnham-Shepard site had a diameter of 1.5 m and a depth of approximately 0.5 m (Figure 8.3). The feature yielded walnut and hickory nut fragments, raspberry (*Rubus* sp.) seeds, *Chenopodium*, and an array of cultigens, including maize, beans (*Phaseolus vulgaris*), and the only known sunflower seeds (*Helianthus annuus*) recovered east of the Hudson River. The mean length of the sunflower seeds is 7.5 mm, indicating their domesticate status. But what was the status of the *Chenopodium*—wild, weedy, cultivated, or domesticated? Bendremer sent a small sample to Bruce Smith who was able to report only that none of it was clearly domesticated, although some of the seeds apparently had relatively thin seeds coats, one of the attributes often associated with domesticated chenopods (Smith, personal communication; see Bendremer 1993:130).

Feature 17 had a diameter of 0.85 m and a maximum depth of 0.4 m. Unlike Features 6 and 8, Feature 17 was not lined with big blue-stem grass. Plant remains recovered from the feature fill include, in addition to *Chenopodium*, hickory nut fragments, *Panicum* seeds, and other grass seeds. In addition, a charred exoskeleton of a *Sitophilus* weevil has been identified in the flotation sample of Feature 17, further strengthening the case for a storage function for this feature, and a reminder of the continuity in some aspects of subsistence from the Late Archaic to the Woodland periods.

All three of these features are clearly associated with the Late Woodland component at the Burnham-Shepard site. Radiocarbon assays, including AMS dates, were run on botanical materials recovered from each of the three features. Feature 6 yielded an AMS date on a bean whose 2-σ calibrated range is A.D. 1299-1449. Feature 8 has a 2-σ date range of A.D. 1282-1431 from an AMS date on maize. Finally, Feature 17 has a 2-σ date range of A.D. 1278-1447 on the basis of a standard radiocarbon date derived from wood charcoal from the feature fill. These dates are calibrated, nearly identical, and indicate that all three features were utilized during the Late Woodland period occupation of the site.

As for their function and duration of use, Features 6 and 8 are relatively large storage facilities that were likely employed for long-term storage. The microstratigraphy from Feature 6 in par-

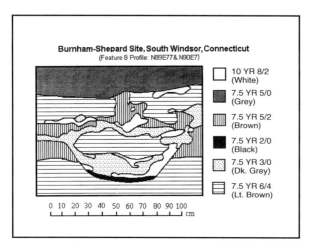

**Burnham-Shepard Site, South Windsor, Connecticut**
(Feature 8 Profile: N89E77 & N90E7)

10 YR 8/2 (White)

7.5 YR 5/0 (Grey)

7.5 YR 5/2 (Brown)

7.5 YR 2/0 (Black)

7.5 YR 3/0 (Dk. Grey)

7.5 YR 6/4 (Lt. Brown)

0 10 20 30 40 50 60 70 80 90 100 cm

**Figure 8.3.** A profile of Feature 8 from the Burnham-Shepard Site (adapted from Bendremer 1993).

ticular quite clearly indicates repeated use. The various microstrata suggest that the feature was partially in-filled and relined periodically to provide a fresh context for the storage of plant materials. Eventually the feature reached dimensions small enough to be considered ill-suited for storage and was abandoned. Feature 17 was, in terms of volume, about half the size of Features 6 and 8. This, combined with its lack of a grass lining, suggests that its storage capabilities were considerably less and that it was likely employed for a shorter time interval.

**Taxonomic Affiliation**
The taxonomic status of the Burnham-Shepard *Chenopodium* is uncertain. We cannot be positive that what was recovered is *Chenopodium berlandieri/bushianum*, although some specimens exhibiting keeled sepals suggest that identification. It is also possible that the specimens recovered from the Burnham-Shepard site represent *Chenopodium macrocalycium*, a coastal variety that is also in the subsection Cellulata. Moreover, the measurements and observations we have made suggest that the Burnham-Shepard samples may include two or more *Chenopodium* populations, perhaps hybridizing. Sorting out the taxonomy of these samples cannot be reliably done by comparing them with Midcontinent varieties alone, since geographic and environmental factors may have produced prehistoric races of *Chenopodium* in

New England that do not conform to those documented in the Midcontinent. More in-depth analyses of both archaeological and modern *Chenopodium* samples from Southern New England are necessary.

**Seed Size**
Seed-size measurements were obtained using a binocular microscope and a glass slide labeled with a micron scale. All seeds were measured at 40x magnification. In all, 96 seeds were measured, 55 from Feature 6, 20 from Feature 8, and 19 from Feature 17. The Burnham-Shepard specimens are small in comparison to modern cultivated *Chenopodium*, as well as Latin American and Midcontinent weedy races. The mean size by feature ranges from $1.10 \pm 0.11$ mm (Feature 8) to $1.12 \pm 0.11$ mm (Feature 17) to $1.18 \pm 0.13$ (Feature 6) (Figure 8.4). The range of sizes from the largest sample (Feature 6) may be normally distributed, while those from the other two are not normally distributed. It is not clear, however, that the uneven distribution is a reflection of an uneven mixture from differing populations. For the sample as a whole, the mean seed diameter is $1.15 \pm 0.126$ mm. The coefficient of variation of this sample is large in comparison to Smith's (1992:125) data for domesticated weedy and wild forms, but again, our sample sizes are small.

Smith has shown that size change is not a character associated with domestication. A word of caution is in order at this point. According to Gremillion (personal communication 1997), although size change cannot strictly be used as an indicator of domesticate status in *Chenopodium*, when cultivated forms are found in association with wild/weedy forms, there does tend to be a difference in seed size. In this case, domesticated forms are often larger than their wild/weedy counterparts. This should not be totally unexpected, since increased seed size permits larger endosperms and thus more vigorous seedlings, rapid germination and maturation, and a higher yield.

Smith has also suggested that there is a geographical size gradient in eastern North American *Chenopodium*, with northern populations larger than southern populations. Figure 8.5

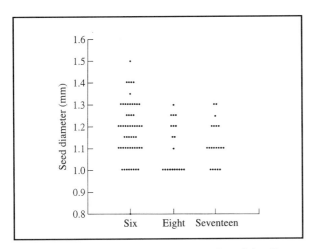

Figure 8.4. A symmetric dot density plot of the diameters of *Chenopodium* seeds from three features at the Burnham-Shepard Site. At p<.05, the distribution of diameters from Feature 6 cannot be distinguished from a normal distribution; the distributions in Features 8 and 17 are significantly non-normal (Lilliefors test).

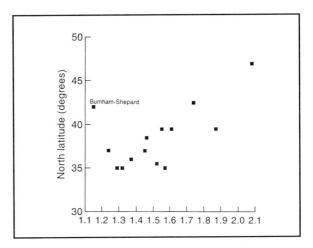

Figure 8.5. Variation in reported mean seed diameters in relation to latitude for wild weedy morphs, and the Burnham-Shepard combined sample. Data are from Asch and Asch (1977:36), Gremillion (1993:501), Smith (1992:144-145), and this paper.

is a scatterplot of mean seed size for geographically locatable *Chenopodium* samples of wild or "weed morph" populations for eastern North America (Asch and Asch 1977:36; Gremillion 1993:501; Smith 1992:144-145). The Burnham-Shepard sample is clearly an outlier; the other reported populations conform to Smith's geographical patterning. Karssen (1970) reported experimental results indicating that reduced day length leads to larger seed size in European *Chenopodium album* populations. The overall cline observed here may reflect a similar pattern in North American *Chenopodium*, with the Burnham-Shepard sample as an outlier.

**Testa Thickness**

Testa thickness, in contrast, is a character that seems to reliably separate domestic cultivars from wild populations (Fritz 1984; Smith 1984, 1992). We measured testa thickness for samples from each of the three features (Figure 8.6). Testa thickness was measured in two ways. The initial testa thickness measurements of all the specimens were derived using the binocular microscope and glass slide micron scale. A smaller number of testa thicknesses were measured using the scanning

electron microscope housed at the University of Connecticut's Department of Scanning Electron Microscopy (Figure 8.7). Testa thicknesses in the Burnham-Shepard specimens are markedly bimodal in all three features; there are both "thin testa" and "wild-type" testa in each sample. This offers the possibility that more than one population of Chenopodium is represented in the samples.

When our samples of testa thickness are compared to Smith's comparative samples from the Midcontinent (Figure 8.8), the means for our samples align with populations intermediate between wild and domesticated forms. In Smith's samples, these are described as weeds of domesticated cultivars, or, more rarely, thin-testa morphs of wild populations. In most wild populations, however, thin-testa morphs have been found at frequencies approximating only 5 percent; our proportions of testa thickness less than 30 mm are far more common.

From the Marble Bluff site in Arkansas that has qualities similar to the Burnham-Shepard material, Fritz (1997) has recently reported a sample of *Chenopodium berlandieri*. She has described both clearly domesticated thin/smooth-testa *Chenopodium* from Marble Bluff, as well as specimens that have "thicker, more pitted seed coats" (Fritz 1997:51). One of the seeds was examined

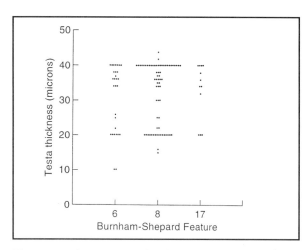

**Figure 8.6.** A symmetric dot density plot of testa thickness for *Chenopodium* seeds from three features at the Burnham-Shepard site.

**Figure 8.7.** Testa thickness for seeds from Features 6 and 8.

with a scanning electron microscope and yielded a testa thickness of 25 μm, intermediate between cultigen (10-20 μm) and wild (40-80 μm) forms. As a result, Fritz (1997:51) concluded that "remnants of reticulate pericarp demonstrate that these specimens represent the species *C. berlandieri*, but the thicker, more pitted seed coats and rounded seed margins implicate them as possible weedy forms rather than clear domesticates or a fully wild population." Perhaps, then, the Burnham-Shepard *Chenopodium* represents a weedy variety, although we cannot yet be sure of what species. On the other hand, Gremillion (1993:506) has reported that in archaeological samples, thick-testa forms become more common after the introduction of maize. It is, therefore, also possible that the Burnham-Shepard *Chenopodium* represents a population reverting back to a wild state.

Still another possibility that cannot be ruled out at this point is that there is an allometric explanation for the testa thickness of the Burnham-Shepard seeds. That is, since the Burnham-Shepard samples are clearly smaller than examples from other domesticated assemblages, it is quite possible that testa thickness and seed size are related to smaller seeds with thinner seed coats. This possibility cannot be ruled out until a small-seeded, modern assemblage can be studied to determine the potential relationship between seed size and testa thickness, if indeed

there is one. We hope to initiate such an investigation in the future. For now, we can conclude only that until we have good samples of *Chenopodium* from pre-maize contexts, we must be cautious in interpreting our observed pattern.

**Reticulation of the Testa Surface**

Testa surfaces of the section Cellulata of *Chenopodium* typically have a characteristic reticulate pattern. In domesticated varieties, however, the testa surface morphology is often less prominently marked and is sometimes even smooth. Smooth seed-coat patterns can be clearly seen in *Chenopodium berlandieri* ssp. *jonesianum*, a Midcontinent variety domesticated prior to approximately 3,000 B.P. (Smith 1985, 1992). The Mexican variety *Chenopodium berlandieri* ssp. *nuttalliae*, or "chia," also displays a smooth seed coat.

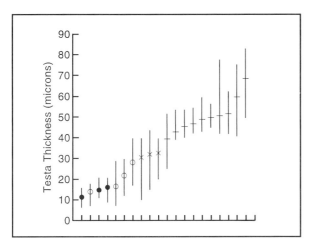

**Figure 8.8.** A comparison of mean and range of testa thickness for various populations of *Chenopodium,* arranged by testa thickness. Solid circles are domesticates, hollow circles are reported as red morph by Smith (1992), the cross represents the three features from Burnham-Shepard, and the single lines indicate wild populations. Data are from Smith (1992:149) and this paper.

In our samples from Burnham-Shepard, we observed examples of both clearly reticulate and comparatively smooth seed-coat patterns. These are illustrated in SEM photos taken on seeds from features 6 and 8, respectively (Figure 8.9). This recalls the bimodality in testa thickness and the uneven distribution in seed size from Feature 8 and 17 and further supports the possibility that more than one population of *Chenopodium* was recovered from the Burnham-Shepard features. It is also possible, however, that the *Chenopodium* seeds recovered from Burnham-Shepard represent a single species with dimorphic seeds.

**Margin Morphology**

In terms of margin configuration, Smith (1985, 1992) and others (Fritz 1984, 1997; Gremillion 1993, 1997) have suggested that a shift from a biconvex, rounded, or equatorial banded seed margin to a truncate margin is indicative of the transformation from wild to domesticated *Chenopodium.* The truncate margin is rectanguloid in cross section and provides greater internal seed volume necessary to house larger embryonic leaves (Smith 1984; Smith and Funk 1985). In

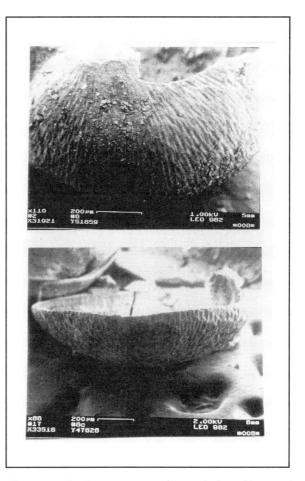

**Figure 8.9.** Seed-coat patterns for seeds from Feature 6 (smooth) and Feature 8 (reticulate).

addition to the development of a truncate margin, Wilson (1981) reported a change in cotyledon shape with domestication. Presumably, such changes were the result of selection for increased seedling vigor in the highly competitive seedbed (Smith 1992).

Examination of the Burnham-Shepard *Chenopodium* samples revealed that the truncate seed-margin configuration was not present in our sample (Figure 8.9). All our specimens exhibit rounded margin configurations. Again, however, if we are dealing with a species different from that which was domesticated in the Midcontinent, selective pressures resulting from the domestication process may not have caused the development of a truncate seed margin. Therefore, it is possible that outward expressions of the domestication process in the Burnham-Shepard samples include a reduction in testa thickness and a shift to a smooth seed-coat pattern, but not the development of a truncate margin. This remains to be demonstrated however.

## DISCUSSION AND CONCLUSION

The harvesting, storage, and consumption of *Chenopodium* has a long history in Connecticut, dating to the end of the Late Archaic period. It is clear that the use of *Chenopodium* by prehistoric populations in the Connecticut River valley is associated with increased duration and intensity of residential occupation. Archaeological sites such as Woodchuck Knoll and Bliss-Howard indicate that anthropogenic environments, created by numerous episodes of reoccupation and favorable for *Chenopodium* and other disturbed-habitat species, were often created and maintained over relatively long periods of time. These environments would have been characterized by numerous disturbed areas (i.e., middens, pathways, pits), and the introduction of large numbers of seeds through gathering activities, clearings, and increased solar insolation, all the ingredients listed in Smith's (1992) coevolutionary floodplain weed theory. Thus, it is possible that the coevolutionary trajectory for plant domestication in the Midcontinent that identifies Late Archaic settlements as the starting point in plant domestication (especially for *Chenopodium*) likely applies as well in the Connecticut River valley, particularly the middle portion of the valley which is characterized by expansive floodplains. Whether or not the domestication of *Chenopodium* took place at this time or any other time prior to or after the introduction of maize horticulture, however, remains an open question.

How do we, then, interpret the Burnham-Shepard *Chenopodium* samples? We are not yet prepared to announce the Burnham-Shepard samples as representative of domesticated *Chenopodium*. It is still unclear to us if the samples represent wild, weedy, cultivated, or domesticated *Chenopodium*. The bimodality in testa thickness points to the sampling of two populations of *Chenopodium*, a wild type (> 40 μm) and a thin-testa type (approximately 20 μm). Again however, since the taxonomy has not

yet been clearly established, we are not confident in assigning domesticate status to the thin-testa type, as has been done in the Midcontinent (Fritz 1984; Smith 1984; Smith and Funk 1984). We are unsure whether we are dealing with *Chenopodium berlandieri* or some other species. It is quite possible that the Burnham-Shepard samples represent another species whose responses to the selective pressures of domestication could be different from that of *Chenopodium berlandieri*. That being the case, we cannot be sure if we are observing the initial responses to the selective pressures of domestication, fully domesticated specimens, a weedy conspecific population, or something else. We must also keep in mind Gremillion's (1993) statements concerning the reversion of domesticated forms to wild forms after the introduction of maize horticulture, a situation that is especially applicable to the Burnham-Shepard site. A specimen representing a reversion to the wild state could conceivably appear similar to the Burnham-Shepard specimens.

Clearly, much more work needs to be done on the Burnham-Shepard *Chenopodium* assemblage before any definitive statements can be offered. First and foremost, we need to address the question of taxonomy. Before we can come to any conclusions concerning domestication, we need to be sure of the species we are examining. As we have mentioned, the presence of keeled sepals on the specimens suggests an identification of either *Chenopodium berlandieri* or *Chenopodium bushianum*. We plan in the future to obtain and examine samples of both of these species for comparative purposes. Second, we must increase our sample size to ensure that our observations are representative of the assemblage as a whole. Third, we would like to collect and analyze samples from other modern, wild populations of *Chenopodium* from the Connecticut River valley to provide a comparative database of local origin. As we have mentioned, it is possible that significant differences in Midcontinent and New England *Chenopodium* populations exist. If this were found to be true, using the extant Midcontinent database for comparative purposes may be unwise. Finally, we would very much like to acquire samples of Connecticut *Chenopodium* from securely dated pre-maize contexts. Examination of pre-maize *Chenopodium* samples will allow us to determine whether the observations we made on the Burnham-Shepard samples existed prior to, and are therefore independent of, the introduction of maize horticulture. If we find variations in *Chenopodium* characteristics similar to those in the Midcontinent prior to the introduction of maize, then the eastern North American independent center of plant domestication (Smith 1992) should be extended to include Southern New England.

## ACKNOWLEDGEMENTS

We thank several individuals for reviewing and commenting on an earlier draft of this chapter. We thank Jeffrey Bendremer for having so carefully excavated the Burnham-Shepard material and for permitting us to reproduce Figures 8.2 and 8.3. We thank Jim Romanow of the University of Connecticut's Department of Scanning Electron microscopy for the SEM microphotographs. Steven Clemants gave useful advice on *Chenopodium* systematics. Gayle Fritz, Patricia Miller, George Milner, and Dean Snow provided important comments and criticisms that improved this chapter. We also thank Kristen Gremillion and Bruce Smith for formerly reviewing this chapter and offering criticisms that resulted in its improvement. In addition, we thank John Hart for organizing an interesting symposium and for asking us to contribute our manuscript to the volume. Finally, thanks are due to Catherine Labadia for comments and the preparation of Figures 8.2 and 8.3.

## END NOTE

1. In the initial publication, American lotus (*Nelumbo lutea*) was also identified by McBride (1978). Although the original specimens cannot be located, photographs of some of the complete specimens indicate that they are most certainly hazelnuts, rather than lotus as McBride suggested.

## REFERENCES CITED

Asch, D. L., and N. B. Asch. 1977. Chenopod as Cultigen: A Re-Evaluation of Some Prehistoric Collections from Eastern North America. *Midcontinental Journal of Archaeology* 2:3-45.

——————. 1985. Prehistoric Plant Cultivation in West-Central Illinois. In *Prehistoric Food Production in North America*, edited by R. I. Ford, pp. 149-204. Anthropological Papers No. 75. Museum of Anthropology, University of Michigan, Ann Arbor.

Bendremer, J. C. M. 1993. *Late Woodland Settlement and Subsistence in Eastern Connecticut*. Unpublished Ph.D. dissertation, Department of Anthropology, University of Connecticut, Storrs.

Bendremer, J. C. M., E. Kellogg, and T. B. Largy. 1991. A Grass-Lined Storage Pit and Early Maize Horticulture in Central Connecticut. *North American Archaeologist* 12:325-349.

Cook, T. G. 1976. Broadpoint: Culture, Phase, Horizon, Tradition, or Knife? *Journal of Anthropological Research* 32:337-357.

Fritz, G. J. 1984. Identification of Cultigen *Amaranth* and *Chenopod* from Rockshelter Sites in Northwest Arkansas. *American Antiquity* 49:558-572.

——————. 1986. *Prehistoric Ozark Agriculture: The University of Arkansas Rockshelter Collections*. Unpublished Ph.D. dissertation. Department of Anthropology, University of North Carolina, Chapel Hill.

——————. 1997. A Three-Thousand-Year-Old Cache of Crop Seeds from Marble Bluff, Arkansas. In *People, Plants, and Landscapes: Studies in Paleoethnobotany*, edited by K. J. Gremillion, pp. 42-62. University of Alabama Press, Tuscaloosa.

Fritz, G. J., and B. D. Smith. 1988. Old Collections and New Technology: Documenting the Domestication of *Chenopodium* in Eastern North America. *Midcontinental Journal of Archaeology* 13:3-27.

Gardner, P. 1993. Carbonized Plant Remains from 36Ti58, ca. A.D. 900-1300, Tioga County, Pennsylvania. In *Archaeological Data Recovery: Site 36Ti58*, edited by P. Miller. Archaeological and Historical Consultants, Inc., Centre Hall, Pennsylvania.

George, D. R. 1997a. A Long Row to Hoe: The Cultivation of Archaeobotany in Southern New England. *Archaeology of Eastern North America* 25:175-190.

——————. 1997b. Recognizing Variability in the Archaeobotanical Record of Late Prehistoric Southern New England. *Bulletin of the Archaeological Society of Connecticut* 60:13-28.

George, D. R., and J. C. M. Bendremer. 1995. Late Woodland Subsistence and the Origins of Maize Horticulture in New England. Paper presented at the 60th Annual Meeting of the Society for American Archaeology, Minneapolis, Minnesota.

Gremillion, K. 1993. Crop and Weed in Prehistoric Eastern North America: The *Chenopodium* Example. *American Antiquity* 58:496-509.

——————. 1997. New Perspectives on the Paleoethnobotany of the Newt Kash Shelter. *In People, Plants, and Landscapes: Studies in Paleoethnobotany*, edited by K. J. Gremillion, pp. 23-41. University of Alabama Press, Tuscaloosa.

Hart, J. P., and N. Asch Sidell. 1996. Prehistoric Agricultural Systems in the West Branch of the Susquehanna River Basin, A.D. 800 to A.D. 1350. *Northeast Anthropology* 52:1-30.

Howe, R. W. 1965. *Sitophilus granarius* (L.) (Coleoptera, Curculiondae) Breeding in Acorns. *Journal of Stored Products Research* 1:99-100.

Karssen, C.M. 1970. The Light Promoted Germination of the Seeds of Chenopodium album, Part 3: Effect of the Photoperiod during Growth and Development of the Plants on the Dormancy of the produced seeds. *Acta Botanica Neerlandica* 19:81-94.

Levinson, H., and A. Levison. 1994. Origin of Grain Storage and Insect Species Consuming Dessicated Food. *Anz. Schladlingskunde, Pflanzenschutz, Umweltschutz* 67:47-59.

McBride, K. A. 1978. Archaic Subsistence in the Lower Connecticut River Valley: Evidence from Woodchuck Knoll. *Man in the Northeast* 15/16:124-131.

Pagoulatos, P. 1986. *Terminal Archaic Settlement and Subsistence in the Connecticut River Valley*. Ph.D. dissertation, University of Connecticut. University Microfilms, Ann Arbor.

——————. 1988. Terminal Archaic Settlement and Subsistence in the Connecticut River Valley. *Man in the Northeast* 35:71-93.

Pfeiffer, J. E. n.d. Late Archaic and Terminal Archaic Cultural Adaptations and the Broadspear Complex. Manuscript in possession of the author.

——————. 1984. The Late and Terminal Archaic Periods of Connecticut Prehistory. *Archaeological Society of Connecticut Bulletin* 47:73-88.

Ritchie, W. A., and R. E. Funk. 1973. *Aboriginal Settlement Patterns in the Northeast*. Memoir 20, New York Museum and Science Service. The University of the State of New York, Albany.

Smith, B. D. 1984. *Chenopodium* as a Prehistoric Domesticate in Eastern North America: Evidence from Russell Cave, Alabama. *Science* 26:165-167.

——————. 1985. The Role of *Chenopodium* as a Domesticate in Pre-Maize Garden Systems of the Eastern United States. *Southeastern Archaeology* 4:51-72.

——————. 1992. *Rivers of Change: Essays on Early Agriculture in Eastern North America*. Smithsonian Institution Press, Washington, D.C.

Smith, B. D., and C. W. Cowan. 1987. Domesticated *Chenopodium* in Prehistoric Eastern North America: New Accelerator Dates from Eastern Kentucky. *American Antiquity* 52:355-357.

Smith, B. D., and V. Funk. 1985. A Newly Described Subfossil Cultivar of *Chenopodium* (Chenopodiaceae). *Phytologia* 57:445-448.

Turnbaugh, W. 1975. Toward an Explanation of the Broad-Point Dispersal in North American Prehistory. *Journal of Anthropological Research* 31:51-69.

Wilson, H. 1981. Domesticated *Chenopodium* of the Ozark Bluff Dwellers. *Economic Botany* 35:233-239.

# CHAPTER 9

# CHANGING STRATEGIES IN THE PRE- AND POST-CONTACT SUBSISTENCE SYSTEMS OF SOUTHERN NEW ENGLAND: ARCHAEOLOGICAL AND ETHNOHISTORICAL EVIDENCE

Jeffrey C. Bendremer

## INTRODUCTION

The investigation of indigenous food-production strategies in New England has really just begun. For several reasons, data bearing upon the nature of pre-contact maize horticulture were lacking from published reports until the 1980s. First, the acidic soils of New England do not favor the preservation of macrobotanical remains. Second, archaeologists in the region have tended to emphasize material culture, such as stone and ceramic objects, over subsistence data. Third, and most importantly, archaeological methods commonly used prior to the 1980s were not designed to detect or extract macrobotanical evidence from Late Woodland sites. More recently, however, archaeologists have given more attention to the recovery and analysis of macrobotanical remains in New England sites (Bendremer 1993; Bernstein 1992a; Chilton, this volume; Ford 1985; Hastorf and Popper 1988; Heckenberger et. al. 1992; Keegan 1987). This has led to the increased identification of macrobotanical remains, including wild and domesticated species, and a growing sophistication in the analysis of the archaeobotanical material. Similarly, New England archaeologists have refined their methods resulting in a significant increase in the paleoethnobotanical database. We now have enough data to begin a comprehensive analysis of native horticultural strategies and overall subsistence systems of the Late Woodland peoples of Southern New England.

Details regarding the origins of food production and the arrival of tropical cultigens in New England have long been debated, primarily because the remains of domesticated plants have, until recently, been nearly absent from archaeological inventories. Some estimated the advent of horticulture in New England at 500 B.C. (Smith 1950; Snow 1980). Others fixed the arrival of maize horticulture later at A.D. 1400 (Galinat 1985) or "post-contact," around A.D. 1500 (Ceci 1979-80). However, the recent discoveries of significant quantities of cultigens at pre-contact sites throughout New England (Bendremer 1993; Bendremer and Dewar 1994) have provided us with a more complete view of Late Woodland subsistence patterns than has been available in the past. From these data it is clear that maize horticulture arrived in New England at about the beginning of the Late Woodland period, ca. A.D. 1,000 (Bendremer 1993; Bendremer and Dewar 1994; Bendremer et. al. 1991; Dincauze 1990; Lavin 1988a; McBride and Dewar 1987; Mulholland 1988). The precise extent and importance of maize horticulture, and what "importance" means in the context of Late Woodland Southern New England, is the subject of ongoing research and debate (Chilton, this volume). Likewise, the possibility of an additional domesticated indigenous plant species, in particular *Chenopodium* sp., is also being actively investigated (George and Dewar, this volume).

## PRE-CONTACT SUBSISTENSE SYSTEMS

McBride and Dewar (1987) have maintained that the Woodland period in Southern New England was marked, in part, by a pattern of increasing social and technological complexity. The Late Woodland period (A.D. 1000-1500) in the lower Connecticut River valley was characterized by a trend toward sedentism, increased site complexity, marked improvements in ceramic technology, increased use of non-local lithic material, and the adoption of maize horticulture (Feder 1984; McBride and Dewar 1987).

The introduction of tropical cultigens (maize, beans, and squash) at about A.D. 1000, however, seems to have occurred with so little obvious change in the coastal settlement and subsistence systems, that McBride and Dewar (1987) described it as a "non-event." Indeed, data gathered from coastal sites such as Mago Point, 72-31, and Selden Island (McBride 1984; Figure 9.1) support the contention that Late Woodland food production was a very minor part of a subsistence strategy best described as a broad-based hunting and gathering subsistence system emphasizing marine and estuary resources (Bendremer 1993; Bernstein 1992b). There certainly is no evidence in the archaeological record of the kind of reliance upon horticulture recorded by early European explorers and colonists, which Chilton (this volume) cautions us may overstate the case, or by groups to the west such as the Iroquois (Demeritt 1991; McBride and Dewar 1987; Bernstein 1990). A similar lack of horticultural data from coastal New York prompted Ceci (1982) to consider increased sedentism and reliance upon maize horticulture a substantially contact phenomenon.

Others have asserted that maize horticulture began prior to European contact (Connecticut Archaeological Survey 1979; McBride 1984; Silver 1980). More recently, excavations by the author and others (Bendremer 1993; Bendremer and Dewar 1994; Bernstein 1992b; Lavin 1988a) have demonstrated the existence of subregional variation; subsistence strategies and the relative importance of maize horticulture varied in different parts of Southern New England. For example, excavations by the author at the Burnham-Shepard site, middle Connecticut River valley (Figure 9.1) have revealed evidence that suggests significant involvement with maize horticulture by the early fourteenth century. Other sites, including Morgan (Lavin 1988a), Pine Hill (Chilton, this volume), and Skitchewaug (Heckenberger et. al. 1992) provide further evidence for the significance of maize horticulture in the middle Connecticut River valley as they contained large samples of maize, beans, and/or squash in, or near, large subterranean storage features (Figure 9.1). The presence of these large storage features, containing considerable quantities of cultigens, suggest that maize and other storable plant foods were a significant component of the diet prior to contact. I do not mean to imply here that maize was a staple food or constituted the bulk or majority of the caloric intake. There is no doubt, however, of the consequential investment represented by maize horticulture in the middle Connecticut River valley during the fourteenth century and possibly earlier. This region is to the north of McBride and Dewar's lower Connecticut River valley study area and contrasts with the subsistence patterns observed there and in coastal Connecticut and New York (Bendremer 1993; Ceci 1982; McBride 1984).

If a number of distinct contemporaneous settlement systems existed in a relatively small region such as Connecticut, then settlement and subsistence patterns in pre-contact New England are certainly more complex than earlier reports suggested. A similar pattern of subregional variation appears to hold for Rhode Island (Bernstein 1992b), the Delaware, Susquehanna, and Hudson River valleys (George and Bendremer 1995) as well as parts of the Mid-Atlantic region (Stewart 1993). It is, therefore, very important that archaeologists begin implementing studies designed to examine regional and subregional variability in settlement and subsistence patterns.

I have always translated this as a need for larger scale regional studies which, by virtue of their wider scope, can detect and assess the full range of strategies heretofore overlooked in the archaeological record. Conversely, Feder (personal communication 1997) has speculated, "Actually, what we need are more small-scale studies, i.e., we should be looking at smaller scales to identify the settlement-subsistence systems within subregions and then compare them to other subregions ... What we need is more communication among those working in these different subregions." Either of these approaches will provide better resolution in archaeological investigations of subregional settlement and subsistence systems despite the time and resource problems inherent in implementing large-scale projects and difficulties in improving communications between those engaged in smaller-scale projects.

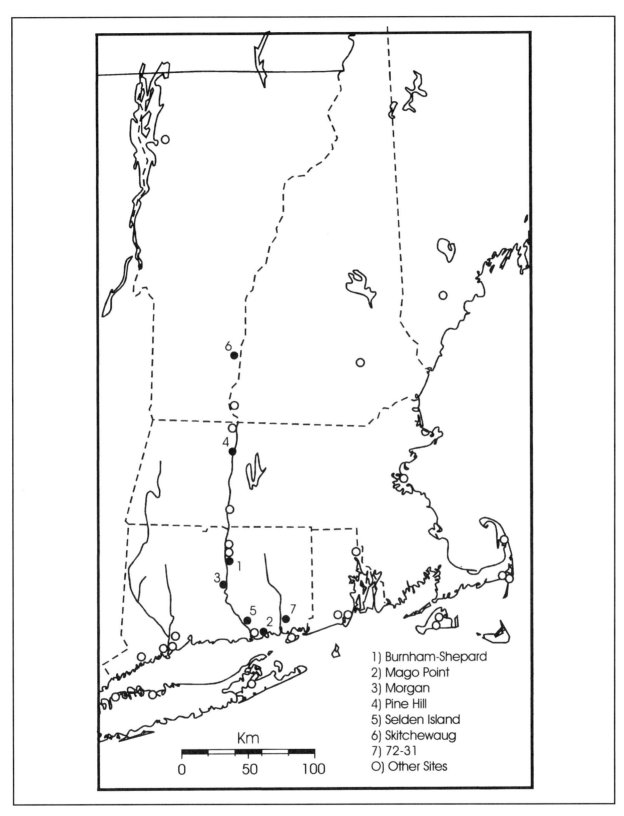

**Figure 9.1.** New England sites with archaeological cultigens mentioned in the text and their relationship to other maize bearing sites (see Bendremer (1993) and Chilton (this volume)).

1) Burnham-Shepard
2) Mago Point
3) Morgan
4) Pine Hill
5) Selden Island
6) Skitchewaug
7) 72-31
O) Other Sites

Km

0    50    100

## VARIETIES OF CULTIGENS

There are at least 48 prehistoric sites where archaeologists have found macrobotanical remains of tropical cultigens in the greater New England region (Bendremer 1993):

| | |
|---|---|
| Connecticut | 16 |
| Coastal and eastern New York | 12 |
| Massachusetts | 9 |
| Rhode Island | 3 |
| Northern New Jersey | 3 |
| New Hampshire | 3 |
| Vermont | 2 |
| Maine | 1 |
| Eastern Pennsylvania | 1 |

The most common report is of maize (*Zea mays*), which has been recovered, often as isolated kernels, at 44 sites. Beans (*Phaseolus vulgaris*) were identified at nine sites. Squash (*Cucurbita* sp.) was discovered at only three sites, in each case associated with both maize and beans (for more on squash, see Hart and Asch Sidell 1997). Sunflower seeds (*Helianthus annuus*), another indigenous cultigen (Yarnell 1978), were discovered at a site also yielding maize and beans. In addition, "corncakes" were found at two sites, and maize cobs (and possible maize cobs) were discovered at four sites. With improved methods for extracting macrobotanical remains, new finds will certainly add to this database (see Chilton, this volume).

Consistent with the inland riverine pattern, the Burnham-Shepard site yielded over 500 whole and 1,000 partial maize kernels in 16 features. (Bendremer 1993; Bendremer and Dewar 1994; Bendremer et. al. 1991). Over 100 maize kernel fragments were also discovered in one of a number of maize-bearing features at the nearby Morgan site (Lavin 1988a). A maize geneticist from the University of Connecticut (Greenblatt, personal communication 1989) concluded that the Burnham-Shepard and Morgan site maize both were a type of Northern Flint maize which most closely resembled an eight-rowed variety. Maize specimens from the Burnham-Shepard and Morgan sites, as well as those discovered at other sites in New England, are close in size and shape to samples of modern eight-rowed Northern Flint measured by the author (Bendremer 1993; Bendremer and Dewar 1994).

Beans and squash have been found at only a few sites in New England. Twelve common beans (*Phaseolus vulgaris*), identified by Lawrence Kaplan (personal communication 1988), were discovered at the Burnham-Shepard site. Although these beans appear to include two distinct shapes, one kidney-shaped and one more rounded, it is unclear from the specimens whether they represent one or two varieties (Bendremer and Dewar 1994; Bendremer et. al. 1991).

The only reported sunflower seeds (*Helianthus annuus*) discovered in the greater New England region were recovered at the Burnham-Shepard site. Domesticated sunflower has been conspicuously absent from archaeological material recovered in New England and is undocumented in early ethnohistorical accounts except by Champlain (1966 [1625]), who reported its use in 1615 in southern Ontario. Thirty-five sunflower seeds, identified by Heiser (personal communication 1989) were recovered from Feature 8, a grass-lined storage pit. It is likely that these sunflower seeds represent a "primitive" domesticated variety (Heiser, personal communication 1990; Bendremer and Dewar 1994; Bendremer et. al. 1991) due to its small achene size (mean = 7.5 mm). The earliest domesticated sunflower discovered was identified by Crites (1993) at the Hayes site in Tennessee. Its uncalibrated AMS age of 4,265 ± 60 B.P. predates, by nearly 1,400 years, other early finds (Brewer 1973; McCollough and Faulkner 1973; Fritz 1986). Sunflower is one of a suite of native North American domesticated crops that became economically important between 250 B.C. and A.D. 200 in areas south and west of Connecticut (Bodner, this volume; Smith 1987, 1989, 1992a, 1992b, 1995). However, other indigenous North American domesticates, such as maygrass (*Phalaris caroliniana*), little barley (*Hordeum pusillum*), knotweed (*Polygonum erectum*), and marsh elder (*Iva annua*), have never been identified in New England. Goosefoot (*Chenopodium berlandieri*), another North American domesticate, has never been identified in New England, but members of the genus

*Chenopodium* are a conspicuous component of many New England botanical assemblages beginning in the Late Archaic (see George and Dewar, this volume). In an analysis of Burnham-Shepard site *Chenopodium*, George and Dewar (this volume) identify what appear to be two populations, one with a thick testa and one with a thin testa. Thin-testa *Chenopodium* is a marker of domestication in Midcontinent sites and has been discovered, along with domesticated *Helianthus* and *Hordeum* in the Susquehanna River basin (Hart and Asch Sidell 1996).

In summary, the most common domestic plant remains discovered in the greater New England region is maize. Sites with more than 10 identified maize kernels were nearly all from inland riverine locations. Although seldom recovered, beans, squash, and sunflower are almost always found in association with maize, and all sites containing multiple domesticates are located in inland riverine environments rather than coastal areas.

Chilton (this volume) maintains that "we should not expect a one-to-one correlation between the amount of maize found and the intensity of maize horticulture," and "we simply cannot expect the presence of one or more cultigens to be a reflection of either importance or diversity in the types of cultigens utilized in the past." If the presence of maize and other cultigens were more homogenous across the region, I would certainly agree. However, there is a fairly well-defined pattern differentiating coastal areas, including the lower Connecticut River valley and Block Island, from inland riverine areas (Bendremer 1993; Bendremer and Dewar 1994). As Largy et al. (this volume) mention in regards to the Goldkrest site, the small amounts of maize found in coastal sites could have been grown elsewhere (Williams and Bendremer 1997). This is much less likely at sites such as Burnham-Shepard, which had (1) multiple domesticated taxa, (2) 16 features containing domesticates, (3) 12 storage features, (4) good soils for cultivation, and (5) larger inventories of maize and other domesticates. These observations are consistent with Ceci's (1979-80, 1982, 1990) evaluation of coastal settlement patterns, poor soils, and the

apparent lack of any significant quantities of archaeological cultigens. Based upon this evidence, it seems clear that maize horticulture and other subsistence activities practiced at seasonal Late Woodland inland riverine sites were different than the subsistence activities at larger, more sedentary coastal sites.

In order to understand food-production strategies and the place of maize horticulture in the overall subsistence system, other important areas of subsistence must be examined. Of particular importance are hunting, fishing, shellfishing, and the collection of wild plant foods. An examination of each of these areas will allow for a comprehensive description of the subsistence system and aid in explanations of the subregional subsistence strategies.

## HUNTING AND GATHERING

### Fish and Shellfish

Shellfish appear to have been an intensively exploited resource as indicated by the number of shell middens discovered along the coasts of New England (Barber 1983; Bernstein 1988; Cerato 1987; Coffin 1940; Hancock 1982; Kerber 1985; Lightfoot and Cerato 1988; McManamon 1984; Powell 1958; Praus 1942; Russell 1942; Sanger 1981, 1988). They were a predictable, low-risk resource, available all year long except when estuaries temporarily froze in winter (Lightfoot and Cerato 1988). However, the relative importance of shellfish and their caloric contribution to the diet of prehistoric aboriginal people have been a matter of some debate (Snow 1980).

The varieties of shellfish recovered from archaeological sites in New England include quahog clam (*Venus mercenaria*), common oyster (*Ostrea virginica*), bay scallop (*Pecten irradians*), softshell clam (*Mya arenaria*), whelks (*Busycon* sp.), mussels (*Mytilus* sp.), moon shell (*Polinices heros*), boat shell (*Crepidula fornicata*), oyster drill (*Urosalpinx cineras*), periwinkle (*Littorina littorea*), razor clam (*Ensus directus*), ark (*Arka transversa*), and basket shell (*Nassarius obsoletus*) (Warner 1972). Of these species, clams (probably both quahog and softshell), common oyster, bay scallop, whelks, mussel, razor clam, and periwinkle are mentioned in ethnohistorical documentation (Higgenson 1846 [1630]; Josselyn 1988 [1674]; Morton 1937 [1669]; Williams 1963 [1643]; Wood 1977 [1634]). Several ethnographic sources mention the desirability of clam as a "sweet kind of shellfish" (Williams 1963 [1643]). Mourt (1967 [1622]) noted that natives were "much taken with the delight of this fish." Although absent from the archaeological record in New England, the exploitation of lobster (*Homerus americanus*) is mentioned in ethnographic sources (Josselyn 1988 [1674]; Wood 1977 [1634]).

In addition, fish is often cited as an important resource for New England natives (Banks 1990; Bellantoni 1987; Warner 1972). Although the archaeological preservation of fish remains in the acidic soils of Southern New England is less likely than that of terrestrial mammals, sites such as Coudert Ledge (McBride 1984), Mago Point (McBride and Dewar 1987), RI 1450 (Bellantoni 1987), RI 1428 (Tveskov 1992), Ft. Shantok (Williams 1972), and others (Bendremer 1993) suggest the importance of fish in the subsistence of New England natives.

Ethnographic records mention four strategies used to exploit marine resources in New England: (1) spear or harpoon fishing of larger species (Josselyn 1988 [1674]; Williams 1963 [1643]; Wood 1977 [1634]); (2) hook and line fishing (Champlain 1966 [1625]; Wood 1977 [1634]); (3) net fishing (De Rasieres 1909 [1628]; Higginson 1846 [1630]; Josselyn 1988 [1674]; Williams 1963 [1643]; Wood 1977 [1634]); and (4) several types of fish weirs (Gookin 1792 [1674]; Morton 1937 [1669]; Mourt 1967 [1622]). The fish species identified in archaeological sites include sturgeon, shark, bluefish, salmon, striped bass, cod, shad, barracuda, bullhead, yellow perch, and grouper (Banks 1990; Banks et. al. 1988; Bellantoni 1987; McBride and Dewar 1987; Tveskov 1992; Warner 1972). Ethnohistorical accounts mention sturgeon, salmon, striped bass, perch, cod, bullhead, barracuda, bluefish, shad, alewives, carp, herring, haddock, eels, fluke, halibut, lamprey, trout, perch, pike, smelt, swordfish, mackerel, pickerel, and others (Table 9.1).

Although fish are available year round,

some species are found in greater concentrations during certain seasons. Josselyn (1988 [1674]) mentioned the Indians "removing from one place to another for convenience of food, sometimes to those places where one sort of fish is most plentiful, other whiles where others are." While the importance of salmon as a seasonal food source during prehistoric times has been called into question (Carlson 1988), other anadromous species (i.e., shad and sturgeon), as well as catadromous species (i.e., eel) were probably important food sources, especially during the spring months (Banks 1990; Warner 1972). In fact, for the aboriginal people living around present day Springfield, Massachusetts, the name of the month that corresponds to parts of March and April refers to catching fish (Pynchon in Thomas 1976). New England Natives generally engaged in salt-water fishing during the warm months while fresh-water fishing and ice fishing during colder times of the year (Williams 1963 [1643]; Wood 1977 [1634]).

## Hunting

Of all the faunal remains present in the archaeological sites of Connecticut, the most ubiquitous is *Odocoileus virginianus* or white-tailed deer (McBride 1984; Williams 1972; Banks et. al. 1988). This may be due, in part, to the fact that large, heavy deer bones are more likely to preserve than more fragile remains of smaller animals. It is clear, however, that white-tailed deer was an important food resource in both prehistoric and post-contact times. The ethnohistorical documents mention deer hunting with bow and arrows (Rosier 1966 [1605]; Wood 1977 [1634]), with traps or snares (Morton 1937 [1669]; Williams 1963 [1643]), and with drives (Mourt 1967 [1622]; Wood 1977 [1634]).

Other faunal species identified in archaeological sites include bear, beaver, dog, moose, rabbit, raccoon, and meadow vole (Table 9.2). Some of the larger and/or more common of these species, such as moose, rabbit, and raccoon, may represent significant sources of food. Other species present in archaeological sites but absent from the ethnohistorical record (e.g., meadow vole and whitefooted mouse) may have lived

**Table 9.1. Fish Remains Identified in Archaeological Sites or Ethnohistorical Accounts in New England.**

| Scientific Name | Common Name | Archaeological Site | Ethnohistoric Account | Source |
|---|---|---|---|---|
| *Acipenser sturio* | Sturgeon | + | + | 1,2,4,5,7,8 |
| *Alosa sapidissima* | Shad | + | + | 1,3,5,6,8 |
| *Anguila rostrata* | Eels | - | + | 2,3,4,5,6,7,8 |
| *Caleichthys felis* | Bullhead | + | + | 8 |
| *Carcharodon carcharais* | Shark[a] | + | + | 4 |
| *Clupea harengus* | Herring | - | + | 1,2,6,8 |
| *Cyclopterus lumpus* | Lumps | - | + | 4 |
| *Cyprinus carpio* | Carp | - | + | 5 |
| *Esox americanus* | Pickerel | - | + | 7 |
| *Esox lucius* | Pike | - | + | 5,8 |
| *Gadus* sp. | Cod | + | + | 2,3,4,5,6,7,8 |
| *Glyptocephalis cynoglossus* | Fluke[a] | - | + | 4 |
| *Hippoglossus hippoglossus* | Halibut[a] | - | + | 5,8 |
| *Archosargus rhomboidales* | Bream[a] | - | + | 5,6,7,8 |
| *Melanogammus aeglefinnus* | Haddock[a] | - | + | 2 |
| *Microgradus tomcod* | Frost Fish[a] | - | + | 3,7,8 |
| *Morone saxatilis* | Striped Bass | + | + | 1,2,4,5,7,8 |
| *Mycteroperca bonaci* | Grouper[a] | + | - | None |
| *Osmerus mordax* | Smelt | - | + | 3,5,8 |
| *Perca flavescens* | Yellow Perch | + | + | 5,8 |
| *Petromyzon marinus* | Lamprey | - | + | 4,7,8 |
| *Pomatomus saltatrix* | Bluefish[a] | + | + | 4 |
| *Promolobus pseudoharengus* | Alewives | - | + | 3,8 |
| *Salmo salar* | Salmon | +(?) | + | 1,4,5,7,8 |
| *Salvelinus* sp. | Trout | - | + | 5 |
| *Sardinops cerulea* | Pilchards | - | + | 5 |
| *Scomber scombrus* | Mackerel[a] | - | + | 2,3,5,7 |
| *Sembastodes paucispinus* | Rockfish[a] | - | + | 4 |
| *Sphyrana borialis* | Barracuda[a] | + | + | 4 |
| *Tautoga onitis* | Tautog[a] | - | + | 7 |
| *Xiphias gladius* | Swordfish[a] | - | + | 4 |

*Note*
[a] Exclusively marine species

*Key to Sources*
1   Gookin 1968 [1792]
2   Higginson 1846 [1630]
3   Johnson 1974 [1654]
4   Josselyn 1988 [1674]
5   Morton 1937 [1669]
6   Mourt 1967 [1622]
7   Williams 1963 [1643]
8   Wood 1977 [1634]
(Bendremer 1993; Bernstein 1992b; Lavin 1988b; Warner 1972)

alongside human beings and were incorporated into sites by accident or were killed as pests. Others, like wolf, might not have been a food source at all, but were killed as a potential threat (Warner 1972). Dogs were hunting companions and, during times of scarcity, a food source (Josselyn 1988 [1674]; Mourt 1967 [1622]; Williams 1963 [1643]).

**Wild Plants**

Wild plant foods provided an important source of nutrition for Connecticut natives in both pre- and post-contact times (see Bernstein, this volume). The fact that few of these plant foods have been identified in archaeological sites reflects, in part, the poor preservation of such materials in the acidic soils of New England. In recent years, with the application of rigorous techniques of water separation and flotation, more botanical remains have been extracted from archaeological sites in New England (Table 9.3).

The ethnohistorical record describes the exploitation of many kinds of wild plant foods. Berries such as strawberry, blueberry, cranberry, and raspberry were collected. Varieties of nuts, such as butternut, walnut (perhaps only native to areas south of New England), chestnut, and hickory nut, were collected and stored (Warner 1972). Tubers (e.g., Jerusalem artichoke and groundnut), which are rarely recovered in New England's archaeological sites, were also consumed.

## REGIONAL VARIATION

The settlement systems of New England Indians in the Contact period were not described in detail in ethnohistorical accounts. Sometimes mentioned, however, is the fact that the Indians of New England moved in a seasonal round depending upon the availability of resources at any given time of year (Gookin 1792 [1674] ; Higgenson 1846 [1630]; Josselyn 1988 [1674]; Thomas 1976; Williams 1963 [1643]). It is probable that this round varied in different parts of Southern New England and even in different parts of Connecticut as it did in the preceding Late Woodland (Bendremer 1993; George and

Bendremer 1995).

The Late Woodland period in eastern Connecticut is characterized by a high degree of regional diversity with respect to settlement and subsistence patterns. The Selden Creek phase (A.D. 750-1500) in the middle Connecticut River valley is characterized by a Late Woodland settlement and subsistence system oriented toward the Connecticut River and its broad, fertile floodplain. Both large and small semi-permanent agricultural hamlets were located on the floodplain and terraces from April or May through at least October. Similarly, small agricultural sites have been observed along the West Branch of the Susquehanna River valley (Hart and Asch Sidell 1996). Riverine resources, as well as wild plant and animals, were exploited by the people living in these warm-weather occupations. Maize horticulture and the storage of domesticated plants became a significant feature of these inland riverine ecoregions by the fourteenth century. Lavin (1988b) has suggested that horticulture became more important in the North-Central Lowlands than elsewhere in eastern Connecticut because inland resources were less abundant and more seasonally restricted. Maize was a "reliable, prolific food source that could be stored for use during the lean months" (Lavin 1988b:113).

In winter, smaller, cold-weather camps, like those described in the ethnohistoric record, were established on high knolls along floodplains or in the uplands. Exploitation of nuts and terrestrial mammals were important at these occupations (Bendremer 1993; Lavin 1988a), as they were in more sedentary coastal villages (Bernstein 1992b). Moreover, the presence of many small, temporary, and task-specific sites in the hills suggests the logistical exploitation of the uplands (Bendremer 1993; McBride 1984). These task-specific sites appear to extend from the immediately adjacent uplands to the area west of the Willimantic River, up to 28 km from the Connecticut river. Another settlement system based upon the year-round exploitation of the uplands appears to be located east of the Willimantic River (Bendremer 1993; McBride, personal communication 1992).

In contrast, large, apparently sedentary vil-

**Table 9.2. Terrestrial Mammal and Bird Species Identified in Archaeological Sites or Ethnohistorical Accounts in New England.**

| Scientific Name | Common Name | Archaeological Site | Ethnohistoric Account | Source |
|---|---|---|---|---|
| *Alces americana* | Moose | + | + | 1,2,4,6,8,9 |
| *Anas rubrides* | Black Duck | + | - | None |
| *Branta canadensis* | Canadian Goose | + | - | None |
| *Castor canadensis* | Beaver | + | + | 9 |
| *Canis familiaris* | Indian Dog | + | + | 4,7,8 |
| *Canis lupus* | Wolf | + | + | 6,8,9 |
| *Erethizon dorsatum* | Porcupine | + | + | 4,6,9 |
| *Erignathus barbatus* | Harbor Seal | + | + | 9 |
| *Glaucomys* sp. | Flying Squirrel | + | + | 2,4,6,7,8,9 |
| *Lutra canadensis* | Otter | + | + | 1,2,3,4,5,6,8,9 |
| *Lynx rufus* | Bobcat | + | + | 2,3,4,7,8,9 |
| *Marmota monax* | Woodchuck | + | - | None |
| *Meleagris gallopavo* | Wild Turkey | + | + | 4 |
| *Mephitis mephitis* | Skunk | + | + | 4,9 |
| *Microtus pennsylvanicus* | Meadow Vole | + | - | None |
| *Mustela vison* | Mink | + | - | None |
| *Peromuscus leucopus* | Whitefoot Mouse | + | - | None |
| *Procyon lotor* | Raccoon | + | + | 1,4,6,8,9 |
| *Odocoileus virginianus* | White-Tailed Deer | + | + | 1,2,3,4,6,7,8,9 |
| *Ondatra zibethica* | Muskrat | + | + | 4,6,9 |
| *Sciurus carolinensis* | Grey Squirrel | + | + | 2,4,6,7,8,9 |
| *Sylvilagus* sp. | Rabbit | + | + | 4,6,8.9 |
| *Tamiasciurrus hudsonicus* | Red Squirrel | + | + | 2,4,6,7,8,9 |
| *Ursus americanus* | Black Bear | + | + | 1,3,4,6,8 |
| *Urocyon cinereoargenteus* | Red Fox | + | + | 4,6,8 |
| *Vulpes fulva* | Grey Fox | + | + | 4,6,8 |

*Key to Sources*
1   Gookin 1968 [1792]
2   Higginson 1846 [1630]
3   Johnson 1974 [1654]
4   Josselyn 1988 [1674]
5   Lechford 1969 [1642]
6   Morton 1937 [1669]
7   Mourt 1967 [1622]
8   Williams 1963 [1643]
9   Wood 1977 [1634]
(Bendremer 1993; Bernstein 1992b; Lavin 1988b; Warner 1972)

**Table 9.3. Partial List of Wild and Domesticated Plant Species Identified in New England Archaeological Sites or Ethnohistorical Accounts.**

| Scientific Name | Common Name | Archaeological Site | Ethnohistoric Account | Source |
|---|---|---|---|---|
| *Amaranthus* sp. | Pigweed | + | - | None |
| *Apios apios* | Groundnut | - | + | 1,4,5 |
| *Carya* sp. | Hickory nut | + | - | None |
| *Castanea dentata* | Chestnut | + | + | 1,2,3 |
| *Chenopodium* sp. | Goosefoot | + | - | None |
| *Corylus* sp. | Hazelnut | + | - | None |
| *Crateagus tomentosa* | Whitehorn Haws | - | + | 2 |
| *Curcubita* sp. | Squash[a] | + | + | 1,2,3,4,8,9 |
| *Cyperus* sp. | Sedge | + | - | None |
| *Fagus grandfolia* | Beechnut | + | - | None |
| *Fragaria vesca americana* | Strawberry | + | + | 2,9 |
| *Galium* sp. | Bedstraw | + | - | None |
| *Helianthus tuberosa* | Jerusalem Artichoke | - | + | 1 |
| *Impatiens* sp. | Jewelweed | + | - | None |
| *Juglans cinerea* | Butternut | + | + | 1,2 |
| *Juglans nigra* | Black Walnut | +(?) | +(?) | 1,2 |
| *Phaseolus vulgaris* | Common Bean[a] | + | + | 1,3,4,7,8 |
| *Phytolacca* sp. | Pokeweed | + | - | None |
| *Polygonatum* sp. | Solomon's Seal | + | + | 4,9 |
| *Polygonum* sp. | Smartweed | + | - | None |
| *Prunus americana* | American Plum | + | + | 2 |
| *Prunus virginiana* | Chokecherry | - | + | 8 |
| *Quercus* sp. | Oak | + | + | 1,3,5,7,8 |
| *Ribes floridum* | Black Currant | - | + | 8 |
| *Ribes rubrum* | Red Currant | - | + | 2,3,8,9 |
| *Rhus* sp. | Sumac | + | - | None |
| *Rubus* sp. | Raspberry | + | + | 2,9 |
| *Sambucus* sp. | Elderberry | + | - | None |
| *Scirpus* sp. | Bullrush | + | - | None |
| *Solanum* sp. | Nightshade | + | - | None |
| *Vaccinium* sp. | Blueberry | + | + | 2,8.9 |
| *Vaccinium macrocarpon* | Cranberry | - | + | 8 |
| *Vitis* sp. | Grape | + | - | None |
| *Zea mays* | Maize[a] | + | + | 1,4,6,7,8,9 |
| *Zizania aquatica* | Wild Rice | + | - | None |

*Note*
[a] Cultivated plant foods

*Key to Sources*
1   Gookin 1968 [1792]
2   Higginson 1846 [1630]
3   Johnson 1974 [1654]
4   Josselyn 1988 [1674]
5   Lechford 1969 [1642]
6   Morton 1937 [1669]
7   Mourt 1967 [1622]
8   Williams 1963 [1643]
9   Wood 1977 [1634]
(Bendremer 1993; Bernstein 1992b, this volume; Lavin 1988b; Warner 1972)

lages on estuaries and tidal marshes along the lower Connecticut River and Long Island Sound (Bendremer 1993; McBride 1984; McBride and Dewar 1987) characterized the coastal region during the Selden Creek phase. The logistically organized exploitation of the uplands was accomplished from smaller temporary and task-specific camps.

A distinct maritime subsistence strategy has been identified on Block Island (Bellantoni 1987; Bendremer 1993). Three different hypotheses for Late Woodland maritime settlement have been proposed for the island: (1) Block Island was inhabited only during the winter and spring months to exploit seasonally abundant resources including seals, migratory waterfowl, and marine shellfish (Bellantoni 1987); (2) Block Island supported year-round inhabitants (McBride, personal communication 1993; Tveskov 1992); and (3) Block Island supported two populations, permanent inhabitants and a transient population from the mainland (Dirrigl and Bellantoni 1993). However, more archaeological work must be completed to resolve questions of Late Woodland settlement systems on Block Island. Like many other Late Woodland coastal sites, evidence for maize horticulture is absent on Block Island.

## MODELS OF LATE WOODLAND MAIZE HORTICULTURE

Several models have been proposed to explain the adoption of maize horticulture in New England. Mulholland (1988), for example, outlined a model of Late Woodland settlement and subsistence change in Southern New England based upon the adoption of maize horticulture. He maintained that arable land became scarcer and more valuable as a result of population increase, environmental degradation, and/or increased competition. These factors served to increase the risk for horticultural people. In this situation, it was important for horticultural populations to have access to estuary and coastal resources in order to augment their resource base (Mulholland 1988). Mulholland tentatively documented a marked increase in riverine and coastal settlement during the Late Woodland period in

New England. The relative proportion of sites in warmer areas also appears to have increased, perhaps as a consequence of the observed settlement of coastal and riverine areas.

Based upon recent data, maize horticulture certainly appears to have been a significant activity in the middle Connecticut River valley during the Selden Creek phase. However, there is very little archaeological data from upland and coastal areas of Southern New England to suggest maize was anything more than a minor component of the subsistence system until the Final Woodland or Contact period. Furthermore, large, essentially non-horticultural, sedentary villages of logistically organized foragers were established in the lower Connecticut River valley and coastal region by the late Middle Woodland period (Bendremer 1993; McBride 1984). Perhaps, as Mulholland suggested, there was a relationship between inland horticultural people and coastal/estuary people in New England. Small quantities of maize have been found at coastal sites while modest quantities of marine shell have been found at inland sites along the Connecticut River. Perhaps these commodities were being exchanged in the Connecticut River valley during the Selden Creek phase (Williams and Bendremer 1995). In the Niantic phase, however, changes in the lower Connecticut River valley and adjacent coastal areas may indicate the adoption, or intensification, of maize horticulture.

There may be some similarities, however, between Selden Creek phase sites in the middle Connecticut River valley and later Niantic phase sites in southern Connecticut. Thin-walled globular vessels, with some of the characteristics of Niantic ware, appear in the middle Connecticut River valley well before they appear in the lower Connecticut River valley (Lavin 1988a; Lavin et al. 1992-93). In addition, if the advent of thin-walled globular ceramics, present by the fourteenth century in the middle valley, are associated with the presence of maize processing (Braun 1980; McBride 1992), then perhaps some of the Niantic and Hackney Pond seasonal camps in the lower Connecticut River valley are the "farmsteads" mentioned in the ethnohistorical record (Snow 1980). Since the best agricultural lands in the lower Connecticut River valley are located inland from the Connecticut River (McBride 1984, 1992), these farmsteads may have replaced the warm-weather, semi-permanent village sites of the Selden Creek phase which were located near important riverine and estuary resources.

## GENDER, SCHEDULING AND SUBSISTENCE

Indigenous societies of New England, like European societies, maintained a division of labor based upon gender and age. Men, for the most part, engaged in year-round hunting activities (Banks et. al. 1988), especially fall and early winter white-tailed-deer-hunting activities and warfare (Salwen 1978; Van der Donck 1968 [1656]; Wassenaur 1909 [1624]). Women, on the other hand, primarily gathered wild plant foods, planted and harvested crops, built and maintained shelters, butchered meat, made clothes, and reared children (Salwen 1978; Van der Donck 1968 [1656]; Wassenaur 1909 [1624]; Williams 1963 [1643]; Wood 1977 [1634]). In coastal areas, men engaged in the procurement of large, marine and riverine vertebrates (both fish and mammals), while women generally collected shallow water invertebrates (Claassen 1991; Verrazzano 1970 [1524-1528]; Williams 1963 [1643]). Inland men's hunting activities were limited, for the most part, to terrestrial mammals.

Yet sex roles were not rigid, as women would also engage in hunting activities, such as drives (De Vries 1909 [1642]; Salwen 1978; Simmons 1978), and men would cut and arrange house poles (Simmons 1978), as well as help clear agricultural land and plant and tend the tobacco crop (Salwen 1978; Simmons 1978; Williams 1963 [1643]). Certain kinds of fishing, particularly during anadromous fish runs, may have been a substantially communal activity (Starna 1990).

The most striking differences between the coastal and inland subsistence strategies were the degree of sedentism exhibited by the occupations and the extent to which these people relied on maize horticulture versus marine and estuary resources, especially shellfish. Although shellfish have sometimes been deemed nutritionally unim-

portant (Cohen 1977), they can comprise an important part of the diet (Borgstrom 1962; Suttles 1968; Waselkov 1982) and contain higher levels of iodine, thiamin, sodium, and minerals critical to human development than terrestrial mammals and wild plant foods (Klippel and Morey 1986). These important resources were gathered, for the most part, by women (Williams 1963 [1643]). Shellfish, furthermore, appear to have constituted a significant component of the subsistence base of Late Woodland, sedentary coastal villages. Thus, the settlement pattern we observe in Southern New England is not surprising because, according to optimal foraging models, "women's foraging activities by and large determine time and frequency of residential mobility" (Kelly 1992:47). This is so because locally gathered resources are exploited and exhausted more quickly than widespread, mobile, hunted resources (Williams and Bendremer 1995).

In coastal areas, rich marine and estuary resources were capable of sustaining relatively large, permanent village occupations where productive, arable soils were scarce and more widely dispersed (Ceci 1982; George and Bendremer 1995). In inland riverine areas, maize horticulture was a more attractive option because of the absence of rich marine resources and the presence of extensive, highly productive, alluvial floodplains (Bendremer 1993). It is possible that intensive maize horticulture would have caused significant scheduling conflicts for coastal women who were primarily engaged in the procurement of more reliable gathered plant and animal resources. Yet inland women may have adopted maize horticulture as a component of their highly diverse subsistence strategy because of the availability of excellent agricultural land and the absence of a reliable, dense, warm-weather resource base. This resulting subsistence system, alternately referred to as tethered mobility (Heckenberger et. al. 1992), foraging horticulturalists (Mulholland 1988), conditional sedentism (Dunford 1992), or mobile farmers (Graham 1994), has rarely been described in the archaeological literature. It seems possible, however, that the adoption of this subsistence strategy would have produced few distinguishing markers in archaeological sites other than the presence, quantity, and variety of cultigens. And even though the overall contribution to caloric intake might have been relatively modest, maize horticulture may still have been an economically and ideologically important activity at inland riverine sites and became even more important throughout the region in the post-contact period.

## POST CONTACT CHANGES IN HORTICULTURE AND REGIONAL ADAPTATIONS

During the early Contact period in New England, maize was an important food staple. The earliest ethnohistorical observation of horticulture in Southern New England comes from Verrazzano (1970 [1524-1528]), who observed planted fields in coastal Rhode Island in 1524. Furthermore, Block (1909 [1614]) observed maize planted on the floodplain of the Middle Connecticut River in 1614. Block observed "few inhabitants" near the mouth of the river but observed "numerous" inhabitants (called "Sequins" and "Nawaas"), large villages, and associated maize fields, upriver in the middle Connecticut River valley (Block 1909 [1630]). A substantial quantity of maize was discovered at the roughly contemporaneous Tubbs site in Niantic, Connecticut (Russell 1947). These early observations of maize horticulture are consistent with McBride and Bellantoni's (1982) assertion that the changes observed at the beginning of the Niantic phase occurred independent of European contact. Probably some of the changes seen at the beginning of the Niantic phase (A.D. 1500-1600), such as the advent of small, long-term seasonal camps and the increased production of globular vessels (McBride 1984), may be partly the result of the adoption or intensification of maize horticulture by people of the lower Connecticut River valley and coastal areas.

It is interesting to note that the different settlement and subsistence systems discussed earlier roughly correspond to the historic territories of the Connecticut tribes at the time of contact: (1) Nipmunk in the northeast hills; (2) Pequot and Mohegan in the eastern coastal zone and lower Connecticut River valley; (3) Podunk, Wangunk, and numerous other river tribes in the middle Connecticut River valley; and (4) Manessis on Block Island. The correlation between pre-contact settlement and subsistence systems, post-contact political and social systems, and environment represents an appreciable degree of continuity from the Late Woodland through the early Colonial period.

In the Thames and Mystic River drainages, large palisaded Pequot and Mohegan villages appeared soon after European contact, during the Hackney Pond phase (A.D. 1600-1700). Similarly fortified villages mentioned in the ethnohistorical record include (1) Podunk Village reported in the middle Connecticut River valley (Block 1909 [1630]); (2) Narragansett villages in southern Rhode Island (Salwen 1978); and (3) "Manisses" villages on Block Island (Bellantoni 1987). Fortified villages appear to have been entirely absent from the lower Connecticut River valley. This suggests that, by the seventeenth century, there was increased warfare, territoriality, population, and/or social complexity in the middle Connecticut River valley, the coastal region, and Block Island. The fortified villages in the coastal zones were sustained by hunting, gathering, and intensive maize horticulture. In addition, wampum manufacturing and the fur trade with Europeans colonists were important economic activities (Ceci 1982, 1990). During the Hackney Pond phase, the coast of eastern Connecticut was inhabited by the Pequot and Mohegan tribes. These dominant tribes had tributary relationships with smaller subordinate tribes (Mulholland 1988). At this time, the lower Connecticut River valley was under the control of the Western Nehantic and Pequot tribes and, later, the Mohegan Tribe. Maize horticulture also became an important subsistence activity on Block Island by the Hackney Pond phase when a sedentary, fortified village was established on the island (Bellantoni 1987). Adjustments in the scheduling of women's activities must have occurred in order to accommodate the intensification of maize agriculture as well as continued warm-weather shellfishing.

The ethnohistorical record indicates that in historic times maize was an important Native

American food crop, which constituted a significant portion of the diet. Planted in May or early June, maize was generally harvested in September but was also consumed early or "green" (Russell 1980; Thomas 1976). Maize was stored in subterranean pits often lined with bark or grass (Mourt 1967 [1622]; Morton 1937 [1669]; Wood 1977 [1643]; Gookin 1792 [1674]). The discoveries at the Burnham-Shepard and Morgan sites suggest that there is considerably continuity in these technologies from pre- to post-contact times.

According to ethnohistorical documents, beans were cultivated with maize and were an important food crop. Ethnohistorical sources recorded their kidney-bean appearance (Gookin 1792 [1674]; Johnson 1974 [1654]; Williams 1963 [1643]; O'Callaghan 1848; Mourt 1967 [1622]; Josselyn 1988 [1674]).

## Subterranean Food Storage Technology

Subterranean storage pits have been reported in ethnohistorical accounts and discovered in the archaeology of many areas in North America, including New England. Storage pits may differ in content, shape, size, depth, association with structures, and lining material. Materials used in the linings of storage pits often included bark (Bushnell 1919; Densmore 1929; Hagen 1958; Hall 1962; Kinietz 1965; Lehmer 1954; Parker 1968; Smith 1972), grass (Bendremer et. al. 1991; Bushnell 1922; Fletcher and LaFlesche 1911; Harrington 1960; Krause 1972; Lehmer 1954; Ritchie and Funk 1973; Will and Hyde 1917; Will and Spinden 1906; Wilson 1917), or both bark and grass (Dragoo 1971; Mills 1904, 1906; Ritchie 1934; Ritchie and Funk 1973).

Although little has been written about the technology associated with food storage among prehistoric peoples of New England, there is evidence of the subterranean storage of *Chenopodium* as early as the Late Archaic period (ca. 2,000-1,400 B.C.) in South Windsor, Connecticut, in the middle Connecticut River valley (McBride 1978). The evidence includes the discovery of weevil remains of the genus *Sitophilus*, associated with *Chenopodium*. These weevils are known as obligate consumers of stored grains (McBride 1978).

The Burnham-Shepard site is characteristic of semi-permanent Late Woodland horticultural camps in the middle Connecticut River valley. With an average volume of $0.56 \text{ m}^3$, most of the 12 storage pits discovered at the Burnham-Shepard site had a relatively small volume compared to those described by Schroedl (1980) for the post-contact Cherokee settlements of Chota and Tanasee. However, these features do appear to be similar in size to those described in the ethnohistorical record for New England. These pits are associated with substantial quantities of domesticated macrobotanical remains as well as a variety of wild plant remains. Subterranean storage features are also a significant characteristic of Late Woodland coastal sites, but these coastal features contain little or no evidence for the storage of domesticated plants.

According to early ethnohistorical accounts, food storage continued to be an important component of aboriginal life in the Historic period (Bradford 1989 [1650]; Champlain 1966 [1625]; Mourt 1967 [1622]; Wood 1977 [1634]). Perhaps it was mentioned frequently because Europeans often stole what stored foods they discovered. Bradford (1989 [1650]) and Mourt (1967) [1622] described the pilfering of Indian storage facilities near Massachusetts Bay Colony.

The New England Indians generally stored food in subterranean storage pits. Wood (1977 [1634]) described these "barnes" as "great holes digged into the ground in forme of a brasse pot, sealed with rinds of trees." This account suggested that some of these pits may have had constricted openings (bottle shaped) and were lined with bark. Morton (1937 [1669]) wrote, "[T]heir barnes are holes made in the earth that will hold a hogshead of corne a peece in them. In these ... they lay their store in great baskets ... with mats under about the sides and on top: and ... they cover it with earth." The use of basketry, mats, and/or woven bags (Champlain 1966 [1625]) is commonly mentioned in these accounts. Bradford (1989 [1650]), Governor of Plymouth Colony, noted, "their stores of corn are contained in great hempen bags, capable of holding five or six bushels." The sizes of these caches varied. Morton's (1937 [1669]) account described contents equivalent to $0.27 \text{ m}^3$ or about 7.88 bushels

(Winchester bushel), although Bradford (1989 [1650]) described a more modest 0.18 m$^3$ to 0.21 m$^3$. Other accounts mentioned bags of maize with three (0.11 m$^3$) or four (0.14 m$^3$) bushels (Russell 1980). Food was also occasionally stored above ground in what English sources described as a "corn crib" (DeForest 1851). It is likely that beans, squash, nuts, tubers, meats, and fish were stored along with maize in these storage facilities (Russell 1980).

## Planting and Fields

The late spring was a time to clear fields, chop the underbrush or weedy growth, and then burn the fields on a calm day (Aupaumut 1824). The burning provided the ground with phosphoric acid and potash, which increase soil fertility. Later, maize, beans, and/or squash were planted in hillocks (Champlain 1966 [1625]; de Rasieres 1909 [1628]; Winthrop 1908 [1678]), some of which could still be observed in the twentieth century (Delabarre and Wilder 1920; Hallowell 1921). Recently, maize mounds have also been identified archaeologically on Cape Cod (Currie 1994; Mrozowski 1994). The Indians around Springfield, Massachusetts, began their year with a month which corresponded to part of April and May called "squannikesos" or "when they set Indian corne" (Pynchon in Thomas 1976). Even the earliest records mentioned both horticulture and burnings (Verrazzano 1970 [1524-1528]).

The Pequots generally spent the summer in larger seasonally occupied villages with little mobility and minimal dispersion (Starna 1990). Maize cultivation necessitated staying close to the villages in summer, although fishing trips and other special purpose expeditions, mostly by men, were also undertaken at this time. The importance of maize cultivation is emphasized in the names of the months used in the aboriginal Agawam calendar described by William Pynchon and reproduced below from Thomas (1976).

### Pynchon Calendar

(1) *squannikesos* - part of Aprill and pt. of May, when they set Indian corne.

(2) *msonesqua n nimock kesos* - pt. of May and June, when ... women weed their corn.

(3) *tow wa kesos* - pt. of June and July, when they hill indian corne.

(4) *matterl la naw kesos* - when squashes are ripe and Indian beans begin to be eatable.

(5) *mi cheen mee kesos* - when Ind corne is eatable.

(6) *pa[s] qui taqunk kesos* - ye midle between harvest and eating Ind corne.

(7) *pap pe narr* - bec: of white frost on ye grass and g[round].

(8) *qunnikesos* - bec: of white frost on ye grass and g[round].

(9) *pap sap qhoho*, or about the 6th of January. Lonatanassick: so called bec: they account it to be the midle of winter.

(10) *squo chee kesos* - bec ye sun hath [not] strength to thaw.

(11) *wapicummilcon* - pt. of febuary and part of march, bec. ye ice in ye River is all gone.

(12) *namossack kesos* - pt. of march and pt. of Aprill, bec of catching fish.

After the harvest, smaller nut-gathering/ hunting camps were established by small family bands (Cronon 1983). Sites like these have been identified for the Late Woodland period in the middle Connecticut River valley. The recent harvest and the abundance of gathered fall plant foods usually meant that this was a time of plenty (Thomas 1976). At this time, migrating water fowl might also be taken (Bradford 1989 [1650]).

The winter was a time when stored foods and meat from hunting were consumed. Ethnohistorical sources indicate that in winter, there was movement by coastal groups away from the coast to warmer inland valleys (Cronon 1983). Although some ethnohistorical sources indicate that winter was a time of larger village occupations in the interior (Thomas 1976), only smaller upland camps have been discovered archaeologically in the lower Connecticut River valley and coastal areas (McBride 1984).

Food scarcity was common in the spring when the stored foods of fall were depleted and few resources were available (Cronon 1983; Higginson 1846 [1630]; Morton 1937 [1669]). It is at this time that spring fishing and fowling camps were established to exploit the first anadromous fish runs of March (as indicated in the Pynchon calendar) and migrating bird species (Starna 1990; Thomas 1976).

The principle variety of maize was almost certainly an eight-rowed Northern Flint like those discovered in pre-contact archaeological sites and described by John Winthrop Jr. in 1678 (1908): "The ear is for the most part, about a span long (nine inches), composed of several, commonly 8 rows of grains, or more, according to the goodness of the ground; and in each row, usually above 30 grains." Although men and women cleared the fields together, the women would plant, cultivate, and harvest the crops (Williams 1963 [1643]). Planting began in late April (Mourt 1967 [1622]) or May (Rasle 1991 [1689-1723]), and harvesting occurred in August and September. Mature maize was husked and dried (Morton 1937 [1669]) and stored in subterranean pits (Mourt 1967 [1622]; Wood 1977 [1634]), although immature "green" maize was also consumed, probably in July or August (Russell 1980). Fields were cleared by burning (Morton 1937 [1669]). They could be planted for eight to ten years (Wood 1977 [1634]) and, subsequently, left fallow to restore fertility (Winthrop 1908 [1678]).

Maize was usually ground and consumed in a stew or porridge with meat, fish, tubers, nuts, and/or vegetables (Gookin 1968 [1792]; Williams 1963 [1643]). Ground corn meal could also be made into boiled unleavened biscuits, "corn cakes" (Gookin 1968 [1792]) or "flat cakes" roasted in hot coals (De Vries 1909 [1642]). These cakes may have been like those discovered at the Indian River and Muskrat Hill sites (Bendremer and Dewar 1993; Warner 1972). Sometimes a roasted corn meal, called "nocake" by the Nipmunk and Massachusett (Gookin 1968 [1792]; Wood 1977 [1634]), and "nokehick" by the Narragansett (Williams 1963 [1643]), was made by parching maize in hot ashes. Afterwards, the ashes were sifted out, and the roasted maize was finely ground. Both beans, and squash were used as a "vegetable," cooked and added to maize and other available wild food stuffs (Wood 1977 [1634]). Beans were harvested in August and September (Russell 1980).

## CONCLUSION

Late Woodland food-production strategies varied considerably across Southern New England. In coastal areas, larger sedentary villages were sustained with local marine and estuary resources and little apparent reliance upon maize horticulture. In these areas, a broad variety of wild plant and animal resources were exploited. Shellfish-collecting was an important women's activity in coastal regions, providing a reliable food source unavailable in inland areas, and may have presented a scheduling conflict with maize horticulture. By the Final Woodland period (ca. A.D. 1500-1600), more intensive maize horticulture was adopted by coastal groups. It was also at this time that more globular, collared pottery styles were adopted, which was much later than their introduction in the middle Connecticut River valley (Lavin 1988a; Lavin et al. 1992-93). These changes occurred near the time of European contact but were not necessarily a result of contact.

Maize horticulture was a notable component of the Late Woodland subsistence system in inland riverine zones. Large storage features, containing significant quantities and several types of cultigens, have been discovered in sites located on, or near, the large alluvial floodplains of the middle Connecticut River valley and other river systems. Globular, collared pottery also occurred here earlier. These sites appear to have been only three-season, semi-permanent hamlets, which in some ways resemble settlement patterns observed elsewhere (see Hart and Asch Sidell 1996). Winter sites are located in higher, more sheltered locations. Temporary and task-specific sites, associated with the exploitation of upland resources, are located as far as 28 km from the Connecticut River. Permanent, fortified villages along the Connecticut River appeared during the Final Woodland, while maize horticulture further intensified.

Apart from the two patterns described above, there is an independent, upland, hunter-gatherer subsistence and settlement system in eastern Connecticut with no evidence of maize horticulture (Bendremer 1993). These Late Woodland settlement and subsistence systems roughly correspond to the historic territories of the Connecticut tribes such as the Nipmunks, Pequots and Mohegans, Podunk, and other river tribes, and the Manessis. Pre-contact settlement and subsistence systems, as parts of indigenous political/social systems and situated in varying environments, exhibit an appreciable degree of continuity from the Late Woodland through the early Colonial period.

More details about subregional variation in subsistence and settlement systems will certainly come to light with further research. It is particularly important that we devise methods to assess subsistence strategies and add to the superficial database we now possess. In addition, archaeologists must realize that they can no longer paint native New England societies of the past with such broad brush strokes. Contemporaneous subsistence systems can, even in a relatively small region, be quite different from each other. These systems can also change significantly in relatively short periods of time. Only from careful, regional analyses can such complex and varied patterns be fully recognized.

## REFERENCES CITED

Aupaumut, H. 1824. *First Annual Report of the American Society for Promoting Civilization and General Improvement of the Indian Tribes of the United States.* New Haven.

Banks, M. 1990. Aboriginal Fish Weirs in Southern New England. *Bulletin of the Archaeological Society of Connecticut* 53:73-83.

Banks, M., J. C. M. Bendremer, and N. Bellantoni. 1988. A Comparison of White-Tailed Deer Processing at Two Coastal Contact Period Sites in Connecticut. Paper presented at the 2nd Annual Faunal Analysis Conference, Princeton University, Princeton.

Barber, R. J. 1983. Diversity in Shell Middens: The View from Morrill Point. *Man in the Northeast* 25:109-125.

Bellantoni, N. 1987. *Faunal Resource Availability and Prehistoric Cultural Selection on Block Island, Rhode Island.* Unpublished Ph.D. dissertation, Department of Anthropology, University of Connecticut, Storrs.

Bendremer, J. C. M. 1993. *Late Woodland Settlement and Subsistence in Eastern Connecticut.* Unpublished Ph.D. dissertation, Department of Anthropology, University of Connecticut, Storrs.

Bendremer, J. C. M., and R. E. Dewar. 1994. The Advent of Maize Horticulture in New England. In *Corn and Culture in the Prehistoric New World*, edited by S. Johannessen and C. A. Hastorf, pp. 369-393. Westview Press, Boulder.

Bendremer, J. C. M., E. Kellogg, and T. B. Largy. 1991. A Grass-Lined Storage Pit and Early Maize Horticulture in Central Connecticut. *North American Archaeologist* 12:325-349.

Bernstein, D. J. 1988. *Prehistoric Subsistence at Greenwich Cove, Rhode Island.* Unpublished Ph.D. dissertation, Department of Anthropology, State University of New York, Binghamton.

————. 1990. Trends in Prehistoric Subsistence on the Southern New England Coast: The View From Narragansett Bay. *North American Archaeologist* 11:321-352.

————. 1992a. Prehistoric Use of Plant Foods in the Narragansett Bay Region. *Man in the Northeast* 44:1-13.

————. 1992b. Prehistoric Seasonality Studies in Coastal Southern New England. *American Anthropologist* 9:96-115.

Block, A. 1909 [1614]. From the New World. Johannes De Laet. In *Narratives of New Netherlands*, edited by J. F. Jameson. Charles Scribner's Sons, New York.

Borgstrom, G. 1962. Shellfish Protein-Nutritive Aspects. In *Fish as Food*, vol 2, adapted by G. Borgstrom, pp. 115-139. Academic Press, New York.

Bradford, W. 1989 [1650]. *Of Plymouth Plantation, 1620-1647*, edited by S. E. Morrison. Alfred A. Knopf, New York.

Braun, D. P. 1980. Experimental Interpretations of Ceramic Vessel Use on the Basis of Rim and Neck Attributes. In *The Navaho Project: Archaeological Investigations Page to Phoenix 500 KV Southern Transmission Line*, edited by D. C. Feiron. Research Paper 1. Museum of Northern Arizona, Research Paper, Flagstaff.

Brewer, A. 1973. Analysis of Floral Remains from the Higgs Site (40LD45). In *Excavation of the Higgs and Doughty Sites: I-75 Salvage Archaeology*, edited by M. C. R. McCollough and C. H. Faulkner. Miscellaneous Paper 12. Tennessee Archaeological Society, Knoxville.

Bushnell, D. J. 1919. Native Villages and Village Sites. *Bulletin of the Bureau of American Ethnology* 69. Smithsonian Institution, Washington, D.C.

————. 1922. Villages West of the Mississippi. *Bulletin of the Bureau of American Ethnology 77.* Smithsonian Institution, Washington, D.C.

Carlson, C.C. 1988. "Where's the Salmon?" A Reevaluation of the Role of Anadromous Fisheries in Aboriginal New England. In *Holocene Human Ecology in Eastern North America.* edited by G.P. Nicholas, pp. 47-80. Plenum Press, New York.

Ceci, L. 1979-80. Maize Cultivation in Coastal New York: The Archaeological, Agronomical, and Documentary Evidence. *North American Archaeologist* 1:45-73.

————. 1982. Method and Theory in Coastal New York Archaeology: Paradigms of Settlement Pattern. *North American Archaeologist* 3:5-36.

————. 1990. Radiocarbon Dating "Village" Sites in Coastal New York: Settlement Pattern Change in the Middle to Late Woodland. *Man in the Northeast* 39:1-28.

Cerrato, R. 1987. Microgrowth Line Analysis of Hard Clams from the Sungic Midden Site (2N3E 1-0), Shelter Island, New York. In *The Prehistoric Hunter-Gatherers of Shelter Island, New York: An Archaeological Study of the Mashomack Preserve*, edited by K. G. Lightfoot, R. Kalin, and J. Moore. Contributions to the Archaeological Research Faculty 46. University of California, Berkeley.

Champlain, S. de. 1966 [1625]. *Voyages of Samuel de Champlain*. Translated from the French by C. P. Otis. Burt Franklin, New York.

Claassen, C. P. 1991. Gender, Shellfishing, and the Shell Mound Archaic. In *Engendering Archaeology: Women and Prehistory*, edited by J. Gero and M. Conkey, pp. 276-300. Blackwell, Cambridge.

Coffin, C. C. 1940. Excavations in Southwest Connecticut. *Bulletin of the Archaeological Society of Connecticut* 10:33-49.

Cohen, M. N. 1977. *The Food Crisis in Prehistory.* Yale University Press, New Haven. Connecticut Archaeological Survey

Connecticut Archaeological Survey. 1979. A Preliminary Inventory of Archaeological Sites in Connecticut. Manuscripts available at the Connecticut Historical Commission, Hartford.

Crites, G. D. 1993. Domesticated Sunflower in Fifth Millennium B.P. Temporal Context: New Evidence from Middle Tennessee. *American Antiquity* 58:146-148.

Cronon, W. 1983. *Changes in the Land: Indian Colonists, and the Ecology of New England*. Hill and Wang, New York.

Currie, D. R. 1994. Micromorphology of a Native American Cornfield. *Archaeology of Eastern North America* 22:63-72.

DeForest, J. W. 1851. *History of the Indians of Connecticut from the Earliest Known Times to 1850.* W.J. Hammersley, Hartford.

Delabarre, E. B., and H. H. Wilder. 1920. Indian Corn Hills in Massachusetts. *American Anthropologist* 22:203-225.

De Lait, J. 1909 [1630]. From the New World. In *Narratives of New Netherlands*, edited by J. F. Jameson. Charles Scribner and Sons, New York.

Demeritt, D. 1991. Agriculture, Climate, and Cultural Adaptation in the Prehistoric Northeast. *Archaeology of Eastern North America* 19:183-202.

Densmore, F. 1929. Chippewa Customs. *Bulletin of the Bureau of American Ethnology* 86. Smithsonian Institution, Washington, D.C..

De Rasieres, I. 1909 [1628]. Letter of Isaack de Rasieres to Samual Bloommaert. In *Narratives of New Netherlands*, edited by J. F. Jameson. pp. 97-113. Charles Scribner and Sons, New York.

De Vries, D. [1633-1643 [1655]] 1909. Korte Historiael Ende Journaels Aenteyckeninge. In *Narratives of New Netherlands*, edited by J. F. Jameson, pp.181-234. Charles Scribner's Sons, New York.

Dincauze, D. F. 1990. A Capsule Prehistory of Southern New England. In *The Pequot: The Fall and Rise of an American Indian Nation*, edited by L. Hauptman and J. Wherry, pp. 19-32. University of Oklahoma Press, Norman.

Dirrigl, F. J., and N. F. Bellantoni. 1993. Comparison of Faunal Assemblages from Fisher's Island, New York and Block Island, Rhode Island. Paper presented at the 33rd Annual Meeting of the North Eastern Anthropological Association, Danbury, Connecticut.

Dragoo, D. W. 1971. The Johnston Site. In *Foundations of Pennsylvania Prehistory*, edited by B. C. Kent, I. F. Smith, and C. McCann, pp. 556-559. Anthropological Series. Pennsylvania Historical Commission, Harris-burg.

Dunford, F. J. 1992. Conditional Sedentism: The Logistical Flexibility of Estuarine Settlements in Circumscribed Environments. Paper presented at the 57th Annual Meeting of the Society for American Archaeology, Pittsburgh.

Feder, K. L. 1984. Pots, Plants and People: The Late Woodland Period in Connecticut. *Bulletin of the Archaeological Society of Connecticut* 47:99-111.

Fletcher, A. C., and F. LaFlesche. 1911. *The Omaha Tribe*. Bulletin of the Bureau of American Ethnology, Twenty-seventh Annual Report. Smithsonian Institution, Washington, D.C.

Ford, R. I. 1985. Patterns of Prehistoric Food Production in North America. In *Prehistoric Food Production in North America*, edited by R. I. Ford, pp. 341-364. Anthropological Papers No. 75. Museum of Anthropology, University of Michigan, Ann Arbor.

Fritz, G. J. 1986. *Prehistoric Ozark Agriculture: The University of Arkansas Rockshelter Collections*. Unpublished Ph.D. dissertation. Department of Anthropology, University of North Carolina, Chapel Hill.

Galinat, W. C. 1985. Domestication and Diffusion of Maize. In *Prehistoric Food Production in North America*, edited by R. I. Ford, pp. 245-278. Anthropological Papers No. 75. Museum of Anthropology, University of Michigan, Ann Arbor.

George, D. R., and J. C. M. Bendremer. 1995. Late Woodland Subsistence and the Origins of Maize Horticulture in New England. Paper presented at the 60th Annual Meeting of the Society for American Archaeology, Minneapolis.

Gookin, D. 1968 [1792]. Historical Collections of Indians in New England. *Collections of the Massachusetts Historical Society Collections, for the Year 1792* 1:141-227. Reprinted 1968, Johnson Reprint Corporation, New York.

Graham, M. 1994. *Mobile Farmers: An Ethnoarchaeological Approach to Settlement Organization among the Raramuri of Northwestern Mexico*. International Monographs in Prehistory, Ethnoarchaeological Series 3. Ann Arbor.

Hagen, W. T. 1958. *The Sac and Fox Indians*. University of Oklahoma Press, Norman.

Hall, R. L. 1962. *The Archaeology of Carcajou Point*. University of Wisconsin Press, Madison.

Hallowell, A. I. 1921. Indian Corn Hills. *American Anthropologist* 23:233.

Hancock, M. 1982. *The Determination of Archaeological Site Seasonality Using the Remains of* Mya arenaria: *Examples from the Maine Coast*. Unpublished Master's thesis, Department of Anthropology, University of Maine, Orono.

Harrington, M. R. 1960. *Ozark Bluff Dwellers*. Indian Notes and Monographs 12. Museum of the American Indian, Heye Foundation.

Hart, J. P., and N. Asch Sidell. 1996. Prehistoric Agricultural Systems in the West Branch of the Susquehanna River Basin, A.D. 800 to A.D. 1350. *Northeast Anthropology* 52:1-30.

————. 1997. Additional Evidence for Early Cucurbit Use in the Northern Eastern Woodlands East of the Allegheny Front. *American Antiquity* 62:523-537.

Hastorf, C. A., and V. S. Popper (editors). 1988. *Current Paleoethnobotany: Analytical Methods and Cultural Interpretations of Archaeological Plant Remains*. University of Chicago Press, Chicago.

Heckenberger, M. J., J. B. Petersen, and N. Asch Sidell. 1992. Early Evidence of Maize Agriculture in the Connecticut River Valley of Vermont. *Archaeology of Eastern North America* 20:125-149.

Higginson, F. 1846 [1630]. New England's Plantation, London. *Collections of the Massachusetts Historical Society*, 1792, pp. 117-124. Boston.

Johnson, E. [1654] 1974. Wonder Working Providence of Sions Savior, London. In *Johnson's Wonderworking Providence, 1628-1651*, edited by J.F. Trumball, pp. 23-143. New York.

Josselyn, J. 1988 [1674]. *John Josselyn, Colonial Traveler: A Critical Edition of an Account of Two Voyages to New England Made during the Years 1638 and 1663*, edited by P. J. Lindholdt. University Press of New England, Hanover.

Keegan, W. F. (editor). 1987. *Emergent Horticultural Economies of the Eastern Woodlands*. Center for Archaeological Investigations, Occasional Papers No. 7. Southern Illinois University at Carbondale.

Kelly, R. L. 1992. Mobility/Sedentism: Concepts, Archaeological Measures and Effects. *Annual Review of Anthropology* 21:43-66.

Kerber, J. E. 1985. Digging For Clams: Shell Midden Analysis in New England. *North American Archaeologist* 6:97-113.

Kinietz, W. V. 1965. *The Indians of the Western Great Lakes, 1615-1760*. University of Michigan Press, Ann Arbor.

Klippel, W. E. and D. F. Morey. 1986. Contextual and Nutritional Analysis of Freshwater Gastropods from Middle Atlantic Deposits at the Hays Site, Middle Tennessee. *American Antiquity* 51:799-813.

Krause, R. A. 1972. *The Leavenworth Site: Archaeology of a Historic Arikara Community*. Publications in Anthropology 3. University of Kansas, Lawrence.

Lavin, L. 1988a. The Morgan Site, Rocky Hill, Connecticut: A Late Woodland Farming Community in the Connecticut River Valley. *Bulletin of the Archaeological Society of Connecticut* 51:7-21.

————. 1988b. Coastal Adaptations in Southern New England and Southern New York. *Archaeology of Eastern North America* 16:101-120.

Lavin, L., F. Gudrian, and L. Miroff 1992-93. Pottery Production and Cultural Process: Prehistoric Ceramics from the Morgan Site. *Northeastern Historical Archaeology* 21-22:44-63.

Lechford, T. 1969 [1642]. *Plain Dealing or News From New England*, edited by D. B. Rutman. Johnson Reprint Co., New York

Lehmer, D. J. 1954. Archaeological Investigations in the Oahe Dam Area, South Dakota. *Bulletin of the Bureau of American Ethnology* 158. Smithsonian Institution, Washington, D.C.

Lightfoot, K. G., and R. M. Cerrato. 1988. Prehistoric Shellfish Exploitation in Coastal New York. *Journal of Field Archaeology* 15:141-149.

McBride, K. A. 1978. Archaic Subsistence in the Lower Connecticut River Valley: Evidence from Woodchuck Knoll. *Man in the Northeast* 15/16:124-131.

————. 1984. *The Archaeology of the Lower Connecticut River Valley*. Unpublished Ph.D. dissertation, Department of Anthropology, University of Connecticut, Storrs.

————. 1992. Prehistoric and Historic Patterns of Wetland Use in Eastern Connecticut. *Man in the Northeast* 43:10-23.

McBride, K. A., and N. Bellantoni. 1982. The Utility of Ethnohistoric Models for Understanding Late Woodland-Contact Change in Southern New England. *Bulletin of the Archaeological Society of Connecticut* 45:51-64.

McBride, K. A., and R. E. Dewar. 1987. Agriculture and Cultural Evolution: Causes and Effects in the Lower Connecticut River Valley. In *Emergent Horticultural Economies of the Eastern Woodlands*, edited by W. F. Keegan, pp. 305-328. Center for Archaeological Investigations, Occasional Papers No. 7. Southern Illinois University at Carbondale.

McCollough, M. C. R., and C. H. Faulkner (editors). 1973. *Excavation of the Higgs and Doughty Sites: I-75 Salvage Archaeology.* Miscellaneous Paper 12. Tennessee Archaeological Society, Knoxville.

McManamon, F. P. 1984. Prehistoric Cultural Adaptations and Their Evolution on Outer Cape Cod. In *Chapters in the Archaeology of Cape Cod,* edited by I. F. P. McManamon, pp. 339-413. Cultural Resource Management Study 8. National Park Service, Boston.

Mills, W. C. 1904. Explorations of the Gartner Mound and Village Site. *Ohio Archaeological and Historical Quarterly* 13:129-189.

—————. 1906. Exploration of the Baum Prehistoric Village Site. *Ohio Archaeological and Historical Quarterly* 15:44-136.

Morton, N. 1937 [1669]. *New England's Memoriall,* edited by H. J. Hall. Scholars Facsimiles and Reprints, New York.

Mourt, G. 1967 [1622]. *A Relation or Journal of the Beginning and Proceedings of the English Plantation Settled at Plymoth in New England.* Recreated with the permission of the Trustees of the Pequot Library, Southport, Connecticut.

Mrozowski, S. A. 1994. The Discovery of a Native American Cornfield on Cape Cod. *Archaeology of Eastern North America* 22:63-72.

Mulholland, M. T. 1988. Territoriality and Horticulture: A Perspective for Prehistoric Southern New England. In *Holocene Human Ecology in Northeastern North America,* edited by G. P. Nicholas, pp. 137-166. Plenum Press, New York.

O'Callaghan, E. B. 1848. *History of New Netherlands or New York Under the Dutch.* D. Appleton, New York.

Parker, A. C. 1968. *Parker on the Iroquois.* Edited with an introduction by W. N. Fenton. Syracuse University Press, Syracuse.

Powell, B. W. 1958. Preliminary Report on a Southwestern Connecticut Site. *Bulletin of the Archaeological Society of Connecticut* 28:12-29.

Praus, A. 1942. Excavations at the Old Lyme Shell Heap. *Bulletin of the Archaeological Society of Connecticut* 13:3-66.

Rasle, S. 1991. [1689-1723] Jesuit Relations. In *Dawnland Encounters: Indians and Europeans in Northern New England.* edited by C. G. Calloway, pp. 61-80. University Press of New England, Hanover.

Ritchie, W. A. 1934. An Algonkin-Iroquois Contact Site on Castle Creek, Broome County, N.Y. *Research Records of the Rochester Municipal Museum* 2:3-48.

Ritchie, W. A., and R. E. Funk. 1973. *Aboriginal Settlement Patterns in the Northeast.* Memoir 20, New York Museum and Science Service. The University of the State of New York, Albany.

Rosier, J. 1966 [1605]. *A True Relation of the Most Prosperous Voyage of Captain George Waymouth, 1605.* University Microfilms, Ann Arbor.

Russell, H. S. 1980. *Indian New England before the Mayflower.* University Press of New England, Hanover.

Russell, L. W. 1942. The Menunketisuck Site. *Bulletin of the Archaeological Society of Connecticut* 14:3-56.

—————. 1947. Indian Burials at Niantic, Connecticut. *Bulletin of the Archaeological Society of Connecticut* 21:39-43.

Salwen, B. 1978. Indians of Southern New England and Long Island: Early Period. In *Northeast,* edited by B. G. Trigger, pp. 160-176. Handbook of North American Indians, Vol. 15, W.C. Sturtevant, general editor. Smithsonian Institution, Washington, D.C.

Sanger, D. 1981. Unscrambling Messages in the Midden. *Archaeology of Eastern North America* 9:37-41.

—————. 1988. Maritime Adaptations in the Gulf of Maine. *Archaeology of Eastern North America* 16:81-100.

Schroedl, G. F. 1980. *Structures and Village Patterns at a Historic Overhill Cherokee Towns of Chota and Tanasee.* Paper presented at the 37th Annual Meeting of the Southeastern Archaeological Conference, New Orleans.

Silver, A. L. 1980. Comment of Maize Cultivation in Coastal New York. *North American Archaeologist* 2:117-130.

Simmons, W. S. 1978. The Narragansett. In *Northeast*, edited by B. G. Trigger, pp. 190-197. Handbook of North American Indians, Vol. 15, W. C. Sturtevant, general editor. Smithsonian Institution, Washington, D.C.

Smith, C. S. 1950. The Archaeology of Coastal New York. *Anthropological Papers of the American Museum of Natural History* 43(2):94-200.

Smith, J. E. 1972. *Like-a-Fishhook Village and Fort Berthold*, Garrison Reservoir, South Dakota. Anthropological Papers 2. National Park Service, Washington, D.C..

Smith, B. D. 1987. The Independent Domestication of Indigenous Seed-Bearing Plants in Eastern North America. In *Emergent Horticultural Economies of the Eastern Woodlands*, edited by W. F. Keegan, pp. 3-47. Center for Archaeological Investigations, Occasional Papers No. 7. Southern Illinois University at Carbondale.

————. 1989. Origins of Agriculture in Eastern North America. *Science* 246: 1566-1571.

————. 1992a. *Rivers of Change: Essays on Early Agriculture in Eastern North America*. Smithsonian Institution Press, Washington, D.C.

————. 1992b. Prehistoric Plant Husbandry in Eastern North America. In *Origins of Agriculture: An International Perspective*, edited by C. W. Cowan and P. J. Watson, pp. 101-119. Smithsonian Institution Press, Washington D.C.

————. 1995. *The Emergence of Agriculture*. Scientific American Library, New York.

Snow, D. 1980. *The Archaeology of New England*. Academic Press, New York.

Starna, W. A. 1990. The Pequots in the Early Seventeenth Century. *The Pequots in Southern New England: The Fall and Rise of an American Indian Nation*, edited by L. M. Hauptman and J. D. Wherry, pp. 33-47. University of Oklahoma Press, Norman.

Stewart, M. 1993. Comparison of Late Woodland Cultures: Delaware, Potomac and Susquehanna River Valleys, Middle Atlantic Region. *Archaeology of Eastern North America* 21:161-178.

Suttles, W. 1968. Coping with Abundance: Subsistence on the Northwest Coast. In *Man the Hunter*, edited by R. B. Lee and I. DeVore, pp. 56-68. Aldine-Atherton, Chicago.

Thomas, P. A. 1976. Contrastive Subsistence Strategies and Land Use as Factors for Understanding Indian-White Relations in New England. *Ethnohistory* 23:1-218.

Tveskov, M. A. 1992. *Early Woodland Settlement and Subsistence on Block Island, Rhode Island*. Unpublished Master's thesis, Department of Anthropology, University of Connecticut, Storrs.

Van der Donck, A. 1968 [1656]. *A Description of the New Netherlands*, edited T. F. O'Donnell. Syracuse University Press, Syracuse.

Verazzano, G. da. 1970 [1524-1528]. *The Voyages of Geovanni da Verrazzano*, edited by L. C. Wroth. Yale University Press, New Haven.

Warner, F. W. 1972. The Foods of the Connecticut Indians. *Bulletin of the Archaeology Society of Connecticut* 37:27-47.

Waselkov, G. 1987. Shellfish Gathering and Shell Midden Archaeology. In *Advances in Archaeological Method and Theory*, Vol. 10, edited by M. B. Schiffer, pp.93-210. Academic Press, New York.

Wassenaur, N. 1909 [1624-1630]. Historisch Verhael. In *Narratives of New Netherlands*, edited by J. F. Jameson, pp. 61-90. Charles Scribner's Sons, New York.

Will, G. F., and G. E. Hyde. 1917. *Corn Among the Indians of the Upper Missouri*. University of Nebraska Press, Lincoln.

Will, G. F., and H. J. Spinden. 1906. *The Mandans: A Study of Their Culture, Archaeology and Language*. Peabody Museum of American Archaeology and Ethnology Papers 3(4). Harvard University, Cambridge.

Williams, L. E. 1972. *Fort Shantok and Fort Corchaug: A Comparative Study of Seventeenth-Century Culture Contact in the Long Island Sound Area*. Unpublished Ph.D. dissertation, Department of Anthropology, New York University, New York.

Williams, M., and J. C. M. Bendremer. 1995. The Archaeology of Maize, Pots, and Seashells: Gender Dynamics in Late Woodland and Contact Period New England. In *Gender in Ancient America*, edited by C. Claassen and R. Joyce, pp. 146-149. Smithsonian Institution Press, Washington, D.C.

Williams, R. 1963 [1643]. *The Complete Writings of Roger Williams*. Russell and Russell, New York.

Wilson, G. L. 1917. *Agriculture of the Hidatsa Indians: An Indian Interpretation*. Studies in the Social Sciences 9. University of Minnesota, Minneapolis.

Winthrop, J. 1908 [1678]. *Winthrop's Journal: History of New England, 1630-1649*, edited by J. K. Hosmer. Charles Scribner and Sons, New York.

Wood, W. 1977 [1634]. *New England's Prospect*, edited by A. T. Vaughan. Commonwealth Series 3. University of Massachusetts Press, Amherst.

Yarnell, R. A. 1978. Domestication of Sunflower and Sumpweed in Eastern North America. In *The Nature and Status of Ethnobotany*, edited by R. I. Ford, pp. 289-299. Anthropological Papers No. 67, Museum of Anthropology, University of Michigan, Ann Arbor.

# CHAPTER 10

# MOBILE FARMERS OF PRE-CONTACT SOUTHERN NEW ENGLAND: THE ARCHAEOLOGICAL AND ETHNOHISTORIC EVIDENCE

Elizabeth S. Chilton

## INTRODUCTION

> *We cannot clearly see any dramatic changes in settlement distribution or size coincident with the adoption of maize horti-culture. Garden crops probably provided only dietary supplements, rather than eco-nomic staples* (Dincauze 1990:30).

> *The Late Woodland period is charac-terized by radical changes in indigenous lifeways. Large semi-permanent villages, maize horticulture, and extensive trade networks all become highly visible in the archaeological record* (Williams and Bendremer 1997:139).

It is generally accepted by New England archaeologists that maize horticulture (1) was introduced into Southern New England by A.D. 1000 (Dincauze 1990; Mulholland 1988), and (2) was not practiced to the same degree across the region (Bendremer, this volume; Cassedy and Webb, this volume; Chilton 1996; George and Bendremer 1995:14; Heckenberger et al. 1992). However, as the above quotes demonstrate, there is a general lack of agreement among New England archaeologists as to the predominance or importance of maize horticulture in the economies of native peoples during the Late Woodland period (1,000-400 B.P.) (Ceci 1979-80, 1990; Demeritt 1991; Silver 1980). While some researchers argue that the adoption of maize hor-ticulture in New England was a "non-event" (McBride and Dewar 1987), others assert that inland peoples practiced intensive horticulture (Bendremer 1993; Lavin 1988a). The significance of this debate is that the use of dichotomous mod-els (i.e., inland vs. coastal, and staple vs. supple-

ment) has impeded a broader understanding of local and regional diversity in subsistence-settle-ment systems. In this chapter, I explore this "maize debate" in Southern New England by reviewing (1) the major issues associated with the debate, (2) the ethnohistoric and archaeological evidence for Late Woodland subsistence and set-tlement, and (3) recent archaeological evidence of maize horticulture from the Pine Hill site in west-ern Massachusetts.

## THE MAIZE DEBATE

Almost 20 years ago, the maize debate in New England centered around whether there was evi-dence for intensive maize horticulture in coastal New England prior to European contact (Ceci 1979-80; Silver 1980). Today, the consensus in the published literature is that intensive maize horti-culture was *not* practiced on the coast until the Contact period or just before (Bernstein 1992, this volume; Little and Schoeninger 1995). The debate continues, however, over the role of maize in the subsistence systems of the interior valleys (Bendremer and Dewar 1994; Lavin 1988a; McBride and Dewar 1987).

One reason for the disagreement about the role of maize horticulture in the interior is a lack of clear archaeological evidence. As Dincauze (1981:58) noted, aboriginal farming is notoriously difficult to detect in New England because of poor preservation conditions. While techniques have improved in recent years, we are still basing our interpretations on scant evidence. For exam-ple, of the 39 sites shown in Figure 10.1 (see also Table 10.1), only four sites have direct radiocar-bon dates of maize (Cassedy and Webb, this vol-ume). Direct dates on maize are important in this context because they leave no doubt about the association between the maize itself and the

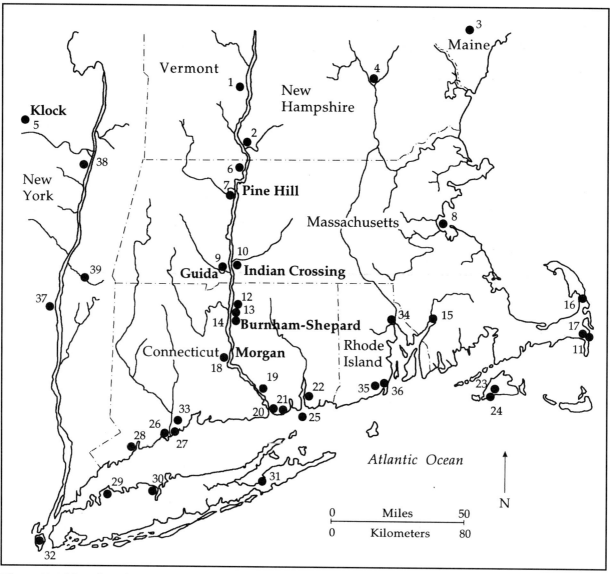

**Figure 10.1.** Map of southern New England, showing the location of archaeological sites with prehistoric cultigens and key sites referred to in the text.

radiocarbon age (Hart, this volume).

Aside from the dearth of evidence, the debate on the importance of maize horticulture has been fueled by (1) the improper and inconsistent use of terms such as "semi-permanent," "intensity," and "staple;" and (2) an improperly assumed correlation between the amount of preserved maize on an archaeological site and its importance in prehistoric subsistence systems. I discuss each of these in turn.

**Improper and Inconsistent Use of Terms**

One problem that both fuels and clouds the debate on the role of maize horticulture is the use of terms that are poorly defined. For example, Bendremer et al. (1991) interpret features and botanical remains at the Burnham-Shepard site as evidence for *"significant involvement* with maize horticulture during the fourteenth century in the southern portion of the Middle Connecticut Valley" (emphasis added; Bendremer, this volume). In this context, it is critical that "significant

**Table 10.1. Archaeological Sites with Prehistoric Cultigens in Southern New England.**

| Number in Figure 10.1 | Site Name | Citation |
|---|---|---|
| 1 | Skitchewaug | Heckenberger et al. 1992 |
| 2 | Fort Hill | Thomas 1979 |
| 3 | Early Fall | Cowie and Petersen 1990 |
| 4 | Campbell | Bunker, personal communication in Bendremer and Dewar 1994 |
| 5 | Klock | Kuhn and Funk 1994 |
| 6 | 19-FR-329 | Garman 1991 |
| 7 | Pine Hill | Chilton 1996 |
| 8 | Calf Island, Worlds End, HL-6 | Luedtke, personal communication in Bendremer and Dewar 1994 |
| 9 | Guida Farm | Byers and Rouse 1960 |
| 10 | Indian Crossing | Mulholland 1988 |
| 11 | Mattaquason Purchase | David Schafer, personal communication, 1997 |
| 12 | 6-HT-116 | Jordan, personal communication in Bendremer and Dewar 1994 |
| 13 | Kasheta | Bendremer et al. 1991 |
| 14 | Burnham-Shepard | Bendremer and Dewar 1994 |
| 15 | Gardner's Neck | Bunker, personal communication in Bendremer and Dewar 1994 |
| 16 | 19-BN-288 | McManamon 1984 |
| 17 | Malluzo | Dunford, personal communication in Bendremer and Dewar 1994 |
| 18 | Morgan | Lavin 1988a |
| 19 | Selden Island | McBride 1984 |
| 20 | Tubbs | Russell 1946 |
| 21 | Mago Point | McBride 1984 |
| 22 | 72-31 | McBride 1984 |
| 23 | Hornblower II | Ritchie 1969 |
| 24 | Lucy Vincent Beach | Chilton and Doucette 1997 |
| 25 | Barlow Pond, Hawk's Nest | Funk and Pfeiffer 1988 |
| 26 | Muskrat Hill | Coffin 1940 |
| 27 | Indian River | Rogers 1943 |
| 28 | Highland | Wiegand, personal communication in Bendremer and Dewar 1994 |
| 29 | Pleasant Hill | Ceci 1979-80 |
| 30 | Matinecock Point | Smith 1950 |
| 31 | Sebonac | Ceci 1979-80 |
| 32 | Bowman's Brook | Ceci 1979-80 |
| 33 | 294A-25-2, 294-AF2-1 | Millis et al. 1993 |
| 34 | RI 2050 | Handsman 1995; Leveillee 1996 |
| 35 | RI 1818 | Leveillee and Harrison 1996 |
| 36 | RI 110k | Leveillee and Harrison 1996 |
| 37 | Hurley | Funk 1976 |
| 38 | Dennis | Funk 1976 |
| 39 | 211-1-1 | Cassedy et al. 1993 |

involvement" be clearly defined. What does this mean in terms of the bulk of the diet, proportion of caloric intake, energy spent, or the organization of labor?

In the same vein, Lavin (1988a:19) has interpreted the evidence from the Morgan site, in the lower Connecticut River valley, as indicating that maize was an "important *staple* for *inland* Indians" (original emphasis). Are we to assume that a staple is something that is critical to the survival or well-being of a community? Does "important" refer to a dietary or cultural value? Heckenberger et al. (1992:137) also suggested that "[a]gricultural products had become an *integral* part of the diet by A.D. 1100" (emphasis added), even though they admitted that "wild plant foods significantly outnumber domesticates." They attributed this to the fact that most of the wild plant remains are inedible. It is clear that in order to come to a more complete understanding of the role of maize in the interior, we need to quantify plant remains in units that make sense for comparison, and we need to define all relative terms more precisely and be consistent in our use of such terms.

## Assumed Correlation between Numbers of Kernels and Proportion of Diet

Another hindrance to a fuller understanding of maize horticulture is the inference by many New England archaeologists that the quantity of maize and other cultigens found at an archaeological site is a reflection of the importance of that resource to the aboriginal inhabitants. For example, Bendremer and Dewar (1994:391) suggested that the presence of (1) more than one type of cultigen at inland sites in Connecticut; (2) storage pits; and (3) "substantial amounts" of horticultural remains indicate intensive horticulture in the New England interior, although they recognized that the large quantity of maize found may, in part, be a "sampling effect." They define "substantial amounts" as more than 1,500 kernels at the Burnham-Shepard site and more than 100 kernels at the Morgan site (see Lavin 1988a). Likewise, Lavin (1988a) reported "numerous maize kernels from virtually all of the features," although precise numbers were not given. On this basis she suggested that maize was a "major food source,"

while acknowledging that it was likely part of a broad-spectrum hunting and foraging base (Lavin 1988a:18).

Can we argue that maize was a "major food source" on the basis of 100 or even 1,500 kernels at one site? Based on Williams' (1963 [1643]) account, there was something in the order of 240 kernels per cob on these eight-rowed Northern Flint cobs. Thus, a few hundred kernels may represent only one or two cobs. Since under most conditions botanical remains will not preserve unless they are charred, there is a complex relationship between excavated remains and the activities that produced those remains. In this same vein, the discovery of more than one type of cultigen simply allows us to identify the *kinds* of plants that were utilized at that particular archaeological site; because the preservation of cultigens is so rare in New England, we simply cannot expect the presence of one or more cultigens to be a reflection of either importance or diversity in the types of cultigens utilized in the past, as suggested by Bendremer and Dewar (1994).

Further complicating the matter, we should also not assume that maize kernels found on archaeological sties were necessarily grown nearby (Demeritt 1991:184). Largy et al. (this volume) suggest that at the Goldkrest site, cobs could have been shucked and kernels transported for eventual consumption elsewhere. Thus, we need to be able to account for the possibility of trade in modeling subsistence systems.

Finally, in terms of the presence of storage pits, in many instances these storage pits contain the remains of wild plants, cultigens, faunal remains, and artifacts of various kinds (Lavin 1988a). Pits may have had multiple uses and may have been used repeatedly over time. For example, Moeller's (1992) analysis of Late Woodland pit features at the Faucett site demonstrates that pits were often used for short-term food "protection" rather than long-term storage. The Late Woodland pit features at the Faucett site are clearly related to the processing of a diverse array of plants and animals (Moeller 1992). Thus, we cannot assume that the presence of pit features correlate directly with the processing and storage of maize (*contra* Bendremer and Dewar 1994).

## EVALUATING THE ETHNOHISTORIC AND ARCHAEOLOGICAL EVIDENCE

Carlson (1994:9) rightly points out that the debate on the intensity of maize horticulture has focused on the *presence* of maize kernels in the archaeological record–not on planting fields, gardens, or other site-based evidence (notable exceptions include Currie 1994, Delabarre and Wilder 1920, Hallowell 1921, and Mrozowski 1994). In order to interpret the significance of maize to native peoples at a particular site or in a given region, it is important to consider the entire cultural context, which includes, but is not restricted to, the full range of subsistence activities, settlement practices, and other technical systems (e.g., ceramics).

### Subsistence

Seventeenth-century accounts of the native New England diet belie claims of maize specialization, and it is likely that the hunting and gathering of a variety of plants and animals formed the core of the diet of aboriginal peoples. These ethnohistoric records should be viewed with some amount of caution since many of the observations took place after native peoples had already suffered from devastating diseases (Morton 1967 [1637]) and other cultural transformations brought about by European colonization.

From his evaluation of the ethnohistoric literature, Bennett (1955) suggested maize comprised 65 percent of the total diet in New England. It is apparent that at the time of contact maize was not as important in New England as it was for groups to the west, such as the Iroquois (Bernstein 1990; Chilton 1996; Demeritt 1991; McBride and Dewar 1987; Vogel and van der Merwe 1977). Bennett (1955:370) also noted that "Indian corn-fields were limited to Connecticut, Rhode Island, central and eastern Massachusetts." However, Bennett's observations reflect a time when production of maize was geared towards trade with the English. Thomas (1979:96-97) asserted that in the middle Connecticut River valley, native peoples relied heavily on maize horticulture. He based this on Pynchon's (1645-50:iii in Day 1967) account of the names of the thirteen months of the

Connecticut valley Indians (Day 1967:244). Since four of the month names refer to the growing and harvesting of maize, Thomas (1979) and Day (1967) concluded that there was a "heavy reliance" on horticulture (see also Bendremer, this volume). However, we simply must assume that by the mid-seventeenth century, native subsistence practices had been significantly transformed by the well-developed trade networks among the English, French, Dutch, and various native groups of the Northeast.

While we know that maize horticulture was practiced by the New England Indians, it may not have consumed much of their time or energy. Cronon (1983:45) indicated that after the planting of maize, native peoples dispersed for two to three months to plant and gather elsewhere while the maize ripened. Thus, the Algonquins of the region may be seen as "mobile farmers," a category for which we currently lack a sufficient archaeological understanding (Graham 1994). Similarly, Mulholland referred to these mobile farmers as foraging horticulturalists (Mulholland 1988). Heckenberger et al. (1992:143) defined the precontact horticultural system as one of "tethered mobility." For Cape Cod, Dunford (1992) defined this kind of restricted mobility within an environmentally circumscribed area as "conditional sedentism."

Wood (1977:86 [1634]) recorded the following about the peoples of the Massachusetts Bay: "In wintertime they have all manner of fowls of the water and of the land, and the beasts of the land and water, pond-fish, with catharres and other roots, Indian beans and clams. In the summer they have all manner of shellfish, with all sorts of berries." In writing about the coast of Maine, Josselyn echoed this diverse menu:

> Their Diet is Fish and Fowl, Bear, Wild-cat, Ratton and Deer; dryed Oysters, *Lobsters* rosted or dryed in the smoak, *Lampres* and dry'd *Moose*-tongues, which they esteem a dish for a *Sagamor*; hard egges ... their *Indian* Corn and Kidney beans they boil ... they feed likewise upon earth-nuts or ground-nuts, roots of water-Lillies, Ches-nuts,

and divers sorts of Berries [emphasis in original; Josselyn 1988 (1674):93].

To this list Roger Williams, who was referring to groups in the vicinity of Narragansett Bay, added the hunting and trapping of numerous animals and the collecting of acorns, chestnuts, walnuts, strawberries, and cranberries (Williams 1963 [1643]).

While most of the ethnohistoric evidence for this period refers to the New England coast, there is also evidence that hunting and gathering were equally important in the New England interior. For the Hudson valley, in a letter from the seventeenth century (in Jameson 1909:105-107), Isaack Rasieres stated that the valley peoples "support themselves with hunting and fishing, and the sowing of maize and beans." In her captivity narrative, first published in 1682, Mary Rowlandson made frequent references to the eating of groundnuts (*Apios tuberosa*), and less frequent references to the eating of various kinds of meat (especially bear and deer) and corn "meal" (VanDerBeets 1973). Rowlandson's narrative did describe a particularly lean point in time, since warfare certainly disrupted usual subsistence practices.

New England Algonquins apparently practiced some wildlife management through the selective burning of the forest understory (Day 1954; Johnson 1993; Martin 1973; Morton 1967:172 [1637]; Patterson and Sassaman 1988; Wood 1977 [1634]). According to Cronon, this selective burning created what ecologists refer to as "edge habitat," which promoted the diverse, mosaic quality of the New England ecosystem (Cronon 1983:51). The effect of this burning was the creation of ideal habitats for a wide variety of plants and animals: beaver, deer, elk, hare, turkey, edible grasses, and many different kinds of edible berries (Cronon 1983:50-51; Whitney 1994).

In terms of the archaeological evidence for maize, as mentioned previously, current interpretations are based on scant evidence. The maize debate took off when Ceci (1979-80) proposed that for coastal New York, maize was not important in the diet until after contact. She suggested that year-round village life, therefore, developed in response to historic economic changes (Ceci 1979-

80:45). As of 1992, only a dozen maize kernels had been found in coastal Southern New England, and this absence of evidence seemed to support Ceci's argument (Bernstein 1992, this volume). More recently, stable isotope analysis conducted by Little and Schoeninger (1995) on human remains from Nantucket supports Ceci's model by demonstrating the continuing importance of oceanic animals in the diet well into the Late Woodland period. Even though the carbohydrate component of the diet may sometimes be underrepresented in isotope values (Parkington 1991), it is clear that maize was not a major component of the diet in coastal Southern New England until after the Contact period (Bernstein, this volume).

Bendremer and Dewar (1994:391) argued that "horticulture may have played an important role at inland riverine sites earlier than at the coastal sites." Lavin's (1988a:19) interpretations of the Morgan site likewise suggest that maize was a staple for interior groups. Lavin further speculated that, in the absence of year-round maritime resources, maize horticulture was the answer to population growth for inland groups (Lavin 1988a:19, 1988b:113). However, on the basis of the archaeological evidence at hand, we cannot be certain that "coastal peoples" did not spend part of the year in the interior, especially those who lived along major canoe routes, such as the Connecticut River. Inter- and intra-regional variation in the importance of horticulture may be explained, at least in part, by environment (Demeritt 1991). For example, the lower Connecticut valley (Connecticut portion) had significantly higher numbers of "growing degree days" than the Massachusetts portion of the Connecticut valley, Rhode Island, and much of the rest of Massachusetts and Connecticut, especially during the "Little Ice Age" (750 to 100 B.P.) (Demeritt 1991:190).

While environmental parameters may tell us what was *possible*, we need archaeological evidence to provide us with more concrete models. Bendremer and Dewar (1994) and Lavin (1988a, 1988b) based their interpretations of the importance of maize horticulture, at least in part, on the quantity of cultigens and features found on particular archaeological sites. It is true that at least three sites in the Connecticut valley (Burnham-Shepard, Morgan, and Pine Hill) have evidence for subterranean food storage or food processing, which included maize. Pit features may indeed be related to the importance of maize in the diet, but at this point we need to critically evaluate the relationships between food storage, food-processing technology, and subsistence. At first glance, there do seem to be more maize sites along the Connecticut River than any other major river in Southern New England (Figure 10.1). Certainly, the broad Connecticut valley floodplain contains some of the most fertile farmland in New England today. But the data used to compile Figure 10.1 are not based on systematic survey, and much more information undoubtedly lies buried in the gray literature and on museum shelves. In the end, it is important for us to look beyond the presence of maize kernels and pit features, and examine the evidence for large-scale changes in subsistence-settlement systems. Stable-isotope analysis and paleopathological analysis of human remains from interior sites would provide valuable information in this regard.

**Settlement Patterns**

There is little evidence for settled village life in the interior of New England, prior to European contact. In terms of archaeological evidence, while McBride's (1984:322) claim that most "New England archaeologists report an increase in artifact … and site density as well as a trend toward fewer, larger sites after A.D. 1000," is apparently true only for the lower Connecticut valley (George and Bendremer 1995). In fact, Ceci (1979-80) reported that there is *no* evidence of pre-contact village-based settlement patterns on Long Island (Ceci 1979-80). Luedtke (1988) described the same scenario for coastal Massachusetts. McBride's (1984) suggestion of increasing site size and density in the lower Connecticut valley is likewise *not* evident in the middle Connecticut valley, where few sites have any evidence of structures. A notable exception is the Pine Hill site, described below.

Concerning the lack of evidence for large Late Woodland villages in Southern New England, some archaeologists claim that such sites simply have not yet been found, or, as Ritchie claimed for the Hudson valley, that they have been obliterated by the large-scale destruction of sites as a result of Euroamerican settlement and digging by amateurs (Ritchie 1958:7; Snow 1980:320). Certainly, the looting of sites has had a serious impact on the visibility of sites in the region (Jordan 1975). Also, due to the large, dynamic floodplain of the Connecticut River valley, sites may have been buried or destroyed (Chilton 1990). Yet we cannot base our models entirely on negative evidence. The relative invisibility of Late Woodland villages in New England may also be due to a high degree of mobility for the small groups that resided in the region (Ritchie 1958:108). I explore this last possibility further.

While settlement pattern data are not plentiful in New England, especially in the interior, it is clear that the large, semi-permanent settlements characteristic of the Late Woodland period elsewhere in the deciduous Woodlands are lacking. New England villages differed from those of the Iroquois of upstate New York in that the inhabitants were often widely dispersed within a "homeland" (Handsman 1991; Johnson 1993:30). Settlement patterns were thus "characterized by a high degree of individual and community dispersion and mobility" (Johnson 1993:246). The basic population unit in Southern New England was most likely the village (Johnson 1993), which consisted of a few hundred inhabitants related through extended kin networks (Cronon 1983:37-38). Mobility may have been a strategy to maintain the environmental diversity and sociopolitical fluidity upon which these communities depended (Chilton 1996).

We know from both ethnohistoric and archaeological accounts that the traditional dwelling throughout New England was the wigwam. The size of wigwams was apparently small. Williams (1963:121 [1643]) described a dwelling for two families as "a little round house of some fourteen or fifteen foot over." Likewise, Higgeson (1968:123 [1629]) stated, "Their houses are verie little and homely, being made with small poles pricked into the ground." Each house was likely shared by one or two related families (Morgan 1965:124; Williams 1963:61 [1643]). For the Hudson valley, Johan de Laet (1625-1640 in Jameson 1909:57) said of the Algonquins living there that "some of them lead a wandering life in the open aire without settled habitation ... Others have fixed places of abode." Thus, it is clear that there was some diversity in settlement practices even within a particular valley. Likewise, Cronon (1983:38) noted that, for some groups, the size and shape of dwellings would change, depending on population density and the time of year (e.g., small wigwams in the summer, multifamily longhouses in the winter).

Williams also commented on the Algonquins' seasonal movements and the flexibility of their habitations:

> In the middle of summer ... they will flie and remove on a sudden from one part of their field to a fresh place ... Sometimes they remove to a hunting house in the end of the year ... but their great remove is from their Summer fields to warme and thicke woodie bottoms where they winter: They are quicke; in a halfe a day, yea, sometimes a few houres warning to be gone and the house up elsewhere [Williams 1963:135 (1643)].

Josselyn (1988:91 [1674]) noted the impermanence of New England communities: "Towns they have none, being always removing from one place to another for conveniency of food ... I have seen half a hundred of their Wigwams together in a piece of ground and they shew prettily, within a day or two, or a week they have all been dispersed." Likewise, Gookin (1968:149 [1792]) and Higgeson (1968:123 [1629]) stated that the New England Indians were inclined to frequently move their dwellings from place to place.

The evidence presented thus far indicates that, in Southern New England, there were no semi-permanent, year-round horticultural villages like those of the late pre-contact Iroquois. Maize may have been ideological and economically important, but it does not appear to have been a resource upon which native peoples depended. In the next section I report on some recent archaeological findings from the middle Connecticut valley in Massachusetts.

## PINE HILL

In western Massachusetts the recovery of prehistoric cultigens is particularly rare. However, in the summer of 1995, students of the University of Massachusetts Archaeological Field School recovered more than 100 charred kernels of maize from a possible storage or food-processing feature at the late prehistoric Pine Hill site in Deerfield, Massachusetts. This is a conservative estimate of the number of kernels recovered since only kernels from in situ samples have been counted thus far; the archaeobotanical analysis for both soil flotation and in situ samples from this feature is currently being conducted by Tonya Largy.

There are only three other sites in western Massachusetts where maize has been reported: (1) Riverside, Gill (Garman 1991); (2) Guida Farm (Byers and Rouse 1960); and (3) Indian Crossing (Mulholland 1988). Only a few kernels were recorded for the Riverside and Indian Crossing sites. There are maize samples from Guida Farm in the Young Collection (Springfield Museum), but the context is problematic. Thus, the archaeobotanical remains from Pine Hill are unique for the area in that they are plentiful, well documented, and well preserved. We have been conducting excavations at this site since 1989, and this is the first maize that we have identified, aside from two kernels found in the shallow plow zone. However, does the presence of a relatively large quantity of maize at the Pine Hill site indicate that the native peoples who lived at the site were intensive horticulturalists?

Pine Hill was tested by the University of Massachusetts Archaeological Field School in the summers of 1980, 1989, 1991, 1993, 1995, and 1997. I report here on the results through the 1995 season, since the rest of the analysis is underway. The site is located on a glacial lake delta remnant in the Deerfield valley; it lies approximately 150 feet above sea level and overlooks the ancient floodplain of the Deerfield River (Figure 10.1). It is quite likely the best preserved Late Woodland site in western Massachusetts. The area is currently used as woodlot, and the only known plowing at the site took place in the nineteenth century. The forest at Pine Hill is a second- or third-growth stand, and parts of the hill have been logged since the first post-plowing growth.

Lithic artifacts recovered from the site include three Late Archaic (5,000-3,000 B.P.) Vosburg points, a Normanskill point, three fishtail points from the Early Woodland (3,000-2,000 B.P.), and several Late Woodland triangles. Several hundred Late Woodland ceramic sherds have also been recovered and are discussed below. While the site is multicomponent, on the basis of the prevalence of certain types of artifacts and the association of artifacts with features, it is clear that most of the prehistoric activity at the site dates to the Late Woodland period. Twenty possible storage or food-processing features (11 of which contained Late Woodland ceramics), and approximately 50 scattered post molds have also been identified (Figure 10.2). No clear pattern has been detected in the post molds; they seem to represent small, overlapping wigwams. Two radiocarbon dates for wood charcoal from pit feature lenses containing ceramics are: (1) cal A.D. 1194-1446; and (2) cal A.D. 1420-1521 (*p*=.67) (Chilton 1996; [13]C-corrected and calibrated at 1-σ with the program CALIB 3.0.3 [Stuiver and Reimer 1993]). Although the site analysis and interpretation are not yet complete, the overlapping distribution of the pit features and post molds and the lack of a substantial midden accumulation indicate that the site most likely represents a seasonal encampment where small groups sporadically coalesced. While one could argue that this is just an aberrant, small site, it is one of the largest Late Woodland occupations known for the middle Connecticut valley. We simply do not have evidence for large, Late Woodland villages in western Massachusetts. Guida Farm may be an exception, but unfortunately most of that site has been destroyed, and most of what we know about the site postdates historic topsoil mining.

## Maize Storage at Pine Hill

In the summer of 1995, charred maize was recovered from what appears to be a subterranean storage or food-processing pit, Feature 148b (see Moeller 1992 for a discussion of food-processing features). Twenty similar features were identified at Pine Hill from 1989-1995 (Figure 10.2). Fifteen of these features have been at least partially excavated. The pits average 1.0 m in diameter and 1.5 m in depth. Almost all the pit features contain several distinct lenses of fill–some dark in color and containing concentrations of ash and charcoal, others barely distinguishable from the surrounding soil. Artifacts recovered from these features include aboriginal pottery, lithic tools, debitage, fire-cracked rock, and charred floral remains. Artifact density within features was low relative to the density of artifacts in the plow zone. For example, only 28 potsherds (of over 500 total) were found in all features combined. Therefore, these features do not seem to be refuse pits, but they may have been used for short-term storage and/or food processing. One pit feature had evidence of a clay lining at the bottom, but no other pit features had any evidence for organic or clay lining of any kind. Flotation and botanical analysis will help resolve the issue of pit function. Seven flotation samples and three excavated samples from three other pit features at Pine Hill were submitted to Tonya Largy for analysis in 1995 (Largy 1995). No cultigens were identified in these samples, but she did identify both charred and uncharred seed taxa, a few nutshells, and a number of tree taxa. Her results suggest that there was burning or clearing taking place at the site, either for cultivation or for habitation (Largy 1995:2).

Feature 148b is the only feature at Pine Hill known to contain maize, although not all the flotation analysis has been completed for the other features. The feature was quarter-sectioned and excavated using the Harris Matrix method (Harris 1989); only one quarter of the feature was excavated (Figures 10.3 and 10.4). There was a small scatter of fire-cracked rock and oxidized soil surrounding the feature just under the shallow plow zone. Based on soil micromorphology, this reddened soil was not from fire but from post-

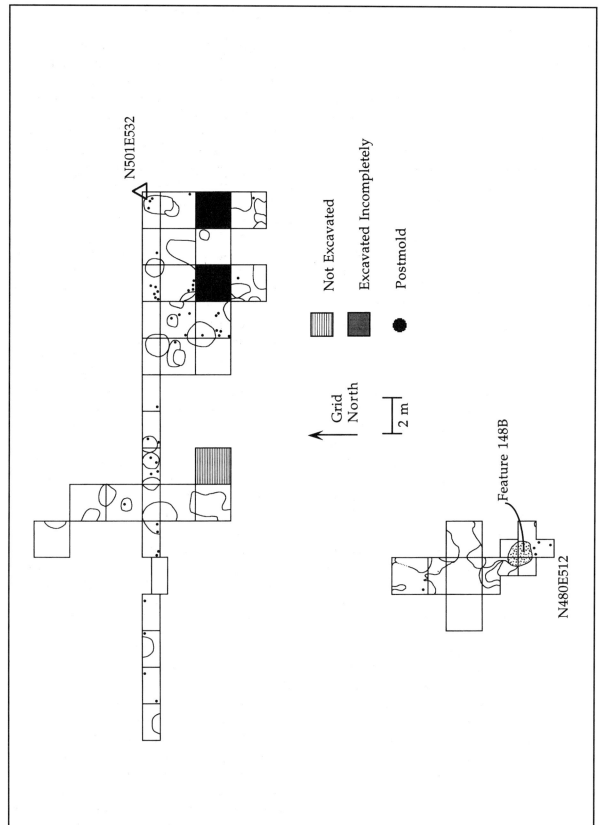

**Figure 10.2.** Plan view of the Pine Hill site, showing the location of excavation units and key features.

depositional chemical processes (Michael Volmar, personal communication 1996). There was a flaked-and-ground hand-ax found in the reddened soil at the top of the feature. The first maize kernels encountered in situ were from directly under the ax. Maize kernels were encountered from just under the plow zone (20-24 cm below surface) to the bottom of the feature, approximately 100 cm below surface. A radiocarbon date for a maize kernel recovered from the feature at 55-60 cm below the surface was cal A.D. 1442-1518 ($p$=.65; $^{13}$C corrected and calibrated at 1-$\sigma$ with the program CALIB 3.0.3 [Stuiver and Reimer 1993]). Approximately 150 flakes were found scattered throughout the pit in various soil lenses. Only two very small potsherds were encountered in the feature–both at the very top. Very little fire-cracked rock was encountered and, again, only at the top of the feature. Numerous other botanicals, including wood charcoal, nutshells, and small quantities of burned bone, were recovered. These have not been quantified yet and await analysis by Tonya Largy.

In sum, the contents of Feature 148b at Pine Hill indicate that maize was a part of the subsistence base of the Native American inhabitants of the site in the latter part of the Late Woodland period. It is possible that other pit features at the site originally contained maize and/or were used for maize storage, and that Feature 148b is the only instance where the maize has been preserved. It is also possible that maize was a relatively minor constituent of the diet for the people who visited the site. The settlement evidence suggests that the site represents seasonal encampments and not year-round settlement. Further analysis of feature contents and settlement patterns will help us to understand more fully the lives of these mobile farmers.

**Ceramic Evidence**

The last piece of the subsistence-settlement puzzle that I discuss in this paper is ceramics. Prehistoric ceramics are very useful for inferring diet, mobility, and settlement patterns. Ceramics have a large number of production-related attributes (Rice 1987:111), and since ceramic technology is additive (as opposed to subtractive, such as

lithic technology), a pot embodies many of the decisions made along the production sequence. Thus, changes over time in the performance characteristics of pottery often reflect changes in the use of "pots as tools" (Braun 1983).

As part of my dissertation research (Chilton 1996), I analyzed ceramics from three Late Woodland sites in the Northeast: two in western Massachusetts (the Guida Farm site, Westfield, and the Pine Hill site, Deerfield) and one in the Mohawk valley, New York (the Klock site, Ephratah; Figure 10.1). The Massachusetts sites were chosen because they represent the best excavated and documented Late Woodland sites in the middle Connecticut valley (Chilton 1996). I chose a Mohawk assemblage in order to compare Iroquoian and Algonquin ceramic technologies. The Klock site was chosen because it was one of the best documented Mohawk sites from the latter part of the Late Woodland period, and was therefore comparable in age to the Connecticut valley sites (Kuhn and Funk 1994).

Several hundred ceramic sherds were recovered from the Pine Hill site. I analyzed ceramic sherds collected through the 1993 field season; nearly 500 sherds were complete enough to be used in the analysis. From these, 56 distinct vessel lots were identified. The Young collection from the Guida Farm site contains approximately 1,000 sherds which were complete enough to be used in this analysis. From these, 108 vessel lots were identified. The collection from the Klock site has over 15,000 ceramic fragments. A random sample of 100 vessel lots was chosen in order to make it comparable in size to the Guida and Pine Hill collections.

In order to establish a vessel lot (i.e., a group of potsherds determined to be *minimally* from the same vessel), at least nine attributes were recorded for each sherd: modal vessel wall thickness, inclusion material (i.e., temper or naturally occurring particles), inclusion size, inclusion density, exterior and interior color, surface treatment (including decoration), and location of the sherd on the vessel. Inclusions were identified using 10X magnification. Since it is extremely difficult to identify rock minerals in fired ceramic pastes, my inclusion designations are consistent,

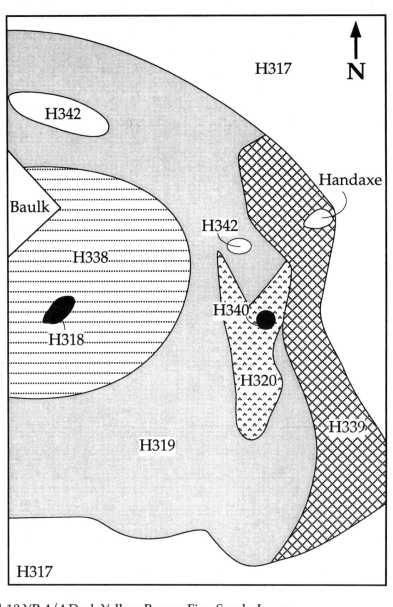

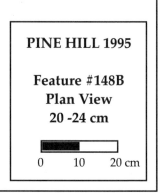

**PINE HILL 1995**

**Feature #148B**
**Plan View**
**20 -24 cm**

H317 – Subsoil-10 YR 4/4 Dark Yellow Brown Fine Sandy Loam
H318 – Fea. 300 -10 YR 2/1 Black Sandy Loam
H319 – Fea. 148B -10 YR 3/2 Very Dark Grey Brown Loamy Sand
H320 – Fea. 148B -2.5 Y 4/4 Olive Brown Slightly Silty Sand
H338 – Fea. 148B -10 YR 2/1 Black Loamy Sand mottled with 10 YR 4/2
         Dark Greyish Brown Slightly Loamy Sand
H339 – Fea. 148B -5 YR 4/4 Reddish Brown Fine Sandy Silt
H340 – Fea. 148B-10 YR 3/3 Dark Brown Sandy Silt
H341 – Fea. 148B-10 YR 4/4 Dark Yellowish Brown Slightly Sandy Silt
H342 – Fea. 148B-2.5 YR 4/4 Dark Brown Fine Silty Sand

**Figure 10.3.** Feature 148B plan view, Pine Hill site, showing Harris Matrix levels (H).

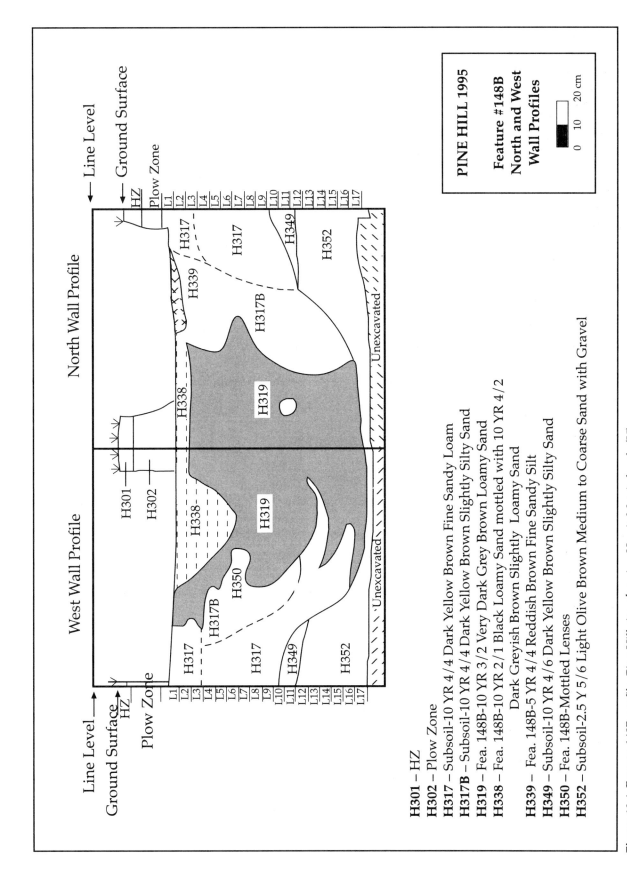

**PINE HILL 1995**

**Feature #148B
North and West
Wall Profiles**

0  10  20 cm

**H301** – HZ
**H302** – Plow Zone
**H317** – Subsoil-10 YR 4/4 Dark Yellow Brown Fine Sandy Loam
**H317B** – Subsoil-10 YR 4/4 Dark Yellow Brown Slightly Silty Sand
**H319** – Fea. 148B-10 YR 3/2 Very Dark Grey Brown Loamy Sand
**H338** – Fea. 148B-10 YR 2/1 Black Loamy Sand mottled with 10 YR 4/2
  Dark Greyish Brown Slightly Loamy Sand
**H339** – Fea. 148B-5 YR 4/4 Reddish Brown Fine Sandy Silt
**H349** – Subsoil-10 YR 4/6 Dark Yellow Brown Slightly Silty Sand
**H350** – Fea. 148B-Mottled Lenses
**H352** – Subsoil-2.5 Y 5/6 Light Olive Brown Medium to Coarse Sand with Gravel

**Figure 10.4.** Feature 148B profile, Pine Hill site, showing Harris Matrix levels (H).

if not exact. John Pretola (University of Massachusetts, Amherst) will be thin-sectioning a subsample from all three sites in order to make more precise inclusion identifications as well as obtain information on construction techniques. Inclusion density was estimated using comparative charts (Terry and Chilingar 1955:229-234). Because the amount of inclusions varies a great deal within ceramic pastes of hand-built pots, estimates of inclusion density are sufficient. The final vessel lot determination is based on overall similarity in the attributes analyzed.

I will summarize a few of the more important technical attributes; other attributes analyzed, but not discussed here, include construction techniques, rim and lip form, and interior and exterior color (Chilton 1996, 1998). The primary temper or inclusion type at Pine Hill and Guida was crushed quartz, followed by feldspar. In contrast, the most common inclusion types at the Mohawk valley Klock site were feldspar (mostly plagioclase) and hornblende. It is important to note here that for cooking vessels, the optimal temper types, such as grog, calcite, crushed burned shell, feldspar and hornblende, have thermal expansion coefficients similar or less than that of clay (Rye 1976: Figure 3). Quartz, on the other hand, is not an optimal temper type for cooking pots; it expands much quicker than clay and can lead to crack initiation. Therefore, on the basis of temper materials used, the Connecticut valley ceramics may not have been ideal cooking pots, on the whole. The significance of this is that the type of maize used by native peoples in the Northeast, which was similar to modern varieties of eight-rowed Northern Flint corn, is unlike sweet corn and needed to be cooked for long periods of time in porridge or stew form (Champlain 1907 [1625]; Fenton 1940). Connecticut valley pots may have been sporadically used for cooking, but they were not ideal for cooking maize over long, hot fires.

Temper density follows a similar yet much more striking pattern. The mean temper densities for vessel lots from Pine Hill and Guida are similar: 15.6 percent and 15.5 percent, respectively. The mean temper density for the Klock site is much lower (just over half) at 8.6 percent. A densely tempered paste is usually stronger. However, the

more temper in a paste, the more potential problems as a result of thermal expansion–especially if the temper is quartz. Therefore, the Connecticut valley vessels would have been less resistant to thermal shock than the Klock site vessels, but more resistant to mechanic shock (Braun 1983).

For vessel wall thickness, the mean and standard deviation are both slightly lower for the Klock site, as compared to the Connecticut valley sites, but the difference is not statistically significant. However, on the basis of body sherd curvature, the Klock vessels are, on average, 70 percent larger than those of Pine Hill and Guida (29 cm vs. 17 cm mean diameter). Wall thickness directly affects resistance to thermal shock. Vessels with thinner walls are less apt to crack when used for cooking. Therefore, since the Klock pots had significantly thinner walls relative to overall size, potters were apparently constructing pots with walls thin enough to withstand the thermal stresses of cooking maize. The Connecticut valley vessels, on the other hand, had thicker vessel walls, relative to overall size. Pots with thick walls are less fragile (more resistant to mechanical shock) but are more likely to crack when exposed to heat (Braun 1983).

Overall, Connecticut valley ceramic vessels would not have held up as well as Klock vessels under long, high temperature cooking, but they would have been adequate for short-term cooking of various plants and animal products. Connecticut valley vessels were generally stronger and smaller and thus would have been more useful for transporting food and water. Therefore, the ceramic evidence, together with subsistence and settlement pattern data, support the notion that Southern New England Algonquins had a diverse diet and did not specialize in maize horticulture.

The Massachusetts Algonquin pots also show a much greater diversity than Iroquois pots in nearly all attributes analyzed: surface treatment, temper type, vessel size and shape, and even vessel color. The great diversity in Algonquin ceramics may, in part, be accounted for by the high degree of mobility and small group size of Algonquin groups in the New England interior. If, as I have suggested elsewhere (Chilton

1996), the Connecticut valley Algonquins were highly mobile with fluid social boundaries, then the social contexts of ceramic manufacture and use were variable. If pots were made at various locations throughout the year, then environmental context would also have been highly variable, which would account for the high degree of attribute variability.

## MOBILE FARMERS OF SOUTHERN NEW ENGLAND

*Allowing for variation, even within the same river valley, opens the debate to questions of social complexity and organization. ... groups with different social, political, economic, or nutritional needs would vary their use of maize across time and space* (Carlson 1994:19-20).

Ceramic, subsistence, and settlement pattern data for much of Southern New England indicate that maize was a dietary supplement and not a staple (Dincauze 1990:30). By "staple," I mean a food item that is necessary for the survival and wellness of the community. So how do we resolve the fact that there are three sites in the Connecticut valley with evidence for subterranean maize storage? Certainly, it is quite possible that maize could more easily be grown in the fertile floodplain of the Connecticut valley than on the patchy soils of the coast, but we need to base our interpretations on more than simply the presence of maize and storage pits. In fact, instead of looking for evidence to support models, I suggest that archaeologists in New England adopt a more scientific, hypothesis-testing approach. I suggest that the most reasonable hypothesis at present is that maize was only one part of a diverse subsistence-settlement system of the New England interior. Evidence that could be used to test, and potentially refute, this hypothesis includes, but is not limited to, the following: (1) evidence for year-round villages, (2) stable isotope analysis of human remains indicating a heavy reliance on maize, and (3) osteological analysis indicating a significant change in diet

and living conditions associated with intensive maize horticulture.

Ultimately, though, the dichotomy between staple and casual use is misdirected; certainly the categories of "agriculturist" and "forager" are not mutually exclusive (Minnis 1985). Instead of viewing subsistence choice as a dichotomy between "non-event" and "intensity," perhaps we should take the suggestion of Watson (1989:564) to heart and view subsistence choice as "a kaleidoscope mosaic where ... domesticated plants are used in varying combinations with a much larger variety of quasi-cultigens ... and a wider variety still of wild ... plants." Also, contrary to the ongoing "coastal versus inland" debate in the literature, there may be more diversity *within* than *between* the subregions of New England.

Subsistence choices in a given subregion likely varied greatly over time due to complex nature of community decision-making. As Bumsted (1980:74) pointed out, the choice of whether to follow a generalist or specialist strategy is a critical one. Choices must provide for the social and nutritional needs of the community, needs which change with the available resources, climate, cultural influences, and interaction spheres (Demeritt 1991:196-197).

Clearly, much more analysis is needed of the botanical remains from the Pine Hill site and other sites in the region. Stable isotope analysis is one way that questions about the dietary importance of maize might be resolved. Yet the issue of the importance and/or intensity of maize horticulture is not something that can be answered with one method or with data from one or two sites. Our understanding of maize horticulture will necessarily rely on evidence of native planting fields, subsistence choices, food-storage practices, and ceramic technologies—all within the diverse social context of New England's native communities.

## ACKNOWLEDGEMENTS

I would like to acknowledge the work of my co-director of the University of Massachusetts Archaeological Field School, Arthur Keene, and fellow staff members Eric Johnson, Claire Carlson, Kathryn Curran, and Michael Volmar. We are currently working on the final site report for the last three field seasons, and much of the analysis has not yet been completed. Thus, the results presented here concerning Pine Hill are preliminary. This research was aided by a Grant-in-Aid of Research from Sigma Xi, The Scientific Research Society, and a Graduate Research Award from the Department of Anthropology, University of Massachusetts, Amherst. I appreciate the comments of the two anonymous reviewers; many of their suggestions are reflected here. I would also like to thank Alan Leveillee for the Rhode Island references, and David Schafer, Desiree Martinez, and Jessi Halligan for their assistance with the production of graphics for this paper. Kathryn Curran produced the original field drawings. Any flaws in this work are solely my responsibility.

## REFERENCES CITED

Bendremer, J. C. M. 1993. *Late Woodland Settlement and Subsistence in Eastern Connecticut.* Unpublished Ph.D. dissertation, Department of Anthropology, University of Connecticut, Storrs.

Bendremer, J. C. M., and R. E. Dewar. 1994. The Advent of Prehistoric Maize in New England. In *Corn and Culture in the Prehistoric New World*, edited by S. Johannessen and C. A. Hastorf, pp. 369-393. Westview Press, Boulder.

Bendremer, J., E. Kellogg, and T. B. Largy. 1991. A Grass-Lined Storage Pit and Early Maize Horticulture in Central Connecticut. *North American Archaeologist* 12:325-349.

Bennett, M. K. 1955. The Food Economy of the New England Indians, 1605-75. *Journal of Political Economy* 63: 369-397.

Bernstein, D. J. 1990. Trends in Prehistoric Subsistence on the Southern New England Coast: The View From Narragansett Bay. *North American Archaeologist* 11:321-352.

————. 1992. Prehistoric Use of Plant Foods in the Narragansett Bay Region. *Man in the Northeast* 44:1-13.

Braun, D. P. 1983. Pots as Tools. In *Archaeological Hammers and Theories*, edited by J. A. Moore and A. S. Keene, pp. 103-136. Academic Press, New York.

Bumsted, M. P. 1980. VT-CH-94: Vermont's Earliest Known Agricultural Experiment Station. *Man in the Northeast* 19:73-82.

Byers, D. S., and I. Rouse. 1960. A Re-Examination of the Guida Farm. *Bulletin of the Archaeological Society of Connecticut* 30:5-39.

Carlson, C. C. 1994. *Hidden Histories and Engendered Archaeologies: Excavations at the Weantinock Indian Planting Fields.* Unpublished Master's thesis, Department of Anthropology, University of Massachusetts, Amherst.

Cassedy, D., P. Webb, A. Dowd, J. Jones, C. Cobb, R. S. Dillon, M. Rheinbold, and T. Millis. 1993. *Iroquois Gas Transmission System Phase III Archaeological Data Recovery Report, Volume 2: The Hudson Valley Region.* Garrow and Associates, Inc., Atlanta. Submitted to Iroquois Gas Transmission System, L.P., Shelton, Connecticut. Copies available from the New York State Office of Parks, Recreation, and Historic Preservation.

Ceci, L. 1979-80. Maize Cultivation in Coastal New York: The Archaeological, Agronomical, and Documentary Evidence. *North American Archaeologist* 1:45-73.

————. 1990. Radiocarbon Dating "Village" Sites in Coastal New York: Settlement Pattern Change in the Middle to Late Woodland. *Man in the Northeast* 39:1-28.

Champlain, S. de. 1907 [1625]. *Voyages of Samuel de Champlain, 1604-1618*, edited by W. L. Grant. Charles Scribner's Sons, New York.

Chilton, E. S. 1990. In Search of Bark Wigwams: Archaeological Investigations of an Early Contact Period site in the Connecticut Valley. Paper presented at the 30th Meeting of the Northeastern Anthropological Association, Burlington, Vermont.

————. 1996. *Embodiments of Choice:Native American Ceramic Diversity in the New England Interior*. Unpublished Ph.D. dissertation, Department of Anthropology, University of Massachusetts, Amherst.

————. 1998. The Cultural Origins of Technical Choice: Unraveling Algonquian and Iroquoian Ceramic Traditions in the Northeast. In *The Archaeology of Social Boundaries*, edited by M. T. Stark, pp.132-160. Smithsonian Institution, Washington, D.C.

Chilton, E., and D. L. Doucette. 1997. *Archaeological Investigations at the Lucy Vincent Beach Site (19-DK-148), Chilmark, Massachusetts*. Manuscript on file at the Massachusetts Historical Commission, Boston.

Coffin, C. C. 1940. Excavations in Southwest Connecticut. *Bulletin of the Archaeological Society of Connecticut* 10:33-49.

Cronon, W. 1983. *Changes in the Land: Indians, Colonists, and the Ecology of New England*. Hill and Wang, New York.

Cowie, E. R., and J. B. Petersen. 1990. *Archaeological Phase II Survey and Testing of the Bonny Eagle Project (FERC No. 2529), Cumberland and York Counties, Maine*. University of Maine at Farmington Archaeology Research Center. Submitted to Central Maine Power Company, Augusta.

Currie, D. R. 1994. Micromorphology of a Native American Cornfield. *Archaeology of Eastern North America* 22:63-72.

Day, G. M. 1954. The Indians as an Ecological Factor in the Northeast Forest. *Ecology* 32:329-346.

————. 1967. An Agawam Fragment. *International Journal of American Linguistics* 33(3): 244-247.

Delabarre, E. B., and H. H. Wilder. 1920. Indian Corn Hills in Massachusetts. *American Anthropologist* 22:203-225.

Demeritt, D. 1991. Agriculture, Climate, and Cultural Adaptation in the Prehistoric Northeast. *Archaeology of Eastern North America* 19:183-202.

Dincauze, D. F. 1981. Paleoenvironmental Reconstruction in the Northeast: The Art of Multidisciplinary Science. In *Foundations of Northeast Archaeology*, edited by D. R. Snow, pp. 51-96. Academic Press, New York.

————. 1990. A Capsule Prehistory of Southern New England. In *The Pequot: The Fall and Rise of an American Indian Nation*, edited by L. Hauptman and J. Wherry, pp. 19-32. University of Oklahoma Press, Norman.

Dunford, F. J. 1992. Conditional Sedentism: The Logistical Flexibility of Estuarine Settlements in Circumscribed Environments. Paper presented at the 57th Annual Meeting of the Society for American Archaeology, Pittsburgh.

Fenton, W. N. 1940. Problems Arising from the Northeastern Position of the Iroquois. *Smithsonian Miscellaneous Collections* 100:159-251.

Funk, R. E. 1976. *Some Recent Contributions to Hudson Valley Prehistory*. New York State Museum Memoir 22. New York State Museum, Albany.

Funk, R. E., and J. E. Pfeiffer. 1988. Archaeological and Paleoenvironmental Investigation on Fishers Island, New York: A Preliminary Report. *Bulletin of the Archaeological Society of Connecticut* 51:69-110.

Garman, J. C. 1991. Prehistoric Maize at Riverside, Gill. *Bulletin of the Massachusetts Archaeological Society* 52(1):1-7.

George, D. R., and J. C. M. Bendremer. 1995. Late Woodland Subsistence and the Origins of Maize Horticulture in New England. Paper presented at the 60th Annual Meeting of the Society for American Archaeology, Minneapolis.

Gookin, D. 1968 [1792]. Historical Collections of Indians in New England. *Collections of the Massachusetts Historical Society Collections, for the Year 1792* 1:141-227. Reprinted 1968, Johnson Reprint Corporation, New York.

Graham, M. 1994. *Mobile Farmers: An Ethnoarchaeological Approach to Settlement Organization among the Rarámuri of Northwestern Mexico.* International Monographs in Prehistory, Ethnoarchaeological Series 3. Ann Arbor.

Hallowell, A. I. 1921. Indian Corn Hills. *American Anthropologist* 23:233.

Handsman, R. 1991. What Happened to the Heritage of the Weantinock People. *Artifacts* 19(1):3-9.

—————. 1995. *A Homelands Model and Interior Sites, A Phase II Archaeological Study of Rhode Island Site 2050, Phenix Avenue, Cranston, Rhode Island.* Report Submitted to the Rhode Island Department of Transportation. Research Report 1, Public Archaeology Program, University of Rhode Island, Kingstown, Rhode Island.

Harris, E. 1989. *Principle of Archaeological Stratigraphy.* 2nd edition. Academic Press, London.

Heckenberger, M. J., J. B. Petersen, and N. Asch Sidell. 1992. Early Evidence of Maize Agriculture in the Connecticut River Valley of Vermont. *Archaeology of Eastern North America* 20:125-149.

Higgeson, Rev. J. 1968 [1629]. New-England's Plantation. In *Collections of the Massachusetts Historical Society, for the Year 1792* 1:117-124. Reprinted 1968, Johnson Reprint Corporation, New York.

Jameson, J. F. 1909. *Narratives of New Netherlands, 1609-1664.* Barnes and Noble, New York.

Johnson, E. S. 1993. *Some by Flatteries and Others by Threatening: Political Strategies in Seventeenth Century Native New England.* Unpublished Ph.D. dissertation, Department of Anthropology, University of Massachusetts, Amherst.

Jordan, D. 1975. Factors Affecting New England Archaeology. *Man in the Northeast* 10:71-74.

Josselyn, J. 1988 [1674]. Two Voyages to New-England. In *John Josselyn, Colonial Traveler: A Critical Edition of Two Voyages to New-England,* edited by P. J. Lindholdt, pp. 1-200. University Press of New England, Hanover, New Hampshire.

Kuhn, R. D., and R. E. Funk. 1994. The Mohawk Klock and Smith Sites. Ms. in possession of authors.

Largy, T. 1995. Archaeobotanical Analysis of Pine Hill, Deerfield, MA. Report submitted to E. S. Chilton, Department of Anthropology, University of Massachusetts, Amherst.

Lavin, L. 1988a. The Morgan Site, Rocky Hill, Connecticut: A Late Woodland Farming Community in the Connecticut River Valley. *Bulletin of the Archaeological Society of Connecticut* 51:7-22.

—————. 1988b. Coastal Adaptation in Southern New England and Southern New York. *Archaeology of Eastern North America* 16:101-120.

Leveillee, A. 1996. National Register Nomination Form. Phenix Avenue Bridge Site, RI 2050.

Leveillee, A., and B. Harrison. 1996. An Archaeological Landscape in Narragansett, Rhode Island: Point Judith Upper Pond. *Bulletin of the Massachusetts Archaeological Society* 57(2):58-63.

Little, E. A., and M. J. Schoeninger. 1995. The Late Woodland Diet on Nantucket Island and the Problem of Maize in Coastal New England. *American Antiquity* 60:351-368.

Luedtke, B. E. 1988. Where Are the Late Woodland Villages in Eastern Massachusetts? *Bulletin of the Massachusetts Archaeological Society* 49(2):58-65.

Martin, C. 1973. Fire and Forest Structure in the Aboriginal Eastern Forest. *The Indian Historian* 6:23-26.

McBride, K. A. 1984. *Prehistory of the Lower Connecticut River Valley.* Unpublished Ph.D. dissertation, Department of Anthropology, University of Connecticut, Storrs.

McBride, K. A., and R. E. Dewar. 1987. Archaeology of the Mashantucket Pequots. In *The Pequots in Southern New England: The Fall and Rise of an American Indian Nation,* edited by L. M. Hauptman and J. D. Wherry, pp. 96-116. University of Oklahoma Press, Norman.

McManamon, F. P. 1984. Prehistoric Cultural Adaptations and Their Evolution on Outer Cape Cod. In *Chapters in the Archaeology of Cape Cod, I,* edited by F. P. McManamon. Cultural Resource Management Study 8, National Park Service, Boston.

Millis, T., D. Cassedy, H. Millis, P. Webb, and N. Asch Sidell. 1993. *Iroquois Gas Transmission System Phase III Archaeological Data Recovery Report, Volume 3: The Connecticut Sites.* Garrow and Associates, Inc., Atlanta. Submitted to Iroquois Gas Transmission System, L. P., Shelton, Connecticut.

Minnis, P. E. 1985. Domesticating People and Plants in the Greater Southwest. In *Prehistoric Food Production in North America,* edited by R. I. Ford, pp. 309-339. Anthropological Papers No. 75. Museum of Anthropology, University of Michigan, Ann Arbor.

Moeller, R. W. 1992. *Analyzing and Interpreting Late Woodland Features.* Occasional Publications in Northeastern Anthropology 12.

Morgan, L. H. 1965. *House and House-life of the American Aborigines.* University of Chicago Press, Chicago.

Morton, T. 1967 [1637]. New English Canaan or New Canaan. In *New English Canaan of Thomas Morton,* edited by C. F. Adams, Jr, pp. 114-349. Burt Franklin, New York.

Mrozowski, S. A. 1994. The Discovery of a Native American Cornfield on Cape Cod. *Archaeology of Eastern North America* 22:47-62.

Mulholland, M. T. 1988. Territoriality and Horticulture: A Perspective for Prehistoric Southern New England. In *Holocene Human Ecology in Northeastern North America,* edited by G. P. Nicholas, pp. 137-166. Plenum Press, New York.

Parkington, J. 1991. Approaches to Dietary Reconstruction in the Western Cape: Are You What You Have Eaten? *Journal of Archaeological Science* 18:331-342.

Patterson, W. A., and K. E. Sassaman. 1988. Indian Fires in the Prehistory of New England. In *Holocene Human Ecology in Northeastern North America,* edited by G. P. Nicholas, pp. 107-135. Plenum, New York.

Rice, P. M. 1987. *Pottery Analysis: A Sourcebook.* University of Chicago Press, Chicago.

Ritchie, W. A. 1958. *An Introduction to Hudson Valley Prehistory.* New York State Museum and Science Service Bulletin 367. Albany.

—————. 1969. *The Archaeology of New York State.* Revised edition. Natural History Press, Garden City.

Rogers, E. H. 1943. The Indian River Village Site, Milford, Connecticut. *Bulletin of the Archaeological Society of Connecticut* 15:3-78.

Russell, L. W. 1946. Indians Burials at Niantic Connecticut. *Bulletin of the Archaeological Society of Connecticut* 21:39-43.

Rye, O. S. 1976. Keeping Your Temper Under Control. *Archaeology and Physical Anthropology in Oceania* 11:106-137.

Silver, A. 1980. Comment on Maize Cultivation in Coastal New York. *North American Archaeologist* 2:117-130.

Smith, C. S. 1950. *The Archaeology of Coastal New York.* Anthropological Papers of the American Museum of Natural History, Vol. 43(2), New York.

Snow, D. R. 1980. *The Archaeology of New England.* Academic Press, New York.

Stuiver, M., and P. J. Reimer. 1993. Extended $^{14}C$ Database and Revised CALIB 3.0 $^{14}C$ Age Calibration Program. *Radiocarbon* 35:215-230.

Terry, R. D., and G. V. Chilingar. 1955. Data Sheet 6. *Geotimes.* Available from the American Geological Institute, Washington, D.C. Reprinted from the *Journal of Sedimentary Petrology* 25: 229-234.

Thomas, P. A. 1979. *In the Maelstrom of Change: The Indian Trade and Cultural Process in the Middle Connecticut River Valley: 1635-1665.* Unpublished Ph.D. dissertation, Department of Anthropology, University of Massachusetts, Amherst, University Microfilms, Ann Arbor.

VanDerBeets, R. (editor). 1973. *Held Captive by Indians: Selected Narratives 1642-1836.* University of Tennessee Press, Knoxville.

Vogel, J. C., and N. van der Merwe. 1977. Isotopic Evidence for Early Maize Cultivation in New York State. *American Antiquity* 42:238-242.

Watson, P. J. 1989. Early Plant Cultivation in the Eastern Woodlands of North America. In *Foraging and Farming: The Evolution of Plant Exploitation*, edited by D. R. Harris and G. C. Hillman, pp. 555-571. Unwin Hyman, London.

Whitney, G. G. 1994. *From Coastal Wilderness to Fruited Plain: A History of Environmental Change in Temperate North America 1500 to the Present*. Cambridge University Press, Cambridge.

Williams, R. 1963 [1643]. *The Complete Writings of Roger Williams*, Vol. 1. Russell and Russell, New York.

Williams, M. B., and J. C. M. Bendremer. 1997. The Archaeology of Maize, Pots, and Seashells: Gender Dynamics in Late Woodland and Contact-Period New England. In *Women in Prehistory: North America and Mesoamerica*, edited by C. Claassen and R. A. Joyce, pp. 136-149. University of Pennsylvania Press, Philadelphia.

Wood, W. 1977 [1634]. *New England's Prospect*, edited by A. T. Vaughan. The Commonwealth Series, W. E. A. Bernhard, general editor. University of Massachusetts Press, Amherst, Massachusetts. Originally published 1634, J. Bellamie, London.

# CHAPTER 11

# PALEOGEOGRAPHIC CHANGES IN WETLAND AND UPLAND ENVIRONMENTS IN THE MILFORD DRAINAGE BASIN OF CENTRAL MAINE IN RELATION TO HOLOCENE HUMAN SETTLEMENT HISTORY

Heather Almquist-Jacobson and David Sanger

Landscapes of northeastern North America have changed significantly during the present interglacial. The most dramatic shift in upland forest vegetation occurred around 4,700 years B.P., with a catastrophic decline in hemlock (*Tsuga*)-dominated forest and subsequent development of beech (*Fagus*)-rich northern hardwood forest (Davis 1983). That shift almost certainly created more productive habitat for several large, upland game species that would have been important to native peoples. In this study, we use paleoenvironmental data to help understand the settlement histories of two archaeological sites (i.e., whether changes in the nature or extent of wetland areas could have stimulated site establishment or abandonment).

Faunal records from many archaeological sites in Maine suggest that prehistoric people relied heavily on wetland mammals, amphibians, and fish in addition to upland species. The distribution of known archaeological sites suggests a strong dependence on waterways for access to resources. Thus, changes in productivity related to the type and extent of wetland systems, which occur naturally as wetlands evolve from open water to marsh, and finally, peatland, may have influenced settlement patterns. Open-water and marsh habitats, in particular, support a broad diversity of plants and animals, and provide transportation routes. Nicholas (1988) argued that early post-glacial (12,000 to 7,000 years B.P.) environments in the northeastern U.S. supported a broader resource base than today, and that glacial lake basins, in particular, were highly productive focal points for settlement until the end of the early Holocene when upland (non-basin) areas became relatively more productive.

The overall goal of this study was to examine the relationship between post-glacial environmental change and human settlement patterns. We have constructed paleogeographic maps of wetlands in the immediate vicinity of two archaeological sites within the Milford Drainage Basin, lower Penobscot River valley, central Maine. (Figures 11.1 and 11.2). The research is part of ongoing archaeological and paleoecological investigations within the Milford Drainage Basin. It includes numerous sites from which Indian peoples would have had ready access to wetlands.

One nearby site, Hirundo, spans from the Middle Archaic (8,000 years B.P.) through the Historic periods (Sanger et al. 1977). The other spans the Late Archaic (6,000 years B.P.) and Ceramic (3,000 to 300 years B.P.) periods. The wetland maps are based on new sedimentologic and macrofossil evidence plus new radiocarbon and pollen-correlation dates from a network of cores collected from a local peatland complex. In addition, we refer to a previously published pollen and charcoal record from a small kettle lake, Mansell Pond (Almquist-Jacobson and Sanger 1995), to characterize major changes in upland vegetation.

## DESCRIPTION OF THE STUDY AREA

The Milford Drainage Basin of the lower Penobscot River valley, Maine, is a broad lowland with a few hills rising to over 90 m a.s.l. and several north-south oriented eskers (Thompson and Borns 1985). The area lies below the highest late-Glacial coastline, and soils generally derive from fine-grained glaciomarine deposits except along the eskers and outwash fans. Local bedrock includes calcareous sandstone of Silurian and Ordovician age (Osberg et al. 1985). The basin lies

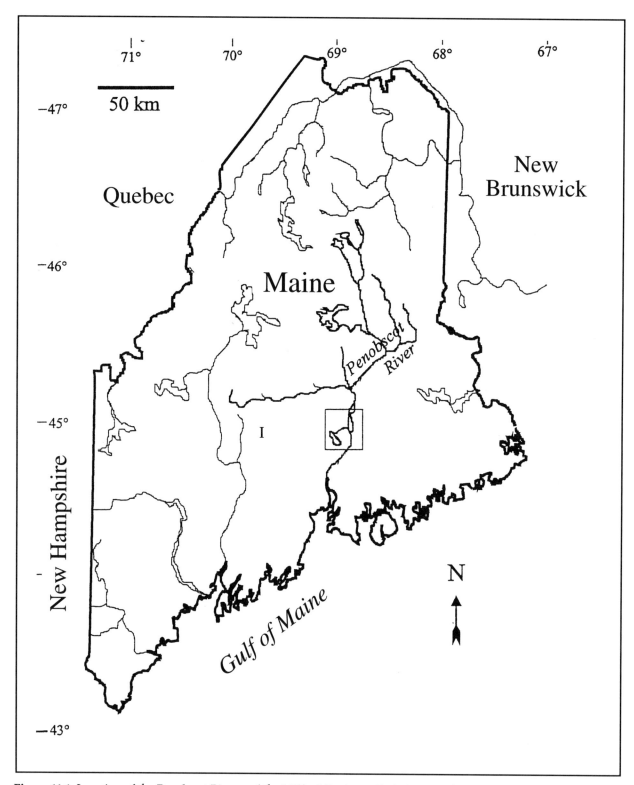

**Figure 11.1.** Location of the Penobscot River and the Milford Drainage Basin in central Maine, USA.

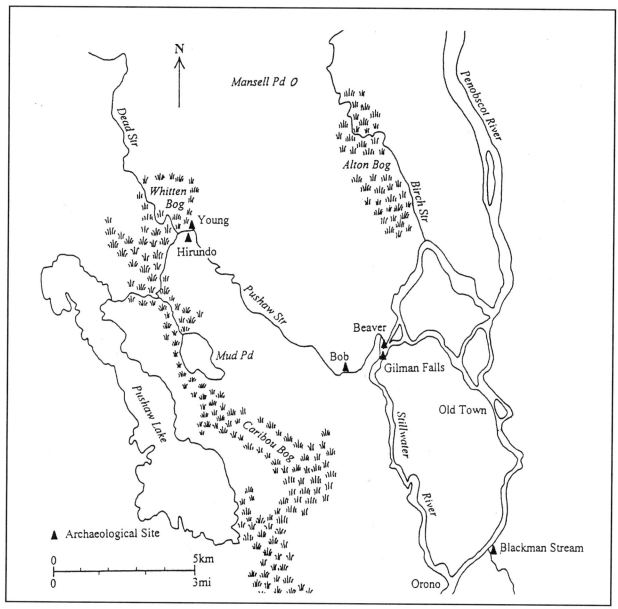

**Figure 11.2.** Location of the Milford Drainage Basin, including the North Caribou Bog Complex, Mansell Pond, and local archaeological sites.

within an important vegetational transition zone between boreal northern hardwood and central hardwood forests (Westveld et al. 1956). Many small streams, several small lakes, and large peatlands lie in relatively flat basins that were covered by silts and clays during a late-Glacial marine transgression (Davis and Jacobson 1985).

The North Caribou Bog peatland complex lies at the juncture of Old Town, Alton, and

Hudson, Maine (44°59' N, 68°47' W). It includes the northern end of Caribou Bog that extends 4 km north from Mud Pond to its upland margin, and Whitten Bog, which lies northeast of Caribou Bog and is separated from it by a northwest-southeast oriented esker (Figure 11.3). The two peatlands cover approximately 8 km$^2$ and 4 km$^2$, respectively. In Caribou Bog, the peat overlies lake sediment in most areas (Cameron et al. 1984; Hu

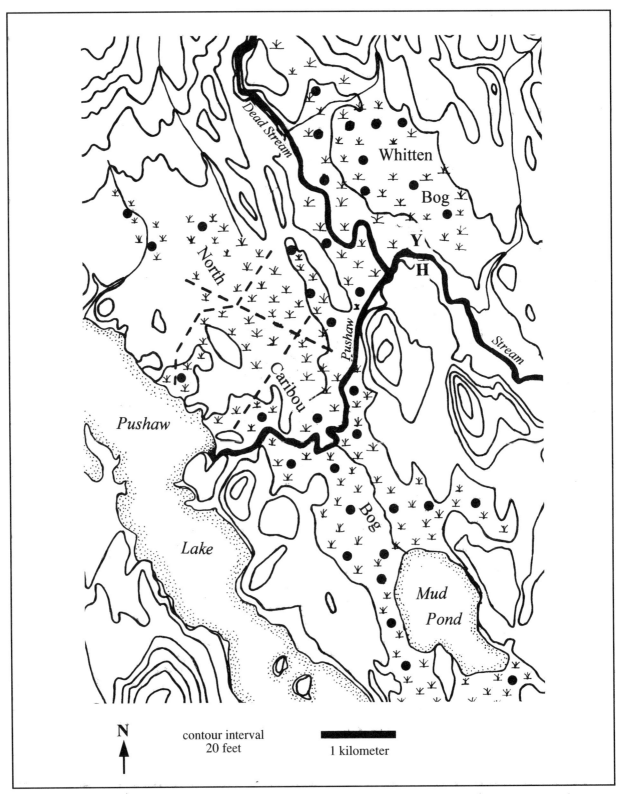

**Figure 11.3.** Map of the study area, including modern extent of open water and peatland and locations of the Young (Y) and Hirundo (H) archaeological sites. Dots depict coring locations; dashed lines depict transects of cores studied by Hu and Davis (1993).

*Almquist-Jacobson and Sanger*

and Davis 1993). The northern portion is raised with peat depths up to 5 m. Hu and Davis's (1993) analysis of 38 cores from that portion of the peatland revealed that the area evolved from a lake with small islands at around 9,000 years B.P. to a mosaic of marsh, peatland, and upland at about 7,000 years B.P. By 6,000 B.P., it was a wooded peatland interspersed with upland and became a continually changing peatland complex thereafter. Preliminary stratigraphic studies of Caribou Bog near the margin of Mud Pond (Figure 11.3; Sanger and MacKay 1973) also showed that peatlands were expanding locally at least between 8,000 and 4,000 years B.P. Whitten Bog includes a raised dome, which is wooded by black spruce (*Picea mariana*) except at the center. Dead Stream cuts through the southwestern portion of the peatland.

The developmental history of Whitten Bog has not been previously studied. Two large archaeological sites, Hirundo (Sanger and MacKay 1973; Sanger et al. 1977) and Young (Borstel 1982), lie on Pushaw Stream adjacent to a prominent set of rapids (Figure 11.3). These sites, which were ideally situated for river fishing as well as exploitation of surrounding wetlands, were repeatedly occupied for thousands of years. The Young site lies on the north side of the stream at the eastern edge of Whitten Bog. Its record spans the Late Archaic (6,000 to 3,000 years B.P.) and Ceramic (3,000 to 300 years B.P.) periods and includes a faunal record dominated by beaver, muskrat, fish, and medium-sized mammals. Hirundo lies on the south side of the stream, opposite the Young site. It spans the Middle Archaic (8,000 to 6,000 years B.P.) through the Historic periods, but no Middle Archaic faunal remains are preserved. The primary faunal elements include beaver, muskrat, bear, fish, and turtle. Although faunal assemblages from the spodosol soils at these sites are almost certainly biased by differential preservation of some bone elements (Knight 1985), they do demonstrate that prehistoric people used at least some local wetland resources. Botanical remains are not preserved. Downstream of these two sites are many other localities from which the wetlands could be accessed by canoe (Sanger 1996).

Mansell Pond lies about 5 km northeast of the North Caribou Bog complex in Alton Township, Penobscot County (45°02'30" N, 68°44'00" W) at 58 m a.s.l. The pond covers 4 ha and has a maximum depth of 7 m, with 8 m of sediment that has accumulated since deglaciation. A 9,200-year pollen and charcoal record including over 110 analyzed levels and 13 radiocarbon dates was published by Almquist-Jacobson and Sanger (1995).

## METHODS

### Core Collection
A network of 35 coring sites was established to cover the current extent of the peatland, except the portion of northern Caribou Bog that was studied previously by Hu and Davis (1993). The spatial resolution of the sampling grid was approximately 500 to 1,000 m (Figure 11.3). Exact coring locations were determined in the field using a handheld geographic positioning devise (GPS). At each sampling point, a complete core was collected using a 5-cm-diameter "Russian" peat corer (Belokopytov and Beresnevich 1955; Jowsey 1966). The cores were wrapped in plastic, returned to the laboratory, and stored at 5°C.

### Determination of the Sediment Depositional Environment
Color, texture, and composition of each sediment core were described. Subsamples for analyses of total organic content, macrofossils, and pollen were taken from selected cores in order to characterize and date each visible sedimentologic change. Bulk density and water content were determined by drying volumetric samples (2 cm$^3$) of determined wet weight at 100°C for 12 hr. Organic content was estimated by loss-on-ignition at 550°C for 2 hr (Bengtsson and Enell 1986). Samples of bulk sediment (~100 cm$^3$) for macrofossil analysis were soaked overnight in 2 percent KOH and passed through 400μm and 225μm sieves with a gentle stream of warm water. The sieved remains were sorted under a Nikon SMZ-U zoom microscope and identified using the reference collection of the Laboratory for Quaternary Paleoecology and Paleohydrology,

**Table 11.1. Uncorrected Radiocarbon Dates.**

| Lab Number | Core | Material | Uncorrected Age (years B.P.) | 13C/12C | Adjusted Age (Calendar years B.P.) | Method |
|---|---|---|---|---|---|---|
| Beta-66756 | W-1 | peat | 5,840 ± 90 | -27.6 | 6,849-6,409 | Std. |
| Beta-66757 | W-7 | peat | 320 ± 60 | -28.9 | 469-0 | Std. |
| Beta-66758 | W-12 | peat | 8,730 ± 90 | -27.4 | 9,903-9,457 | Std. |
| Beta-66759 | W-13 | peat | 8,080 ± 80 | -27.8 | 9,203-8,572 | Std. |
| Beta-78604 | W-3 | peat | 7,270 ± 80 | -27.9 | 8,133-7,833 | Std. |
| Beta-78605 | W-8 | peat | 9,330 ± 110 | -25.1 | 10,795-10,033 | Std. |
| Beta-78606 | W-9 | peat | 9,140 ± 80 | -26.5 | 10,294-9,952 | Std. |
| Beta-78607 | W-11 | peat | 9,180 ± 100 | -27.4 | 10,359-9,941 | Std. |
| Beta-68466 | C-7 | peat | 2,410 ± 140 | -30.8 | 2,747-1,986 | Std. E.C. |
| Beta-68467; CAMS-10468 | C-11 | wood | 8,740 ± 60 | -30.8 | 9,845-9,459 | AMS |
| Beta-68468 | C-14 | marsh sed. | 9,500 ± 70 | -27.8 | 10,894-10,227 | Std. |
| Beta-68469 | C-15 | peat | 8,220 ± 110 | -29.1 | 9,423-8,658 | Std. E.C. |
| Beta-68470 | C-18 | peat | 7,990 ± 110 | -28.1 | 9,144-8,423 | Std. E.C. |
| Beta-78602 | C-20 | peat | 8,620 ± 100 | -26.3 | 9,864-9,390 | Std. |
| Beta-78603 | C-23 | peat | 7,760 ± 70 | -26.9 | 8,584-8,364 | Std. |

*Key*

W    Whitten Bog      C    Caribou Bog
Std.    Standard method      E.C.    Extended counting time.

Calendar years are calculated using CALIB 3.0.1 and 2σ (Stuiver and Reimer 1993).

University of Maine, and by reference texts including Martin and Barkley (1961), Montgomery (1977), and Lévesque et al. (1988).

Unconsolidated sediment was characterized as representing peatland, marsh, or lake, based on physical characteristics and macrofossil content (Figure 11.4). Peatland was characterized by moss (*Sphagnum*)- or sedge (*Carex*)-dominated peat with or without wood; common macrofossils included sedge (*Carex*), marsh St. John's wort (*Triadenum*), and leather leaf (*Chamaedaphne*). Marsh was characterized by highly inorganic sediment with or without coarse organic detritus. Rush (*Juncus*) or cattail (*Typha*), loosestrife (*Lysimachia*), and water plantain (*Alisma*) dominated the macrofossil assemblages. Lake was represented by (1) highly inorganic sediment with very few macrofossils, (2) gyttja (organic mud) with seeds of water lily (*Nuphar* and *Nymphaea*) and spike rush (*Eleocharis*), or (3) gyttja with abundant seeds of stone wort (Characeae), quill wort (*Isoetes*), water-nymph (*Najas*), pondweed (*Potamogeton*), and grass (Poaceae).

## Determination of the Timing of Transitions in Sediment Depositional Environment

The timings of transitions between sediment types within 18 selected cores were determined to within a few hundred years using radiocarbon dating and to within 1,000 years using pollen correlation. Thirteen samples of peat and one sample of marsh sediment were dated by Beta Analytic, Miami, Florida, using standard methods. Those samples were pretreated with HCl before conversion to methane. One wood sample was analyzed by accelerator mass spectrometry (AMS). Chemical pretreatment to eliminate carbonates and target-material conversions for that sample were performed by Beta Analytic Inc.; the AMS measurement was made at Lawrence Livermore National Laboratory in California. Dates of all samples (Table 11.1) are based on the 5,568-yr [14]C half-life and the NBS oxalic acid standard, with standard deviations quoted including ±1 of the counting statistics of background, sample, and standard counts (Steventon and Kutzbach 1987).

Eight sediment ages were determined using pollen correlation. Those subsamples (0.5

182                                                          *Almquist-Jacobson and Sanger*

Milford Drainage Basin
Macrofossil Assemblages of Selected Samples

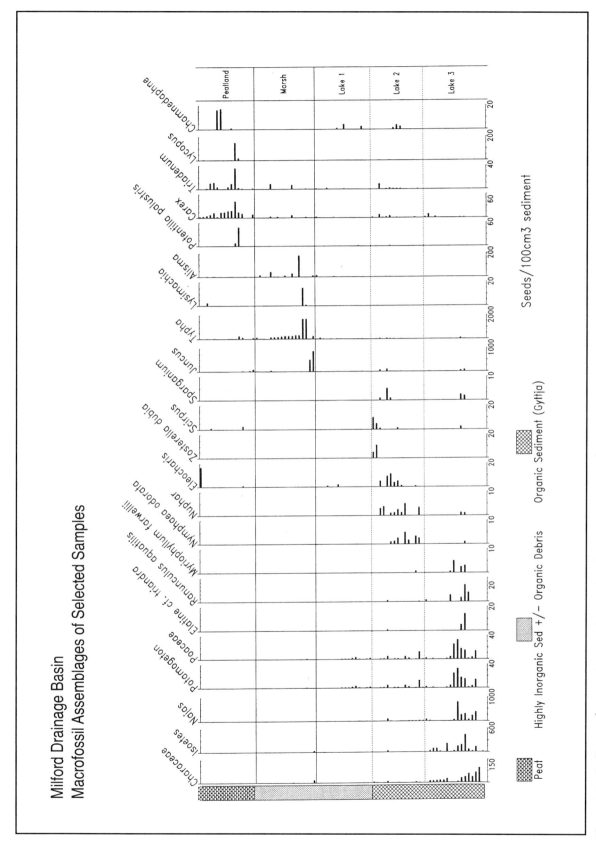

**Figure 11.4.** Sediment characteristics and macrofossil assemblages of eighty selected samples (along y-axis) interpreted as representing peatland, marsh, and lake environments.

cm$^3$) were processed by standard chemical methods to concentrate fossil pollen (Faegri et al. 1989). Terrestrial pollen sums of at least 250 grains were counted at 400X. Identifications were aided by the pollen reference collection of the Laboratory for Quaternary Paleoecology and Paleohydrology, University of Maine, and by reference texts including McAndrews et al. (1973), Faegri et al. (1989), and Moore et al. (1991). Botanical nomenclature follows Gleason and Cronquist (1991). Percentages of pollen types are based on the terrestrial pollen sum. The pollen assemblage of each sample was assigned an age to the nearest 1,000 years based on comparison with the well-dated pollen record from Mansell Pond (Figure 11.5; Almquist-Jacobson and Sanger 1995).

## Construction of Paleogeographic Maps

The timing and nature of changes in sediment depositional environment at each core location were compiled and maps of the study area were prepared for every 1,000-year interval since 10,000 years B.P. The maps represent changes in the spatial extent of the various landscape units identified (lake, marsh, peatland, upland) as a function of time. They do not depict topographic changes.

## RESULTS AND DISCUSSION

### Changes in Wetland and Upland Systems

The 10,000 years B.P. map (Figure 11.6a) explains why no Paleoindian (11,000 to 10,000 years B.P.) remains have been discovered along the present streams in the study area; a large lake covered much of the lowlands. Between 10,000 and 9,000 years B.P. (Figure 11.6b), the lake receded slightly and limited areas of marsh developed. A small peatland became established under what is today the raised portion of Whitten Bog. Upland vegetation consisted of a semi-open woodland including light-demanding trees and shrubs such as spruce (*Picea*), poplar (*Populus*), eastern larch (*Larix*), fir (*Abies*), hazel (*Corylus*), green alder (*Alnus viridis*), and shrub birch (*Betula*) among others, as well as grasses (Poaceae), sedges (Cyperaceae), composites (Asteraceae), bracken fern (*Pteridium aquilinum*), and staghorn clubmoss (*Lycopodium clava-*

*tum*). The frequency of charcoal in the Mansell Pond lake sediments (Figure 11.5) suggests that fire was relatively common.

Between 9,000 and 8,000 years B.P., the peatland area expanded to over half its modern extent. Peatland and small pockets of marsh separated the open water into three lakes joined by streams (Figure 11.6c). White pine (*Pinus strobus*) entered the area around 9,000 years B.P., and dominated the landscape for around 1600 years. A rapidly changing suite of secondary species, including decreasing amounts of the more boreal tree types and a brief but significant presence of mountain maple (*Acer spicatum*) accompanied the increase in pine. By around 8400 B.P., more temperate trees, including oak (*Quercus*) in particular, but also ash (*Fraxinus*), elm (*Ulmus*), speckled alder (*Alnus incana*), and sugar maple (*Acer saccharum*), appeared. The reduction in percentages of herb pollen and fern and moss spores indicates that the pine forest was significantly more closed than previously. Charcoal abundances indicate that fire was still a factor on the landscape (Figure 11.5). No evidence of human habitation is confirmed for this period.

From 8,000 to 6,000 years B.P. (Figure 11.6d), Caribou Bog expanded slightly in all directions, replacing the rush marsh along the esker and reducing the open-water area in the northernmost part to a small cattail marsh. The open-water area bordering Whitten Bog also gradually developed into cattail marsh. On the uplands, eastern hemlock (*Tsuga canadensis*) abruptly replaced white pine at around 7,400 years B.P. Abundances of elm, ash and sugar maple (*Acer saccharum*) increased, while oak began to decline slightly. This assemblage probably represents a mosaic vegetation similar to that described by Davis et al. (1991), with extensive, almost pure hemlock stands interspersed with stands of mixed hardwoods. Charcoal abundances indicate that fire was much reduced. At other sites in the region, the abundance of hemlock persisted until around 4,850 years B.P., when hemlock populations across northeastern North America were decimated, apparently by a pathogen (Allison et al. 1986; Davis 1981). At Mansell Pond, however, hemlock first declined abruptly around 6,400 years B.P.,

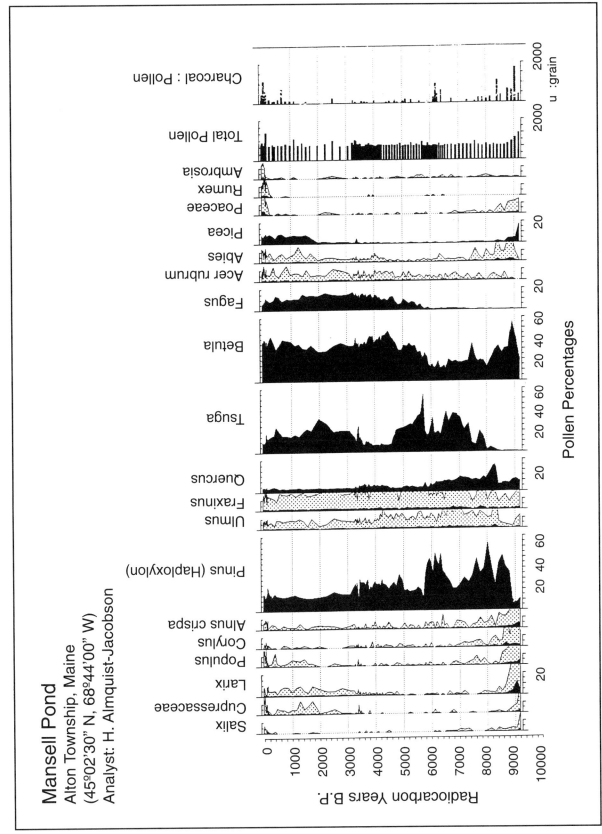

**Figure 11.5.** Summary pollen and charcoal diagram from Mansell Pond (adapted from Almquist-Jacobson and Sanger 1995).

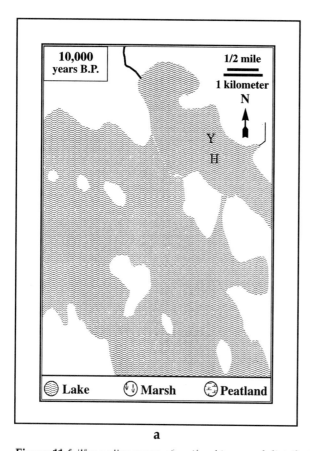

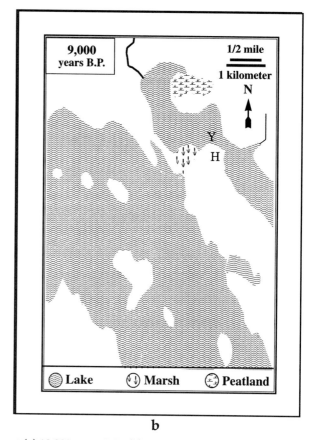

| a | b |

**Figure 11.6.** Time-slice maps of wetland type and distribution at (a) 10,000 years B.P.; (b) 9000 years B.P.; (c) 8000 years B.P.; (d) 6000 years B.P.; (e) 1000 years B.P., and; (f) modern. Y and H show locations of the Young and Hirundo archaeological sites, respectively.

and was replaced by white pine and increased prevalence of fire. Human populations were well established by this period at the Hirundo site and at two other sites (Beaver and Gilman Falls) located 19 km downstream (east) on Pushaw Stream (Sanger 1996; Sanger et al. 1977).

Soon after 5,700 years B.P., hemlock abruptly replaced pine, and beech entered the area and began to increase gradually, together with birch. The forest became more closed, and fire was again much reduced. Although the changes in local forest type suggest increased moisture availability, the only detectable change in wetland configuration between 6,000 and 5,000 years B.P. was the transition of a small cattail marsh into peatland.

From 5,000 to 1,000 years B.P. (Figure 11.6e), the extent of the various wetland areas has remained remarkably stable, while upland forests changed considerably. The regional hemlock decline occurred around 4,700 years B.P., and

thereafter the upland forests consisted largely of birch and beech. Red maple (*Acer rubrum*) was present, probably as an early successional species on wet sites. White pine and oak probably occupied drier sites. Abundances of elm decreased around 4,200 years B.P. Hemlock expanded again at 3,400 years B.P., apparently replacing pine and oak (Figure 11.5) and creating a mosaic with stands dominated by birch and beech. However, hemlock did not regain its former prominence, and stands were probably smaller than those of the early Holocene.

Spruce and fir expanded around 2,000 years B.P. (Figure 11.5), while hemlock, beech, ash, and sugar maple began a long-term, gradual decline. Other boreal elements including juniper and cedar (*Juniperus* and *Thuja*, which cannot be distinguished palynologically), poplar, eastern larch, and herbs expanded as well. Such trends in northeastern North America have been attributed

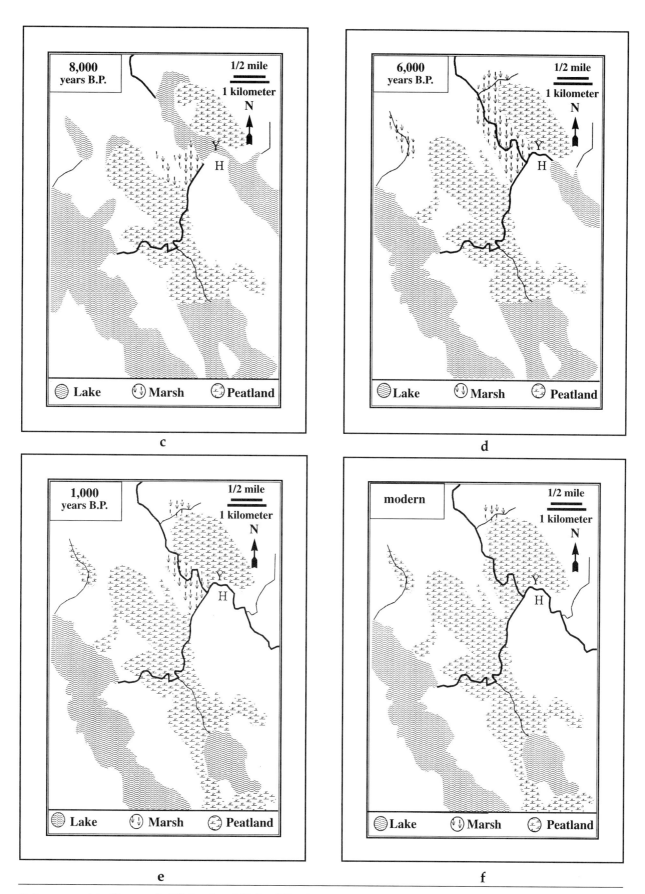

to broad-scale climatic cooling (Gajewski 1987, 1988; Russell et al. 1993).

Upland forests changed little between 1,000 years B.P. and European settlement (Figure 11.6f), but Whitten Bog invaded the last significant expanse of cattail marsh in the area. Settlement does not appear to have had any significant effect on the extent of the wetland areas, although increased fire frequency on the landscape may have influenced peatland vegetation locally. In general, however, it appears that wetland areas remained largely undisturbed by Europeans.

## Potential Relationships Between Environmental Changes and Settlement Patterns

Recent archaeological surveys have revealed about 100 sites along the Penobscot River and its tributary streams (Sanger et al. 1994; Sanger 1996). Those sites range in size and, presumably, in duration of occupation. Although the earliest archaeological sites within the Penobscot River system as a whole may date to about 9,500 years B.P. (Sanger et al. 1992), the oldest radiocarbon-dated archaeological materials from the Milford Drainage Basin date to only about 8,000 years B.P. (Sanger 1996). The abundance of open water shown by our paleogeographic reconstructions suggests that the lack of earlier archaeological evidence reflects either a true lack of human habitation or simply a lack of sampling at appropriate elevations.

By 8,000 years B.P., the reduction of open water and development of restricted waterways would have significantly increased both the extent of habitable uplands and the safety and ease of water transport. In addition, the development of cattail marshes after 8,000 years B.P. would have provided an important local resource. The Young site, in particular, was not occupied until after 6,000 years B.P., when the adjacent lake became a cattail marsh, and was abandoned by 300 years B.P., when that marsh was overgrown by peatland.

The primary occupation period of all sites in the study region was 5,000 to 300 years B.P. (Late Archaic through Ceramic periods). In addition, faunal records from many of those sites appear to record an increase in the use of beaver during this period (Almquist-Jacobson and Sanger 1995; Spiess 1992). Ethnographic evidence shows that beaver was an important source of both pelts and fat for native people. However, an increase in beaver usage cannot be attributed to wetland expansion because the extent of wetland areas remained relatively stable. Instead, changes in the composition of forests surrounding the wetlands may have stimulated growth of beaver populations. In Maine today, beavers prefer wetlands near abundant sources of white birch, poplar, and red maple. Abundances of those northern hardwoods increased at around 4,700 (birch and maple) and 2,000 (poplar) years B.P. Of course, increased abundances of beaver through this or any other mechanism would not rule out changes in cultural preference (Spiess 1992) as a factor contributing to the increase in beaver remains found at local sites.

## CONCLUSIONS

Comparison of the timing of the establishment and abandonment of the Young, Hirundo and other nearby settlements and changes in the local environment, suggests three environmental factors that may have played important roles in stimulating and maintaining those settlements. These factors are (1) development of restricted waterways, (2) expansion of cattail (*Typha*) marsh, and (3) increase in northern hardwoods. In general, the nature and configuration of wetland resources appear to have had a considerable influence on settlement locations throughout the Holocene. Rather than becoming less attractive during the middle Holocene, as suggested for sites in Southern New England (Nicholas 1988), the lowland areas of the Milford Drainage Basin appear to have remained vitally important. That long-term significance of wetlands may have arisen because, in the north, the expansion of northern hardwoods was likely to have been as beneficial to beaver as to deer. In comparison, climate conditions in Southern New England would have precluded significant expansion of boreal wetland mammals, even when forage conditions improved.

Therefore, although the Holocene development of upland forests in the Milford Drainage

Basin is controlled by climate and disturbance, while wetland evolution is primarily controlled by autogenic sedimentary processes, the two systems are related. In fact, the relative value of wetland areas to prehistoric people may have depended in part on the nature of the upland resource.

## ACKNOWLEDGEMENTS

This research was supported by the Bangor Hydro-Electric Company through a grant to D. Sanger for a study of human occupation of the Milford Basin. Funds for some of the radiocarbon analyses were provided by a grant from the National Science Foundation EPSCoR Program. Norton G. Miller kindly reviewed an earlier manuscript.

## REFERENCES CITED

Allison, T. D., R. E. Moeller, and M. B. Davis. 1986. Pollen in Laminated Sediments Provides Evidence for a Mid-Holocene Forest Pathogen Outbreak. *Ecology* 67: 1101-1105.

Almquist-Jacobson, H., and D. Sanger. 1995. Holocene Climate and Vegetation in the Milford Drainage Basin, Maine. U.S.A., and Their Implications for Human Prehistory. *Vegetation History and Archaeobotany* 4: 211-222.

Belokopytov, I. E., and V. V. Beresnevich. 1955. Giktorf's Peat Borers. *Torf. Prom.* 8: 9-10.

Bengtsson, L., and M. Enell. 1986. Chemical Analysis. In *Handbook of Holocene Palaeoecology and Palaeohydrology*, edited by B. E. Berglund, pp. 423-454. John Wiley and Sons, New York.

Borstel, C. L. 1982. *Archaeological Investigations at the Young Site, Alton, Maine.* Occasional Publications in Maine Archaeology 2. The Maine Historic Preservation Commission, Augusta, Maine.

Cameron, C. C., M. K. Mullen, C. A. Lepage, and W. A. Anderson. 1984. *Peat Resources of Maine.* Vol. 2: Penobscot County. Bulletin 29. Maine Geological Survey, Augusta.

Davis, M. B. 1981. Outbreaks of Forest Pathogens in Forest History, In *Proceedings of the IV International Palynological Conference* (1976-77), Vol. 3, pp. 216-227. Birbal Sahni Institute of Paleobotany, Lucknow, India.

————. 1983. Holocene Vegetational History of the Eastern United States. In *Late-Quaternary Environments of the United States.* Vol. 2. The Holocene, edited by H. E. Wright, Jr., pp. 166-181. University of Minnesota Press, Minneapolis.

Davis, M. B., S. Sugita, R. R. Calcote, and L. Frelich. 1991. Effects of Invasion of *Tsuga canadensis* on a North American Forest Ecosystem. In *Proceedings of the 1st European Ecosystem Conference*, pp. 1-11. Firenze, Italy.

Davis, R. B., and G. L. Jacobson, Jr. 1985. Late Glacial and Early Holocene Landscapes in Northern New England and Adjacent Areas of Canada. *Quaternary Research* 23: 341-368.

Faegri, K., P. E. Kaland, and K. Krzywinski. 1989. *Textbook of Pollen Analysis.* John Wiley and Sons, New York.

Gajewski, K. 1987. Climatic Impacts on the Vegetation of Eastern North America during the Past 2000 years. *Vegetation* 68: 179-190.

————. 1988. Late Holocene Climate Changes in Eastern North America Estimated from Pollen Data. *Quaternary Research* 29: 255-262.

Gleason, H. A., and A. Cronquist. 1991. *Manual of Vascular Plants of Northeastern United States and Adjacent Canada.* 2nd edition. New York Botanical Garden, New York.

Hu, F. S., and R. B. Davis. 1993. Postglacial Development of a Maine Bog and Environmental Implications. *Canadian Journal of Botany* 73: 638-649.

Jowsey, P. C. 1966. An Improved Peat Sampler. *New Phytologist* 65: 245-248.

Knight, J. A. 1985. *Differential Preservation of Calcined Bone at the Hirundo Site, Alton, Maine.* Unpublished MSc Thesis, Institute for Quaternary Studies, University of Maine, Orono, Maine.

Lévesque, P. E. M., H. Dinel, and A. Larouche. 1988. *Guide to the Identification of Plant Macrofossils in Canadian Peatlands.* Publication No. 1817. Land Resource Research Centre, Ottawa, Ontario.

Martin, A. C., and W. D. Barkley. 1961. *Seed Identification Manual.* University of California Press, Berkeley.

McAndrews, J. H., A. A. Berti, and G. Norris. 1973. *Key to the Quaternary Pollen and Spores of the Great Lakes Region.* Life Sciences Miscellaneous Publication, Royal Ontario Museum.

Montgomery, F. H. 1977. *Seeds and Fruits of Plants of Eastern Canada and Northeastern United States.* University of Toronto Press, Toronto.

Moore, P. D., J. A. Webb, and M. E. Collinson. 1991. *Pollen Analysis.* Blackwell Scientific, London.

Nicholas, G. P. 1988. Ecological Leveling, the Archaeology and Environmental Dynamics of Early Postglacial Land Use. In *Holocene Human Ecology in Northeastern North America,* edited by G. P. Nicholas pp. 257-296. Plenum Press, New York.

Osberg, P. H., A. M. Hussey, II, and G. M. Boone. 1985. *Bedrock Geological Map of Maine.* Maine Geological Survey and Department of Conservation.

Russell, E. W. B., Davis, R. B., Anderson, R. S., Rhodes, T. E., and D. S. Anderson. 1993. Recent Centuries of Vegetational Change in the Glaciated North-Eastern United States. *Journal of Ecology* 81: 647-664.

Sanger, D. 1996. Gilman Falls: Implications for Early and Middle Archaic of the Maritime Peninsula. *Canadian Journal of Archaeology* 20: 7-28.

Sanger, D., W. R. Belcher, J. P. Fenton, and M. Sweeney. 1994. *Gilman Falls: A Middle Archaic Quarry and Workshop in Central Maine.* Report to Bangor Hydro-Electric Company. MacKay Archaeological Laboratory, University of Maine, Orono, Maine.

Sanger, D., W.R Belcher, and D.C. Kellogg. 1992. Early Holocene Occupation at the Blackman Stream Site, Central Maine. In *Early Holocene Occupation in Northern New England,* edited by B. S. Robinson, J. B. Petersen, and A. K. Robinson, pp. 149-161. Occasional Publications in Maine Archaeology, No. 9, Augusta.

Sanger, D., R. B. Davis, R. G. MacKay, and H. W. Borns. 1977. The Hirundo Archaeological Project–An Interdisciplinary Approach to Central Maine Prehistory. In *Amerinds and their Paleoenvironments in Northeastern North America,* edited by W. Newman and B. Salwen, pp. 457-471. Annals of New York Academy of Sciences 288.

Sanger, D., and R .G. MacKay. 1973. The Hirundo Archaeological Project Preliminary Report. *Man in the Northeast* 6: 21-29.

Spiess, A. E. 1992. Archaic Period Subsistence in New England and the Atlantic Provinces. In *Early Holocene Occupation in Northern New England,* edited by B. S. Robinson, J. B. Petersen, and A. K. Robinson, pp. 163-185. Occasional Publications in Maine Archaeology 9. Augusta.

Stuiver, M., and P. J. Reimer. 1993. Extended $^{14}$C Database and Revised CALIB 3.0 $^{14}$C Age Calibration Program. *Radiocarbon* 35:215-230.

Steventon, R. L., and J. E. Kutzbach. 1987. University of Wisconsin Radiocarbon Dates XXIV. *Radiocarbon* 29: 397-415.

Thompson, W. B., and H. W. Borns, Jr. 1985. *Surficial Geologic Map of Maine.* Maine Geological Survey and Department of Conservation.

Westveld, M., R. I. Ashman, H. I. Baldwin, R. P. Holdsworth, R. S. Johnson, J. H. Lamvert, H. J. Lutz, L. Swain, and M. Standish. 1956. Natural Forest Vegetation Zones of New England. *Journal of Forestry* 54:332-338.

# CHAPTER 12

# PREHISTORIC PLANT USE IN MAINE: PALEOINDIAN TO CONTACT PERIOD

Nancy Asch Sidell

## INTRODUCTION

This chapter presents the first summary of prehistoric plant use in Maine. Large samples of systematically collected and analyzed plant remains are needed to outline regional trends in plant use and environmental change through time. However, the plant remains from many Maine sites have not been systematically analyzed due to funding constraints. Some excavators have focused on hand collection of the most visible charred remains for $^{14}$C dating, while others have done flotation or fine water-screening of selected soil samples for use in subsistence analysis. As a first step toward developing a regional archaeobotanical synthesis, this paper considers ten of the best sampled[1] components of more than 30 components from 22 archaeological sites that have been analyzed. The ten components from ten sites span over 10,000 years of prehistory (Table 12.1) and are located in a variety of habitats in western and central Maine.

## SIGNIFICANCE OF THE TEN SELECTED COMPONENTS

From oldest (1) to youngest (10), the ten components were selected for the following reasons:

(1) The 10,580-10,500-year-old (cal 2σ 12,677-12,191 B.P.) carbonized remains from the Hedden site (Figure 12.1) in the Kennebunk Plains provide a unique glimpse of early coastal plains vegetation.

(2) The deeply stratified Sharrow site spans 9,000 years of prehistory at the junction of the Sebec and Piscataquis rivers in Milo, Maine. The well-sampled Middle Archaic component has yielded one fragment of *Cucurbita pepo* L., a pepo gourd that could not have grown wild in central Maine, directly dated to 5,695 B.P. (cal 2σ 6,732-6,293 B.P.).

(3, 4, 5) The best sampled Late Archaic components are found at the Hunter Farm site, located on the estuarine Androscoggin River at Topsham; Site 27.60, on five acres of sandy hilltop near Warren; and Fort Halifax, a stratified site at Winslow on a sandy point bar at the junction of the Sebasticook and Kennebec rivers.

(6, 7) Along the Saco River, about 20 km upstream from where Champlain observed maize cultivation in 1605, maize was grown at the Little Ossipee North site by 570 B.P. (cal 2σ 655-530 B.P.) and at the Early Fall site by 460 B.P. (cal 2σ 550-320 B.P.).

(8, 9, 10) Dating to the Late Ceramic and Contact periods, the Sandy River, Tracy Farm, and Norridgewock Mission sites were all part of the "Norridgewock Village" located at the junction of the Sandy and Kennebec rivers. For the Mission site (occupied ca. A.D. 1694-1754), Father Rasles' accounts of Abnaki life provide limited information on historic plant use for comparison with the abundant archaeological record.

## HISTORIC VEGETATION

Nine of the ten selected archaeological sites are located in the "transition hardwoods-white pine-hemlock zone" where today the beech, birches, and maples of the north mix with the oaks and

**Table 12.1. Radiocarbon Dates from Selected Maine Components.**

| Site Name (Site No.) | Component | Lab No. | Age (B.P. ± 1 S.D.) | Calibrated Calendric Date [a] 2σ (cal date) B.P. | Carbonized Material Dated |
|---|---|---|---|---|---|
| Hedden (4.10) [b] | Paleoindian | Beta-68806 | 10,500 ± 60 | 12,600 (12,419) 12,191 | Spruce wood |
| | | Beta-70668 | 10,580 ± 60 | 12,677 (12,508) 12,305 | Pine wood |
| Sharrow (90.2D) [c] | Middle Archaic | Beta-18234 | 6,320 ± 110 | 7,392 (7,212) 6,941 | Unknown floral remains |
| | | Beta-34297 | 6,000 ± 130 | 7,176 (6,854, 6,821, 6,814) 6,500 | Wood |
| | | Beta-34296 | 5,900 ± 100 | 6,981 (6,732) 6,477 | Wood |
| | | Beta-18233 | 5,820 ± 100 | 6,884 (6,661) 6,357 | Wood |
| | | AA-7491 | 5,695 ± 100 | 6,732 (6,473) 6,293 | Cucurbit rind |
| Hunter Farm (15.110) [d] | Late Archaic | Beta-11020 | 4,730 ± 90 | 5,646 (5,559, 5,461, 5,341, 5,338) 5,289 | ? |
| | | Beta-29811 | 4,160 ± 70 | 4,858 (4,811, 4,761, 4,690) 4,446 | ? |
| 27.60 [e] | Late Archaic | Beta-45012 | 4,140 ± 80 | 4,857 (4,805, 4,767, 4,639, 4,637, 4,614, 4,581, 4,578) 4,418 | Red oak gp., ash wood |
| | | Beta-54197 | 4,030 ± 120 | 4,838 (4,512, 4,473, 4,449) 4,147 | Red oak gp., ash wood |
| | | Beta-45009 | 4,030 ± 90 | 4,826 (5,412, 4,473, 4,449) 4,238 | Red oak gp., ash, pine, cherry wood |
| | | Beta-45010 | 4,020 ± 90 | 4,823 (4,507, 4,479, 4,446) 4,234 | Red oak gp., ash, pine wood |
| | | Beta-54198 | 3,150 ± 160 | 3,699 (3,363) 2,893 | Red oak gp., pine wood |
| Fort Halifax (53.35) [f] | Late Archaic | Beta-24688 | 3,280 ± 80 | 3,690 (3,471) 3,350 | ? |
| | | Beta-29809 | 3,160 ± 60 | 3,473 (3,368) 3,217 | Pine wood |
| | | Beta-29810 | 3,130 ± 30 | 3,387 (3,354) 3,263 | Pine wood |
| | | Beta-30913 | 3,100 ± 80 | 3,468 (3,341, 3,281, 3,278) 3,074 | Wood charcoal |
| Little Ossipee North (7.7) [g] | Ceramic | Beta-83651 | 1,010 ± 60 | 1,055 (930) 782 | Pine, oak wood |
| | | Beta-89980 | 850 ± 60 | 919 (732) 663 | Pine, maple, birch, white oak gp. wood |
| | | Beta-102060 | 570 ± 40 | 655 (600) 530 | Maize cupule |

**Table 12.1. Continued**

| Site Name (Site No.) | Component | Lab No. | Age (B.P. ± 1 S.D.) | Calibrated Calendric Date [a] 2σ (cal date) B.P. | Carbonized Material Dated |
|---|---|---|---|---|---|
| Early Fall (7.13) [h] | Ceramic | Beta-29079 | 460 ± 60 | 550 (509) 320 | Unidentified charcoal associated with maize |
| | | Beta-29671 | 570 ± 70 | 660 (574) 501 | Unidentified charcoal associated with maize |
| | | Beta-29672 | 460 ± 80 | 635 (509) 309 | Unidentified charcoal |
| Sandy River (69.24) [i] | Contact | Beta-44409 | 40 ± 70 | 510 (309) 0 | Wood, bark, pitch charcoal |
| | | Beta-43974 | 300 ± 80 | | Wood charcoal |
| Tracy Farm (69.11) [i,j] | Contact | Beta-43970 | 1,140 ± 70 | 1,232 (1,057) 927 charcoal | Butternut shell, wood, pitch |
| Norridgewock Mission (69.2) [i,k] | Contact | Beta-43969 | 530 ± 70 | 650 (535) 471 pine wood | Maple, sugar maple, red oak gp., |

*Notes*

a   Calibrated at 2σ with CALIB rev. 3.0.3 (Stuiver and Reimer 1993)
b   Spiess and Mosher 1994; Spiess et al. 1995; Asch Sidell 1995
c   Petersen 1991; Petersen and Asch Sidell 1996
d   Asch Sidell 1989
e   Spiess 1993
f   Asch Sidell 1990
g   Cowie and Petersen 1990; Will et al. 1996
h   Cowie and Petersen 1990
i   Cowie and Petersen 1992; Cowie et al. 1992; dates for Tracy Farm and Norridgewock Mission sites do not agree with assessment of age based on associated artifacts (Ellen Cowie, personal communication)
j   Asch Sidell 1998
k   Asch Sidell 1996

**Figure 12.1.** Site Location Map.

hickories more typical of the central U.S. (Figure 12.2). The original forest of this zone at settlement contained red oak, white ash, red maple, and sugar maple mixed with white oak, chestnut, beech, basswood, ironwood, white pine, and hemlock (Westveld et al. 1956). Several southern species reach their northern limit and some northern species reach their southern limit in southwestern Maine (Little 1971, 1977; Richards et al. 1983). The tree species that are of special interest for reconstruction of diet (i.e., nut and fruit trees) are not distributed uniformly across the landscape. Figure 12.3 maps the modern distribution of all species of nut trees in Maine.

## PREHISTORIC VEGETATION

At the time of Paleoindian occupation of the Hedden site, rapid vegetation changes were taking place in much of Maine in response to changes in climate and ocean shoreline location. By 12,000 B.P. according to R. B. Davis and Jacobson (1985), there was probably a closed forest in southern Maine, dominated by spruce, balsam fir, birches, and poplar. Also present were ash, jack pine, larch, ironwood, and elm. Before 11,000 B.P., oak and maple had migrated into southernmost Maine, while ice blocks remained in the north (Figure 12.4). White pine joined the assemblage before

*Asch Sidell*

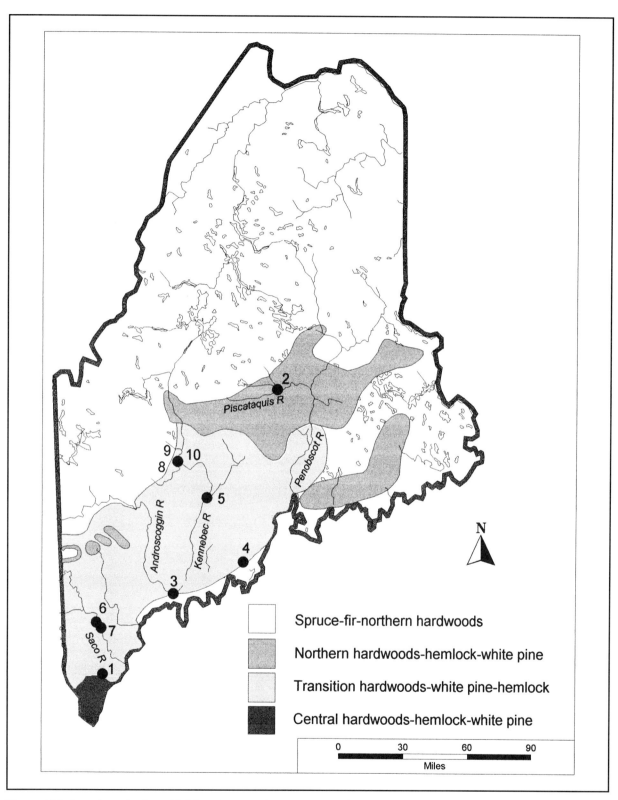

**Figure 12.2.** Location of selected Maine sites in relation to presettlement forest types. Sites are (1) Hedden; (2) Sharrow; (3) Hunter Farm; (4) 27.60; (5) Fort Halifax; (6) Little Ossipee North; (7) Early Fall; (8) Sandy River; (9) Tracy Farm; (10) Norridgewock Mission.

---

*Prehistoric Plant Use in Maine: Paleoindian to Contact Period*                    195

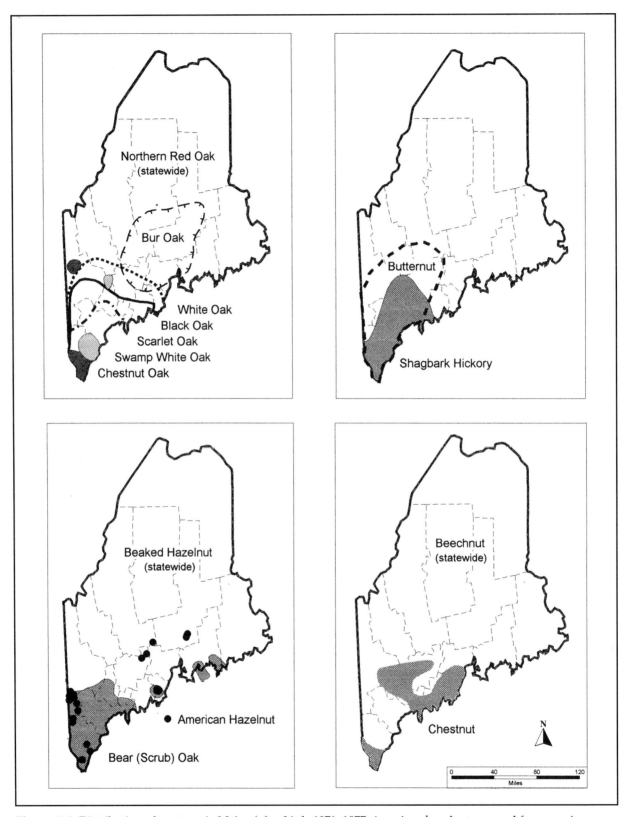

**Figure 12.3.** Distribution of nut trees in Maine (after Little 1971, 1977; American hazelnut mapped from specimens on file in University of Maine Herbarium at Orono).

*Asch Sidell*

10,000 B.P., replacing some of the spruce.

Most species of nut trees had not migrated into Maine by the time of Paleoindian occupation (Davis 1983). M. B. Davis hypothesized that oak reached southwestern Maine about 9,000 years ago and beech about 6,000 years ago (see maps in Davis 1983). R.B. Davis and Jacobson's (1985) model of early Holocene landscapes shows oak arriving in the Hedden site area at about 11,000 B.P., and rapidly spreading to cover the entire state by 10,000 B.P. The models differ because R. B. Davis and Jacobson mapped first arrival of the species, while M. B. Davis mapped the date when large populations become established.

Identification of wood charcoal, nuts, and seeds from archaeological sites provides direct evidence for environmental reconstruction at the site-specific level. Wood charcoal, bark, and pitch are the most abundant types of plant remains from archaeological sites in Maine (Table 12.2). The wide variety of firewood recovered at most sites consists primarily of pine and oak, with beech, maple, ash, birch, and other species (Table 12.3). The most unusual site in terms of wood charcoal composition is the Paleoindian Hedden site (Spiess et al. 1995). Paleoindian sites in New England and the Maritimes are generally found shallowly buried in sandy soil with few plant remains. In contrast, the Hedden site is deeply buried beneath sand dunes in the Kennebunk Plains, where today 1,123 acres of sandplain grasslands and pitch pine / scrub oak woodland are protected by the State of Maine and the Nature Conservancy as habitat for five endangered or threatened plants and animals (Hill 1989).

The Hedden site is unique because a widespread burning event occurred just before, during, or after the Paleoindian occupation (Spiess et al. 1995). Carbonized plant remains were found in a 20-cm layer of windblown sand above a pebbly sand glacial outwash surface. Although plant remains occurred in proximity to artifacts, the charcoal was not concentrated in particular areas, and it was also found outside the apparent area of occupation. How do we know if any of the charcoal is cultural? The overall assemblage of wood, bark, pitch, seeds, spruce needles, etc., is not unlike that found at most archaeological sites in

Maine where charcoal is generally associated only with the cultural levels. It is possible that the very tiny fragments of Hedden charcoal could have been widely dispersed by wind as was the sand which formed the dunes covering the site, so that now it is not possible to tell if the charcoal was dispersed from campfires. Nevertheless, it is not unreasonable to assume that, if the Hedden plant remains are not of cultural origin, they are still an indication of plants that would have been used by the prehistoric people who frequented the site. In other words, if raspberries were growing at Hedden site, they would undoubtedly have been used for food.

The Hedden site flotation samples were very small, and the wood charcoal was preserved as tiny fragments, making it difficult to attain genus- or species-level identifications. Assuming collection of the nearest available deadwood for use as firewood, or burning of fallen branches if the wood is noncultural, the wood analysis suggests a forest composed predominantly of pine (*Pinus* spp.) and spruce (*Picea* spp.), with minor amounts of ring-porous and diffuse-porous species. The presence of spruce is also indicated by the ubiquity of spruce needles and / or spruce cone scale fragments in 15 of 16 flotation samples. A single fir needle fragment (*Abies balsamea* [L.] Mill.) identifies fir as a component of the forest. The presence of seeds of fleshy fruits indicates that the forest at about 10,500 B.P. in southwestern Maine near Hedden was quite open, allowing sunlight for the growth of brambles (*Rubus* spp., raspberry, blackberry, or dewberry), bunchberry (*Cornus canadensis*), bristly sarsaparilla (*Aralia hispida* Vent.), and grape (*Vitis* sp.). The single grape fragment, which was found in association with cultural artifacts, may have been carried to the site from a nearby stream valley. Today, a small stream fringed with mesic vegetation cuts into the dunes very close to the Hedden site. No nut fragments were recovered, but more extensive sampling is required to determine whether nut trees grew in the area.

In the Early Archaic component at the Little Ossipee North[2] site in southwestern Maine, a study of 191 wood fragments from four flotation samples and 8 hand-picked samples revealed a

**Table 12.2. Selected Maine Sites: Percentage Composition of Carbonized Plant Remains.**

**CARBONIZED PLANT REMAINS (%)**

| Site / Component | 4.10 PI | 90.2D MA | 15.110 LA | 27.60 LA | 53.35 LA | 7.7 Ceramic | 7.13 Ceramic | 69.24 Contact | 69.11 Contact | 69.2 Contact |
|---|---|---|---|---|---|---|---|---|---|---|
| Wood | 68.10 | 77.48 | 83.66 | 82.49 | 89.97 | 53.71 | 63.74 | 56.30 | 72.45 | 71.41 |
| Bark | 10.20 | 17.21 | 6.54 | 6.97 | 3.70 | 30.38 | 22.25 | 19.90 | 16.96 | 19.95 |
| Twig | 6.90 | 0.26 | 0.19 | 0.78 | 0.01 | 2.77 | 0.90 | 0.74 | 1.12 | 0.47 |
| Pitch | 13.50 | 3.97 | 8.13 | 8.78 | 6.17 | 9.84 | 8.50 | 4.42 | 5.63 | 3.51 |
| Nutshell | – | 0.23 | 0.75 | 0.04 | 0.10 | 1.24 | 3.17 | 2.01 | 0.63 | 1.73 |
| Nutmeat, acorn | – | – | 0.03 | – | – | – | – | 0.17 | 0.01 | 0.23 |
| Bud | – | – | – | – | – | (2) | 0.01 | – | P | 0.01 |
| Grass stem | – | – | – | – | – | – | – | – | 1.15 | 0.16 |
| Stem/vine type A | – | – | – | 0.15 | – | – | – | – | – | – |
| Stem | – | – | – | – | – | – | P | – | – | 0.04 |
| Stem and rhizome | – | – | – | – | – | – | – | 0.27 | 0.11 | – |
| Rhizome | – | 0.01 | – | – | – | 0.06 | 0.09 | 0.66 | 0.47 | 0.21 |
| Tuber | H | 0.01 | – | – | – | – | – | – | 0.02 | – |
| Gall | 0.20 | – | – | – | – | 0.004 | – | – | 0.08 | 0.01 |
| Fungus | – | 0.01 | – | – | – | – | 0.07 | – | – | – |
| Cedar branch tip | – | – | – | – | – | – | – | – | – | – |
| Fir needle | P | – | – | – | – | (5) | – | – | 0.02 | P |
| Pine needle | – | – | – | – | – | P+ | – | – | P | P |
| Spruce needle | P | – | – | – | – | – | – | – | P | – |
| Spruce cone scale | 0.90 | – | – | – | – | – | – | – | P | – |
| Cone scale | – | – | – | – | – | 1.32 | – | – | – | – |
| Cone | – | – | – | – | – | 0.07 | – | – | – | – |
| Cucurbita rind | – | 0.01 | – | – | – | – | 0.03 | 0.02 | 0.01 | 0.01 |
| Maize | – | – | – | – | – | 0.01 | 0.78 | 13.88 | 0.79 | 1.54 |
| Bean | – | – | – | – | – | – | 0.01 | – | 0.004 | 0.03 |
| Seeds | P | 0.20 | 0.14 | 0.26 | P | 0.08 | 0.25 | 0.15 | 0.15 | 0.26 |
| Unknown | 0.20 | 0.64 | 0.56 | 0.54 | 0.05 | 0.52 | 0.21 | 1.48 | 0.40 | 0.43 |
| Total | 100.0 | 100.0 | 100.0 | 100.0 | 100.0 | 100.0 | 100.0 | 100.0 | 100.0 | 100.0 |

# Table 12.2. Continued

## SAMPLE STATISTICS

| | | | | | | | | | | |
|---|---|---|---|---|---|---|---|---|---|---|
| Charcoal wt. (g) | 5.5 | 152 | 74 | 160 | 322 | 336 | 101 | 88 | 643 | 216 |
| No. samples | 16 | 44 | 31 | 44 | 75 | 6 | 20 | 7 | 60 | 31 |
| No. features sampled | n/a | 3 | 10 | 44 | 13 | 5 | 2 | 3 | 20 | 11 |

## SAMPLING

| | | | | | | | | | | |
|---|---|---|---|---|---|---|---|---|---|---|
| Flotation/Water screen | F | WS | F | F | F | WS + F | WS | WS | WS + F | WS |

*Notes*

P present in 0.5-2 mm fraction

H in handpicked (non-flotation, non-water-screened) samples

PI Paleoindian

MA Middle Archaic

LA Late Archaic

Summary of Site 69.2 does not include data from feature with concentration of entire corn cobs.

Summary of Site 69.11 includes only samples analyzed quantitatively. An additional 56 samples were scanned to obtain quantitative information only on seeds, nutshell, and cultivated plants. A total of 890 g from 48 features was examined.

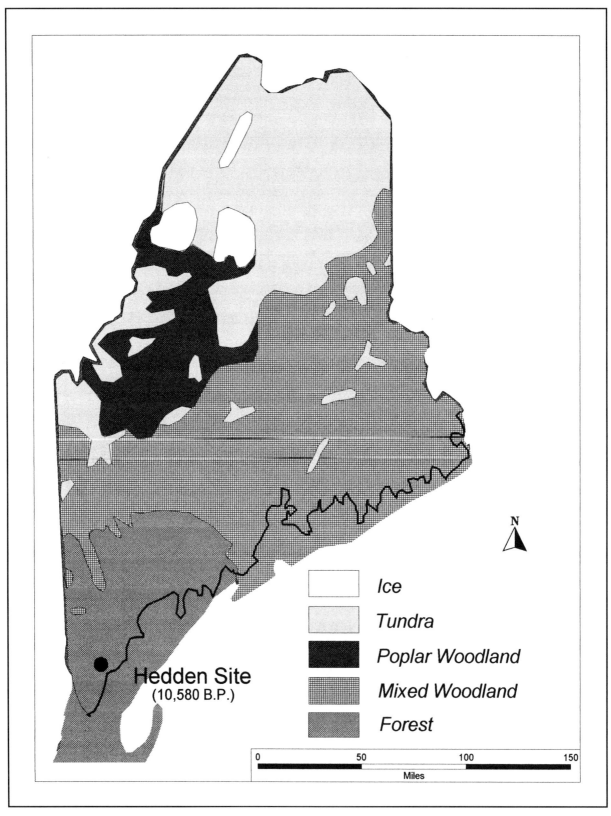

**Figure 12.4.** Reconstructed landscape at 11,000 B.P. (after R.B. Davis and Jacobson 1985).

**Table 12.3. Selected Maine Sites: Percentage Composition of Wood Charcoal.**

| Site Component | 4.10 PI | 90.2D MA | 15.110 LA | 27.60 LA | 53.35 LA | 7.7 Ceramic | 7.13 Ceramic | 69.24 Contact | 69.11 Contact | 69.2 Contact |
|---|---|---|---|---|---|---|---|---|---|---|
| **WOOD (%)** | | | | | | | | | | |
| Acer spp., maple | — | 0.48 | 0.97 | — | 3.26 | 0.67 | 6.87 | — | 3.01 | 3.57 |
| A. saccharum, sugar maple | — | 9.90 | 2.27 | 0.36 | 2.84 | — | — | 22.32 | 2.48 | 8.27 |
| Alnus spp., alder | — | — | — | — | — | 6.00 | — | — | — | — |
| Betula spp., birch | — | 1.93 | 3.56 | 0.12 | 12.72 | 0.67 | 0.60 | — | 3.46 | 6.58 |
| B. populifolia, gray birch | — | — | — | — | — | — | — | — | — | 0.19 |
| Crataegus spp., hawthorn | — | 1.21 | — | — | — | — | — | — | — | — |
| Fagus grandifolia, beech | — | 0.72 | 4.53 | 3.68 | 7.57 | 19.33 | 2.09 | 1.79 | 8.20 | 3.01 |
| Fraxinus spp., ash | — | 8.94 | 10.36 | 5.22 | 11.99 | — | 0.30 | 12.50 | 7.07 | 5.64 |
| Juglans cinerea, butternut | — | — | — | — | — | — | — | 0.89 | 2.33 | 1.69 |
| Larix laricina, larch | — | — | — | — | — | — | — | — | — | 0.75 |
| Ostrya virginiana, ironwood | — | 7.49 | — | 0.36 | 3.47 | — | — | — | 1.50 | 2.26 |
| Picea spp., spruce | 1.79 | 3.14 | — | 1.30 | — | — | — | — | 1.58 | — |
| Picea/Pinus, spruce/pine | 19.73 | — | — | — | — | — | — | — | — | — |
| Pinus spp., pine | 28.70 | 25.85 | 26.21 | 32.03 | 28.60 | 58.00 | 60.60 | 2.68 | 55.53 | 40.60 |
| Populus spp., poplar | — | — | — | — | 0.21 | — | 0.60 | — | 0.23 | 1.88 |
| Prunus spp., cherry | — | 0.48 | — | 0.12 | — | — | — | — | 0.23 | 1.32 |
| Quercus spp., oak | — | — | 31.39 | — | 7.68 | 8.67 | 0.30 | — | 0.07 | — |
| Quercus spp., red oak group | — | 28.50 | H | 46.74 | 6.73 | 5.33 | 2.69 | 0.89 | 8.28 | 10.34 |
| Quercus spp., white oak group | — | — | H | — | 7.15 | 0.67 | — | — | 0.60 | — |
| Tilia americana, basswood | — | 0.24 | — | 1.19 | 0.21 | — | — | 15.18 | 0.08 | 0.56 |
| Tsuga canadensis, hemlock | — | — | — | 0.71 | — | — | — | — | — | — |
| Ulmus americana, American elm | — | 2.17 | — | — | 0.84 | — | 0.30 | — | 0.45 | 4.14 |
| Coniferous | 42.15 | 3.86 | 8.09 | 4.03 | 1.26 | — | 12.54 | 23.21 | 1.28 | 2.82 |
| Ring porous | 2.24 | 0.97 | 1.29 | 0.47 | 0.63 | — | 2.98 | — | — | — |
| Diffuse porous | 1.35 | 2.90 | 1.29 | 1.78 | 2.94 | 0.67 | 4.78 | 19.64 | 3.24 | 4.89 |
| Unidentifiable | 4.04 | 1.21 | 10.03 | 1.90 | 1.89 | — | 5.37 | 0.89 | 0.38 | 1.50 |
| **Total** | 100.0 | 100.0 | 100.0 | 100.0 | 100.0 | 100.0 | 100.0 | 100.0 | 100.0 | 100.0 |
| **No. fragments** | 223 | 414 | 309 | 843 | 951 | 150 | 335 | 112 | 1329 | 564 |

*Notes*

H from handpicked (1/4-in screen) samples.

Samples are from flotation or fine water-screening, except Site 4.10 which includes 123 fragments of hand-picked wood.

wood assemblage dominated by sugar maple (*Acer saccharum* Marsh.), pine (*Pinus* spp.), hemlock (*Tsuga canadensis* [L.] Carr.), oak (*Quercus* spp., red oak group), ash (*Fraxinus* spp.), and possibly spruce (*Picea* spp.), with minor amounts of cherry (*Prunus* spp.), poplar (*Populus* spp.), ironwood (*Ostrya virginiana* [Mill.] K. Koch), and beech (*Fagus grandifolia* Ehrh.) (Will et al. 1996). This site provides the earliest evidence for the arrival of beech in Maine. One fragment of beech wood was present in a sample dated to 9,350 ± 90 B.P. (cal 2σ 10,793-10,044 B.P.). However, an additional date on red oak group charcoal from lower down in the same feature was 7,980 ± 100 B.P. (cal 2σ 9,190-8,500 B.P.), indicating possible disturbance.

In central Maine, Almquist-Jacobson and Sanger (this volume) show oak pollen at Mansell Pond for at least the past 9,200 years, and beech pollen after 5,700 B.P. About 30 km to the north at the Sharrow site, direct evidence was found for older beech wood and nutshell in the Middle Archaic deposits (Tables 12.3 and 12.4). Beech wood charcoal was identified in three samples from Feature 20; a date on unidentified floral remains from the feature was 6,320 B.P. ± 110 (cal 2σ 7,392-6,941 B.P.). A carbonized beechnut shell (*Fagus grandifolia* Ehrh.) was preserved in a hearth feature with a wood charcoal date of 5,820 ± 110 B.P. (cal 2σ 6,884-6,357 B.P.).

Plant remains from Maine archaeological sites dating 6,000 B.P. to 300 B.P. suggest forests composed of mixed hardwoods and pine, as expected. Typically, pine and oak together make up 50 percent or more of the wood charcoal (Table 12.3).

## HISTORIC RECORDS OF PLANT USE

Bennett (1955) studied the food economy of the New England Indians from 1605-1675 by referring to early historic records. He concluded that there were no conspicuous differences among southeastern New England Indian tribes in composition of diet and that maize provided about two-thirds of the food calories, with fish and game providing a fifth. In Maine, the Indians relied more heavily on hunting, fishing, and gath-

ering because maize was too risky a crop east of the Kennebec River (Bennett 1955:372). Bennett suggested that moving down the coast from northeastern Maine to the Massachusetts border, the proportion of maize in the food supply rose on a gradient from nothing to a substantial fraction.

In 1605, Champlain explored the mouth of the Kennebec River where he was informed by the natives "that the Indians who cultivated Indian corn lived far inland, and had ceased to grow it on the coasts on account of the war they used to wage with others who came and seized it" (Biggar 1922-1936:321). As Champlain proceeded down the coast he observed Indian gardens and a village at the mouth of the Saco River. Cultivated plants included Indian maize, beans, squashes, pumpkins, and tobacco.

Father Gabriel Druillettes of Quebec City founded a mission at the Norridgewock Indian village on the Kennebec River in 1646 and ministered to it until 1652 (Calvert 1991). In the 1680s, the Jesuit brothers Vincent and Jacques Bigot of Canada revived the mission and made many trips to the Kennebec and Penobscot rivers. In 1690, in Quebec, Father Sebastian Rasles learned the Abnaki language and lifeways from Maine Indians who had recently emigrated to Canada. He began a dictionary of the Abnaki language in 1691 and was finally assigned to reside at the Norridgewock Mission in 1695. It is Rasles' letters that document that maize was grown in interior Maine by the Indians at Norridgewock late in the seventeenth century (Thwaites 1959, 67). Prior to 1693, the Abnaki lived on the west bank of the Kennebec River at the Tracy Farm site; in 1694, they moved to the east bank of the river at the Norridgewock Mission site, known as Old Point (Prins and Bourque 1987). The mission at Old Point was located on an interval of about 250 acres across from the mouth of Sandy River, where the Kennebec River bends to flow on three sides of the village. The Minot and Heath map of 1719 (Calvert 1991:Plate XX) shows "plowing fields" for maize on both sides of the Kennebec south of Sandy River.

Rasles' writings do not give us a very detailed picture of Indian uses of plant foods other than maize. In a letter to his brother in

**Table 12.4. Selected Maine Sites: Nutshell.**

| Site | 4.10 | 90.2D | 15.110 | 27.60 | 53.35 | 7.7 | 7.13 | 69.24 | 69.11 | 69.2 |
|---|---|---|---|---|---|---|---|---|---|---|
| Component | PI | MA | LA | LA | LA | Ceramic | Ceramic | Contact | Contact | Contact |
| **NUTSHELL** | | | | | | | | | | |
| *No. fragments >2 mm* | | | | | | | | | | |
| Acorn | – | 37 | 11 | – | 7 | 293 | 12 | 2 | 28 | 88 |
| Beechnut | – | 1 | – | – | – | 22 | – | – | 3 | 4 |
| Butternut | – | – | – | – | – | – | – | 104 | 335 | 141 |
| Hazelnut | – | – | 16 | 4 | 2 | 5 | 283 | – | 20 | 1 |
| Total | 0 | 38 | 27 | 4 | 9 | 320 | 295 | 106 | 386 | 234 |
| *Percentage Composition* | | | | | | | | | | |
| Acorn | – | 97.37 | 40.74 | – | 77.78 | 91.56 | 4.07 | 1.89 | 7.25 | 37.61 |
| Beechnut | – | 2.63 | – | – | – | 6.88 | – | – | 0.78 | 1.71 |
| Butternut | – | – | – | – | – | – | – | 98.11 | 86.79 | 60.26 |
| Hazelnut | – | – | 59.26 | 100 | 22.22 | 1.56 | 95.93 | – | 5.18 | 0.43 |
| Total | 0 | 100.00 | 100.00 | 100.00 | 100.00 | 100.00 | 100.00 | 100.00 | 100.00 | 100.01 |
| **SUMMARY STATISTICS** | | | | | | | | | | |
| Wt. total charcoal examined (g) | 5.5 | 152 | 74 | 160 | 322 | 336 | 101 | 88 | 890 | 216 |
| Nutshell index (No. frags >2 mm/g charcoal) | – | 0.25 | 0.37 | 0.03 | 0.03 | 0.95 | 2.91 | 1.20 | 0.49 | 1.07 |
| Percentage nutshell and nutmeat | – | 0.23 | 0.78 | 0.04 | 0.10 | 1.24 | 3.17 | 2.18 | 0.63 | 1.96 |
| Ubiquity in features (%) | – | 100 | 20 | 7 | 9 | 80 | 100 | 100 | 83 | 82 |
| No. features sampled | n/a | 3 | 10 | 44 | 13 | 5 | 2 | 3 | 48 | 11 |

*Notes*

For Site 69.11, nutshell numbers are raw counts; the nutshell index takes into account subsampling corrections; the ubiquity calculation is based on 36 features, excluding features with only 1/4-in screen-size charcoal and one feature with only 0.2 g charcoal.

October of 1723, after game had been depleted in the area, he observed that the Norridgewock

> seldom have any food but Indian corn, beans, and pumpkins ... When they are without corn, they search the cultivated fields for potatoes,[3] or even for acorns, which they value as highly as corn [Thwaites 1959, 67:213-215].

Rasles' dictionary of the Abnaki language included a calendar dividing the year into moons named after subsistence activities. Those months with names relating to agriculture or plants are (Rasles 1833:321):

> April - the moon when they sow
> May - when they cover the Indian corn
> June - when they hill up the corn
> July - when the blueberries are ripe
> September - when they gather acorns[4]

The cycle of planting, cultivating, and harvesting the maize determined where the Norridgewock would be at certain times of the year. Rasles described the annual cycle relating to maize:

> They plant corn only in the spring, and do their last tilling about Corpus Christi day [mid-June]; after that, they consider to which place by the Sea they shall go to seek food until the time of harvest, which generally takes place shortly after the Assumption [mid-August] ... They have from it something to live upon, although in a very wretched way, until after All Saints' day [November 1], when they return a second time to the Sea [Thwaites 1959, 67:215-219].

> During the winter months they live better at the sea than during the summer, because besides acorns, shellfish, fruit, etc., they have game, Canada geese, ducks, and a hundred other types of game, and in such a quantity that the sea is covered with them; ... We live in our winter quarters until around Candlemas [February 2] or Ash Wednesday, at which time they disperse to hunt beavers and moose, and I return to the village over the snow on snowshoes ... and we arrived in good health at the village with the women and children. As for the men, they finished their spring hunting and returned to the village to plant. This is their usual routine [Calvert 1991:264-265, translation of Letter of August 17, 1714].

It should be noted that this annual round of activities cannot necessarily be projected back into prehistory. Sanger (1996) has cited evidence of year-round occupation of coastal areas from analysis of growth rings in softshell clams and other indicators. He has suggested that there were distinct coastal and interior populations extending back at least 5,000 years before the arrival of Europeans into the Gulf of Maine, and that seasonal transhumance between coastal areas in the summer and interior areas in the winter may have resulted from European presence.

## THE ARCHAEOLOGICAL RECORD

### Methods

Most plant remains discussed here were recovered by flotation or fine water-screening rather than by hand excavation of visible charcoal. Soil samples were processed either by a water flotation machine with 1-mm mesh (Maine Historic Preservation Commission and, recently, University of Maine at Farmington); by water-screening using 1-mm, 1/8-in, and 1/4-in mesh (University of Maine at Farmington); or by water flotation in a bucket (Archaeological Research Consultants, Inc.) to recover charcoal. Each technique seemed to successfully recover seeds, although flotation recovered far more of the tiniest charcoal and seeds, such as blueberry and strawberry. Comparing the number of seeds per gram of charcoal in flotation and water-screened samples at Site 69.11, flotation of 12 samples weighing a total of 25 g yielded a seed index of 13.0, whereas 92 water-screened samples weighing 531 g produced only 1.0 seed per gram of charcoal. These seed indices cannot be used to propose a correction factor for water-screened samples until a series of samples from similar contexts are processed by both methods.

In the archaeobotanical laboratory, samples were sieved, cleaned, and sorted according to techniques developed at the Center for American Archeology (D. L. Asch and N. B. Asch 1985). Charcoal larger than 2 mm was sorted and quantified by counting rather than by weighing categories; charcoal 0.5-2 mm was scanned for presence/absence of rare categories, and all seeds were removed. In many cases, total charcoal weights were estimated by using a riffle sampler to obtain a subsample for thorough removal of noncarbonized materials. A 20-piece subsample of wood larger than 2 mm was identified from each sample when possible; 30 fragments were identified in samples with a large number of species present.

Sampling strategies and sample sizes varied among the ten sites (Table 12.2). To ensure comparability of data among the 10 components, only flotation and water-screened samples are included in the calculations of overall sample composition (Table 12. 2). Percentage composition of wood computations (Table 12.3) include hand-picked charcoal from one site to increase the sample size and accuracy of the calculations. Sample volumes were not available from most sites. Therefore, any density calculations are expressed as a ratio of the number of fragments (of nuts or maize larger than 2 mm, or seeds larger than 0.5 mm) in relation to the total weight of all types of charcoal larger than 0.5 mm recovered from flotation and water-screened samples. This ratio is preferable to the usual densities based on volume of processed soil because it eliminates differences that may be related to excavation technique, such as selecting areas of concentrated charcoal as opposed to random sampling that includes areas of low charcoal concentration.

**Food Remains**

Archaeobotanical remains show that a variety of wild plants were used in Maine throughout pre-history. Plant food remains at Maine sites are usually less than one percent of the total charcoal recovered from Paleoindian, Middle Archaic, and Late Archaic sites (Table 12.2). After 1,000 B.P., there is an overall increase in density of nutshell, seeds, and cultivated plants, particularly maize, for the components included in this summary. The food remains are considered in more detail in the sections that follow.

## NUTSHELL

As mentioned earlier, nut trees were not distributed uniformly across the landscape in prehistory (Figure 12.3). Another factor to consider is that the nuts are available on a variable cycle, with beechnut, butternut, and hazelnut yielding a large crop every two to three years, hickory every one to three years, and northern red oak every three to five years (Young and Young 1992).

Red oak, beaked hazelnut, and beech occur statewide today as they probably have for the past 10,000 years (or at least 6,000 years in the southern half of the state in the case of beech). Based on distribution of modern vegetation, trees yielding edible nuts during the Ceramic and Contact periods (3,000-150 B.P.) in southwestern Maine would have included butternut, two types of hazelnut, four or five species of oak, and possibly shagbark hickory and chestnut.

No nutshell was recovered from the Paleoindian Hedden site (Table 12.4). Most Archaic sites in Maine have a very low frequency of nutshell, usually less than 1 percent (Table 12.2). Ceramic and Contact period components generally have a higher percentage of nutshell, up to about 3 percent.

At the Norridgewock Mission site where Father Rasles documented use of acorns, 31 samples from 10 features (excluding a concentration of entire maize cobs) yielded a mean of 1.9 percent nutshell and nutmeat. Although present in low frequency, nutshell was quite ubiquitous, occurring in 9 of 11 features (including the maize concentration). Fragments of butternut (*Juglans cinerea* L.) shell were found in 7 of 11 features, acorn (*Quercus* spp.) and/or acorn nutmeat in three, hazelnut (*Corylus* spp.) in one, and beech-nut (*Fagus grandifolia* Ehrh.) also in one feature. In other words, all the types of nuts that grow in that part of central Maine today were recovered from the Norridgewock Mission site.

It is interesting that butternut, which comprises 60-98 percent of the nutshell at the three Norridgewock Village sites, was recovered only from those sites, although 8 of the 10 sites studied are within the modern range of butternut. On July 1, 1796, the Rev. Paul Coffin stood at the mouth of Sandy River overlooking Norridgewock point and intervale (former site of the Norridgewock Mission) and Sandy River and its intervales (former maize fields) on both sides. He was performing missionary work among the white people who had settled above Winslow on the Kennebec River after 1770. Traveling upriver on July 2, Coffin noted in his journal that abundant "oilnut trees" grew on the islands and bordering the shoreline of Sandy River (Woodman 1855:88-89). This is the only native plant that he recorded other than grass growing with the oilnut trees on an island in Sandy River. The favorable location of the Norridgewock Village sites with regard to oilnuts suggests that, although Rasles did not mention it, the sweet butternuts could have been an important source of dietary fat and protein, used either as is or by boiling to extract the oil. Butternuts contain about 64 percent fat and 25 percent protein, as compared to red oak acorns which have only about 22 percent fat and 6 percent protein (Asch et. al. 1972:11).

## ROOTS/TUBERS

Most of the fragmentary roots, tubers, and rhizomes recovered from Maine sites have not been identifiable to species. They are generally not groundnut tubers (*Apios americana* Medic.), a type often referred to in historic accounts of settlers captured by the Indians (Russell 1980:156). Groundnut has been identified only at Site 74.148, located on Pushaw Stream, a tributary to the Stillwater River in the Penobscot River drainage. At Site 74.148, 11 tubers weighing 2.7 g were recovered in a 1/4-in mesh from a component

dating to 3,560 ±70 B.P. (cal 2σ 4,072-3,638 B.P.) (Mack et al. 1998).

## SEEDS

A great variety of carbonized seeds have been recovered from Maine sites (Table 12.5). Dividing the seeds into categories according to probable use, and excluding maize fragments and cucurbit rind, it is evident that seeds from edible fleshy fruits are a large fraction of the recovered seeds throughout prehistory (Table 12.6). Seeds from plants that could have been used medicinally or for beverages comprise another important category.

Starting after 1,000 B.P. and possibly associated with the introduction of domesticated plants, grass seeds appear in the archaeobotanical assemblage for the first time, ranging from 1.7 percent of all Ceramic period seeds to 4-11 percent of Contact period seeds. Also starting after 1,000 B.P., there is an increase in the category of economic/weed seeds culminating in the presence of 18.5-37 percent edible seeds of possible "weedy" plants at Contact period sites. Several of these species are considered in detail in the sections that follow. If a seed can potentially fit into more than one category of economic use, it has been placed in only one of those categories or in "other" seeds.

### Fleshy Fruits

A large portion of the seeds recovered from all sites were from a wide variety of edible fleshy fruits. All of the seeds from the Late Archaic Fort Halifax site were from fleshy fruits, although only eleven seeds were recovered altogether. Other sites with a high proportion of seeds from fleshy fruits include the Paleoindian Hedden site (73 percent), the Middle Archaic component of the Sharrow site (56 percent); the Late Archaic Hunter Farm site (79 percent); the Ceramic component of Little Ossipee North (95 percent) and Early Fall site (38 percent); and the three Contact period Norridgewock Village sites, Sandy River (32 percent), Tracy Farm (36 percent), and Norridgewock Mission (28 percent). The site with the lowest percentage of fleshy fruits (Site 27.60,

12.5 percent) had a very small number of seeds overall.

The Little Ossipee North site, with 95 percent fleshy fruits, had a particularly interesting assemblage of dried whole blueberries (*Vaccinium* spp.) and individual blueberry seeds, as well as seeds of raspberry/blackberry/dewberry (*Rubus* spp.), strawberry (*Fragaria* spp.), huckleberry (*Gaylussacia baccata* [Wang.] K.Koch), elderberry (*Sambucus* spp.), grape (*Vitis* spp.), cherry (*Prunus* spp.), and bunchberry (*Cornus canadensis* L.). The seeds were widespread on a living surface that included numerous tiny fragments of white pine (*Pinus strobus* L.) needles and acorn nutshell.

Seeds of at least twelve kinds of fleshy fruits were recovered from the Norridgewock Village sites. At Norridgewock Mission the fruits represented were strawberry, huckleberry, Canada plum (*Prunus nigra* Ait.), pin cherry (*P. pensylvanica* L.), chokecherry (*P. virginiana* L.), raspberry/blackberry/dewberry, elderberry, blueberry, grape, and wild raisin (*Viburnum cassinoides* L.). Additional species recovered from Tracy Farm were bunchberry and hawthorn (*Crataegus* spp.).

**Economic/Weed Seeds**

The seeds of plants that are sometimes considered weeds, but nevertheless could be of economic importance, include tick trefoil (*Desmodium* spp.), hog peanut (*Amphicarpa bracteata* [L.] Fern.), chenopod (*Chenopodium* spp.), amaranth (*Amaranthus* spp.), and sunflower (*Helianthus* spp.). These seeds may have been by-products of horticultural activities after 1,000 B.P., and may have been collected for food in times of scarcity.

Both hog peanut and tick trefoil are legumes with tiny seeds produced in pods. Two hog peanut seeds were recovered at Sandy River site in association with four tick trefoil seeds. From Tracy Farm, there were a total of 11 hog peanut and 373 tick trefoil seeds. Hog peanut produces small seeds (3.4 x 3 x 1.5 mm) in pods and large seeds in fleshy single-seeded subterranean fruits (Martin and Barkley 1961:173). The archaeological seeds are from aerial pods. Both types of seeds can be eaten as a cooked vegetable, with the aerial seeds available in the fall and the underground

fruits from fall to early spring. The underground fruits are also eaten raw.

Tick trefoil (*Desmodium* spp.) was found on the living surface in the Ceramic period occupation at Little Ossipee North site and is quite ubiquitous in the Contact period at the Norridgewock Village, occurring in 27 percent of the features at Norridgewock Mission, 47 percent at Tracy Farm, and 33 percent at Sandy River site. Tick trefoil has a segmented, hairy pod which clings to clothing and animals, meaning it could be classified alternatively as a bristly weed. There are no historic references to the use of tick trefoil for food. However, there is archaeological evidence for its economic importance at Cloudsplitter Rockshelter in Kentucky where "wild bean loments" were quite common in the deposits. The pods were found stored in a small circular pit with 7 liters of seeds known to have been cultivated prehistorically in the eastern U.S.: sumpweed (*Iva annua* L.), sunflower (*Helianthus annuus* L.), goosefoot (*Chenopodium berlandieri* Moq.), maygrass (*Phalaris caroliniana* Walt.), and erect knotweed (*Polygonum erectum* L.) (Cowan 1985:240; Fritz 1990:405).

At Norridgewock Mission, weed seeds of possible economic importance comprise 18.5 percent of all seeds, including *Chenopodium berlandieri* Moq. (goosefoot) and *Desmodium* spp. (tick trefoil). Nineteen carbonized *C. berlandieri* seeds were recovered from Feature 1 and two seeds from Feature 63. The seeds are reticulate and biconvex with a mean diameter of 1.5 mm, uncorrected for shrinkage due to carbonization. According to a revised checklist of the vascular plants of Maine (Richardset. al. 1983), *Chenopodium* is represented in Somerset County by two species: the non-native *C. album* L. and the native species *C. hybridum* L. v. *gigantospermum* (Aellen) Rouleau. Nomenclature in the checklist is based upon *Gray's Manual of Botany* (Fernald 1973 [1950]), which subsumed *C. berlandieri* under *C. paganum* Reichenb. Using seed characteristics rather than vegetative characteristics for classification, the Norridgewock Mission seeds can be attributed to *C. berlandieri* Moq. var. *bushianum* (Aellen) Cronq., commonly called pitseed goosefoot (Aellen and Just 1943; D. L. Asch and N. B. Asch 1985; Gleason and Cronquist 1991).

Although this species has not been identified from Somerset County, it is likely that it does grow there today. *C. berlandieri* is the goosefoot species that was domesticated by Indians of the midwestern and eastern United States about 3,500 years ago and was cultivated until at least 800 years ago, after the introduction of maize and beans (Fritz 1990). At Norridgewock Mission, the *C. berlandieri* would have grown as a weed in the maize fields and in disturbed soil around the village, and the seeds could represent a food that was used when the maize supply was exhausted.

One carbonized *C. berlandieri* seed, 1.6 mm in diameter with a thick seed coat, was also recovered at the Late Archaic Hunter Farm site. One seed tentatively identified as *Amaranthus* sp./ *Chenopodium* sp. from the Early Fall site lacked a seed coat.

One achene resembling sunflower (*Helianthus* spp.), but too small to be the cultivated or weedy common sunflower (*H. annuus* L.), was recovered from the Tracy Farm site in association with maize, cucurbit rind, wild rye, and tick-trefoil seeds. Uncorrected for shrinkage due to carbonization and for a broken shell, the achene is >3.8 mm x 2.2 mm.

**Medicinal/Beverage Plants**
The use of medicinal and beverage plants is poorly documented at most archaeological sites because parts of the plant may have been used which are not readily preserved by burning, such as leaves, or which are difficult to identify, such as roots. For sumac (*Rhus* spp.), a plant that is recorded frequently at archaeological sites, it was the seeds which were used fresh or stored to make an acidic beverage. In this study, seeds of sumac were found in two of the ten components (Table 12.5).

Bristly sarsaparilla (*Aralia hispida* Vent.) seeds were recovered from two flotation samples at the Paleoindian Hedden site. Bristly sarsaparilla was also represented at Early Fall, Little Ossipee North, and Tracy Farm sites (Table 12.5). Wild sarsaparilla (*A. nudicaulis* L.) seeds were identified only from Tracy Farm site. Wild sarsaparilla grows in woodlands, and bristly sarsaparilla in rocky and sandy open woods and clearings (Fernald 1973 [1950]). Both types of sarsaparilla

are found in every county in Maine today (Richards et. al. 1983:48). Kavasch (1981) noted that the black fruits of *Aralia hispida* and *A. nudicaulis* ripen early; they are tasty trailside nibbles, but quite seedy and therefore not desirable to eat in any quantity. Richardson (1981) warned that *Aralia* berries are not edible and contain a poisonous glycoside. The fruit of *A. nudicaulis* was eaten by Indians in British Columbia (King 1984:76). However, most ethnohistoric accounts of sarsaparilla refer to the roots, not the fruits. The Penobscot Indians of Maine used sarsaparilla to help kidney function and made a tea from sarsaparilla and sweetflag roots to treat arthritis and rheumatism (Russell 1980:37). The Indians of New England subsisted on sarsaparilla roots during hunting expeditions or warfare (Fernald and Kinsey 1958).

Sweetfern (*Comptonia peregrina* [L.] J.M. Coulter) seeds were present in 8 of 11 Norridgewock Mission features and comprised 27.4 percent of all seeds from the site. From the Late Archaic 27.60 site, 5 of eight 8 were sweetfern, originally reported as Type NS-38. Sweetfern is a shrub up to 1.5 m tall that grows in dry, sandy soil in all Maine counties. The young nutlets may be eaten and the mature ones ground for seasoning; the fresh or dried leaves make an excellent tea (Richardson 1981). Algonquin groups in Canada use sweetfern as a medicinal plant (Black 1980). It has been used by various Indian groups as a treatment for diarrhea and stomach cramps, for itching, to hasten parturition, as a poultice for toothache, as an astringent and stimulant, and as ceremonial incense (King 1984).

Bedstraw (*Galium* spp.) seeds were common in the Middle Archaic component of Sharrow site. Bedstraw was used by many Indian groups to make a medicinal tea (King 1984), but the seeds can also be classified as a bristly weed seed that is introduced to sites by clinging to people and animals.

When only one or a few seeds are recovered from an archaeological site, it is uncertain if the plant was being used or if the seeds are incidental inclusions. Common lousewort or wood-betony (*Pedicularis canadensis* L.) seeds were recovered in one sample from the Tracy Farm site. It is a plant

**Table 12.5. Selected Maine Sites: Seeds.**

| Site<br>Component | 4.10<br>PI | 90.2D<br>MA | 15.110<br>LA | 27.60<br>LA | 53.35<br>LA | 7.7<br>Ceramic | 7.13<br>Ceramic | 69.24<br>Contact | 69.11<br>Contact | 69.2<br>Contact |
|---|---|---|---|---|---|---|---|---|---|---|
| *Amaranthus/Chenopodium*, amaranth/goosefoot | – | – | – | – | – | – | – | – | 1 | – |
| *Amphicarpa bracteata*, hog peanut | – | – | – | – | – | – | – | 2 | 11 | – |
| *Andropogon gerardi*, big bluestem | – | – | – | – | – | – | – | – | 1 | – |
| *Aralia hispida*, bristly sarsaparilla | 3 | – | – | – | – | 1 | 7 | – | 43 | – |
| *A. nudicaulis*, wild sarsaparilla | – | – | – | – | – | – | – | – | 3 | – |
| *Chenopodium* spp., goosefoot | – | – | 1 | – | – | – | 1 | – | 32 | 21 |
| *Comptonia peregrina*, sweetfern | – | – | – | 5 | – | – | – | – | – | 46 |
| *Cornus* spp., dogwood | – | – | – | – | – | – | 1 | – | – | – |
| *C. alternifolia*, dogwood | – | 1 | – | – | – | – | – | – | 11 | 1 |
| *C. canadensis*, bunchberry | 5 | – | – | – | – | 1 | 1 | – | 11 | – |
| *Crataegus* spp., hawthorn | – | 34 | – | – | – | – | – | 2 | 10 | – |
| *Cucurbita* spp., squash | – | – | – | – | – | – | – | – | – | 1 |
| Cyperaceae, sedge family | – | – | – | – | – | 1 | – | – | 2 | – |
| *Desmodium* spp., tick trefoil | – | – | – | – | – | 8 | – | 4 | 373 | 10 |
| *Elymus* spp., wild rye | – | – | – | – | – | – | – | – | 126 | – |
| Fabaceae, bean family | – | 1 | – | – | – | – | – | – | – | – |
| *Fragaria* spp., strawberry | – | – | – | – | – | 137 | – | – | 7 | 2 |
| *Galium* spp., bedstraw | – | 20 | – | – | – | – | – | – | – | – |
| *Gaylussacia baccata*, huckleberry | – | – | – | – | – | 35 | – | – | – | 1 |
| *Helianthus* spp., sunflower | – | – | – | – | – | – | – | – | 1 | – |
| Liliaceae, lily family | – | – | 1 | – | – | – | 8 | – | – | – |
| *Pedicularis canadensis*, lousewort | – | – | – | – | – | – | – | – | 2 | – |
| *Phaseolus vulgaris*, bean | – | – | – | – | – | – | 1 | – | 2 | 4 |
| *Picea* spp., spruce | – | – | – | – | – | – | 4 | – | – | – |
| *Pisum sativum*, peas | – | – | – | – | – | – | – | – | – | 4 |
| Poaceae, grass family | – | – | – | – | – | 17 | 2 | 2 | 2 | 6 |
| *Polygonum* spp., smartweed | – | – | – | – | – | – | 1 | – | 1 | – |
| *Prunus* spp., cherry | – | – | – | – | – | 2 | – | – | 24 | 3 |
| *P. nigra*, Canada plum | – | – | – | – | – | – | – | – | – | 2 |

**Table 12.5. Continued**

| Site | 4.10 | 90.2D | 15.110 | 27.60 | 53.35 | 7.7 | 7.13 | 69.24 | 69.11 | 69.2 |
|---|---|---|---|---|---|---|---|---|---|---|
| Component | PI | MA | LA | LA | LA | Ceramic | Ceramic | Contact | Contact | Contact |
| *P. pensylvanica*, pin cherry | – | – | – | – | – | – | 6 | 2 | 8 | 1 |
| *P. virginiana*, chokecherry | – | – | – | – | – | – | – | – | 12 | 2 |
| *Ranunculus* spp., buttercup | – | – | 1 | – | – | – | – | – | – | – |
| *Rhus* spp., sumac | – | – | – | – | – | – | 13 | – | 7 | – |
| *Rubus* spp., bramble | 2 | 2 | – | 1 | 11 | 691 | 30 | 4 | 230 | 24 |
| *Sambucus* spp., elderberry | – | 1 | 1 | – | – | 12 | 5 | – | 31 | 1 |
| *Triticum aestivum*, wheat | – | – | – | – | – | – | – | – | 3 | – |
| *Vaccinium* spp., blueberry | – | – | – | – | – | 77 | – | – | 46 | 3 |
| *Viburnum* spp., viburnum | – | – | – | – | – | – | – | – | – | 2 |
| *Viburnum* cf. *cassinoides*, wild raisin | – | – | – | – | – | – | – | – | – | 1 |
| *Vitis* spp., grape | 1 | – | 10 | – | – | 3 | 2 | – | 25 | 5 |
| Unknown/unidentifiable | – | 7 | – | 2 | – | 25 | 34 | 9 | 113 | 28 |
| **Total** | 11 | 66 | 14 | 8 | 11 | 1,010 | 116 | 25 | 1,138 | 168 |
| **SUMMARY STATISTICS** | | | | | | | | | | |
| Total charcoal examined (g) | 5.50 | 152 | 74 | 160 | 322 | 336 | 101 | 88 | 890 | 381 |
| Seed index (# >0.5 mm/g) | 2.00 | 0.43 | 0.19 | 0.05 | 0.03 | 3.01 | 1.15 | 0.28 | 1.94 | 0.72 |
| Maize index (# fragments >2 mm/g) | – | – | – | – | – | 0.01 | 0.70 | 8.30 | 0.62 | 0.95 |

*Notes*

Includes all seeds larger than 0.5 mm.

Site 69.11 seed index includes a correction factor for subsampling; the index varied from 13.01 in 12 flotation samples to 0.99 in 92 water-screened samples.

Site 69.2 seed and maize index calculations do not include a concentration of cobs weighing 165 g (1/4-in screen size); including that concentration changes the ratios to 0.44 and 8.39, respectively.

**Table 12.6. Selected Maine Sites: Economic Categories of Seeds.**

| Site | 4.10 | 90.2D | 15.110 | 27.60 | 53.35 | 7.7 | 7.13 | 69.24 | 69.11 | 69.2 |
|---|---|---|---|---|---|---|---|---|---|---|
| Component | PI | MA | LA | LA | LA | Ceramic | Ceramic | Contact | Contact | Contact |
| **PERCENTAGE COMPOSITION** | | | | | | | | | | |
| Domesticated seeds | – | – | – | – | – | – | 0.86 | – | 0.44 | 5.36 |
| Fleshy fruits | 72.73 | 56.06 | 78.57 | 12.50 | 100.00 | 94.85 | 37.93 | 32.00 | 35.50 | 27.98 |
| Economic/weed seeds | – | – | 7.14 | – | – | 0.79 | 0.86 | 24.00 | 36.73 | 18.45 |
| Medicinal/beverage plants | 27.27 | 30.30 | 7.14 | 62.50 | – | 0.10 | 17.24 | – | 4.83 | 27.38 |
| Grass seeds | – | – | – | – | – | 1.68 | 1.72 | 8.00 | 11.34 | 3.57 |
| Other | – | 13.64 | 7.14 | 25.00 | – | 2.57 | 41.38 | 36.00 | 11.16 | 17.26 |
| **Total seeds** | 100.00 | 100.00 | 99.99 | 100.00 | 100.00 | 100.00 | 100.00 | 100.00 | 100.00 | 100.00 |
| **SAMPLE SIZE** | | | | | | | | | | |
| No. seeds | 11 | 66 | 14 | 8 | 11 | 1,010 | 116 | 25 | 1,138 | 168 |

*Notes*

Summary includes all seeds larger than 0.5 mm.

Domesticated seeds are cucurbit, bean, pea, and wheat.

Seeds of fleshy fruits include blackberry/raspberry/dewberry, blueberry, bunchberry, Canada plum, cherry, elderberry, grape, hawthorn, huckleberry, strawberry, viburnum, and wild raisin. Economic/weed seeds include amaranth/goosefoot, goosefoot, hog peanut, sunflower, and tick trefoil. Medicinal or beverage seeds are bedstraw, bristly sarsaparilla, wild sarsaparilla, buttercup, common lousewort, sumac, and sweetfern. Grass seeds are big bluestem, wild rye, and grass family. Other seeds are bean family, dogwood, lily family, sedge family, smartweed, spruce, and unknown.

of woods and clearings. Lousewort was eaten as greens by the Iroquois, but most references list medicinal uses for this plant. The entire plant was used to make a tea for reducing internal swelling; the root was useful for treating anemia, external swelling, tumors, and as a physic and aphrodisiac (Black 1980; King 1984).

Similarly, buttercup (*Ranunculus* spp.) was represented by only one seed at the Late Archaic 15.110 site. Various parts of the plant were used for medicinal purposes by many Indian groups (Black 1980; King 1984; Largy, this volume), but on the basis of only one seed it is not possible to say if Maine Indian groups were collecting and using buttercup.

### Grass Seeds

Grass seeds appear in the archaeological record after 1,000 B.P. in Maine. Many of the small grass family (Poaceae) seeds have not been classified to genus (Table 12.5). One big bluestem seed (*Andropogon gerardi* Vitman) was identified at the Norridgewock Mission site and 126 wild rye (*Elymus* spp.) seeds have been identified from Tracy Farm site samples. Although wild rye seeds were eaten by western Indians (King 1984), there are few ethnographic references to the use of grass seeds for food in eastern North America. Several references to use of grass roots for medicinal purposes have been summarized by Black (1980). It is also possible that the grass seeds are present as by-products of using grass stems and leaves for technological purposes such as thatching, pit lining, matting, and fire starting (N. B. Asch and D. L. Asch 1985).

### Other Seeds

Various other seeds recovered in small quantities include dogwood (*Cornus* spp.), sedge family (Cyperaceae), bean family (Fabaceae), lily family (Liliaceae), smartweed (*Polygonum* spp.), spruce (*Picea* spp.), and unknown or unidentifiable seeds. The seeds of the lily family were found in small quantities at two sites. Many plants in the lily family have edible young shoots and rootstocks, but most of the fruits are not considered edible. The fleshy fruits of false Solomon's seal (*Smilacina* spp.) are edible but slightly cathartic (Peterson 1978).

## CULTIVATED PLANTS

The first possibly cultivated plant to appear in Maine was pepo gourd (*Cucurbita pepo* L.), represented by a rind fragment found at the deeply stratified Sharrow site in central Maine. The tiny rind fragment has been directly dated to 5,695 ± 100 B.P. (cal 2σ 6,732-6,293 B.P.) and occurred in a feature dating to 6,320 ± 110 B.P. (cal 2σ 7,392-6,941 B.P.). The pepo gourd could not have grown wild in Maine, and therefore must have been intentionally introduced. There is no evidence for long-distance trade networks at that time, which leaves open the possibility that it was a cultivated plant in Maine (Petersen and Asch Sidell 1996). Although this would seem to be a marginal environment for growing of pepo gourd, Bartlein and Webb (1985) estimated that the mean July temperature at 6,000 B.P. in central Maine was at least 1°C warmer than today. Furthermore, it has now been demonstrated that the Sharrow pepo gourd is not an isolated occurrence in the northeastern United States; the Memorial Park site in north-central Pennsylvania, east of the Allegheny Front, also has mid-Holocene cucurbit directly dated to 5,404 ± 552 B.P. (cal 2σ 7,386-4,856 B.P., AA-19129) (Hart and Asch Sidell 1997). The earliest directly dated pepo gourd in North America (7,100 ± 300 B.P., NRSL-298, cal 2σ 8,418-7,385 B.P.) that is likely to represent a cultivated plant is found at the Koster site in west-central Illinois in an occupation dating about 7,000 B.P. (cal 2σ 7,932-7,536 B.P., combined S.D. of 3 dates) (Asch 1994:31-33).

The next evidence for use of cultivated plants in Maine comes from the Little Ossipee North site in the central Saco River valley, where two maize (*Zea mays* L.) cupule fragments were recovered from a feature dating to 1,010 ± 60 B.P. (cal 2σ 1,055-782 B.P.) (Will et al. 1996). Direct dating of one of the cupules has yielded a date of 570 ± 40 B.P. (cal 2σ 655-530 B.P.) (Richard Will, personal communication). Besides abundant wood, bark, and pitch, the Ceramic component contained nutshell fragments and a wide variety of seeds of edible fruits that were associated with a buried soil horizon and several stone hearth features. Most of the seeds came from a living surface dated to 850 ± 60 B.P. (cal 2σ 919-663 B.P.). One hypothesis to explain the discrepancy between age of the maize and age of the wood in Feature 5 is that the stone-ringed hearth acted as a catch basin for materials picked up in flood waters. It appears that a large flood event sometime after 850 B.P. (most likely at about 650 ± 60 B.P., cal 2σ 674-533 B.P., Beta-83652, from nearby Chartier Field site) capped the Little Ossipee North site with about one foot of fine silt (Will et al. 1996). It is possible that the cupules were moved into the hearth feature during that flood event (Rick Will, personal communication). Another possibility is that the 1,010 B.P. date on Feature 5 is misleading and may represent admixture of charcoal from an earlier occupation.

At the Early Fall site, located about 3 km downstream from Little Ossipee North in the central Saco River valley, 70 percent of the feature samples contained remains of cultivated plants, including maize, 11 fragments of *Cucurbita pepo* rind, and one bean (*Phaseolus vulgaris* L.) (Asch Sidell 1990). Radiocarbon dates on associated charcoal are 570 ± 70 B.P. (cal 2σ 660-501 B.P.) and 460 ± 60 B.P. (cal 2σ 550-320 B.P.) (Cowie and Petersen 1990; Ellen R. Cowie, personal communication). The maize consisted of both cob and kernel fragments. The abundance of cob fragments indicates that the maize was grown near the site and shelled at the site for consumption, rather than having been imported as shelled maize from another location.

It was unexpected to find that 70 percent of the water-screened samples from Early Fall site contained the remains of cultivated plants in low frequencies, a percentage that is comparable to Mississippian sites in the Midwest where maize is thought to have been an important part of the diet. For example, at the Audrey North and Hill Creek sites in the lower Illinois River valley, maize occurred in 74 percent and 76 percent of the feature samples, respectively (N. B. Asch and D. L. Asch 1985:162). However, the frequency of maize (percentage of all fragments larger than 2 mm) was much higher at the Illinois sites (6.4 percent at Audrey North and 5.9 percent at Hill Creek), whereas the Early Fall site had only 0.8 percent maize fragments. At Fort Ancient sites where testing and flotation have been extensive,

Wagner (1987:229) found maize in 75-86 percent of the samples.

To put these discoveries of Maine maize in perspective, it is useful to look at the Crawford et. al. (1997) summary of the spread of maize. In the midwestern U.S., the earliest maize dates are from the Holding site in the American Bottom (2,077 ± 70 B.P., cal 2σ 2,300-1,870 B.P.). Early dates are also found in Ohio (Edwin Harness site, 1,730 ± 85 B.P., cal 2σ 1,830-1,410 B.P.) and Tennessee (Icehouse Bottom site, 1,775 ± 100 B.P., cal 2σ 1,920-1,420 B.P.). By about 1,570 B.P. (cal 2σ 1,690-1,290 B.P.), maize had spread to the Grand Banks site in southern Ontario; and at 1,190 ± 40 B.P. (cal 2σ 1,220-980 B.P.), maize is found at the Memorial Park site in Pennsylvania. In northern New England the earliest date associated with maize kernels and beans in a storage pit is 850 ± 50 B.P. (cal 2σ 909-557 B.P.) at the Skitchewaug site in Vermont (Heckenberger et. al. 1992). However, this is not an AMS date on maize or bean fragments and, therefore, cannot be directly compared with the 570 B.P. date from Little Ossipee North.

The high frequency of seeds (3 seeds per gram of charcoal) in the Ceramic occupation at Little Ossipee North could be associated with an opening up of the landscape for horticulture. The edges of agricultural fields, as well as abandoned fields in the early stages of succession, provide ideal habitat for the collection of berries and edible seeds of wild legumes, grasses, and other weeds. However, the maize cupules may be more recent than the majority of the seeds, which were in a context dated to 850 B.P. This suggests that earlier maize may yet be found in Maine along the Saco River valley.

In addition to the maize at Ceramic sites in the central Saco River valley, I have recently identified two maize cupule fragments from a Ceramic/Contact context at the Conant site (ME 35-15) in the central Androscoggin River valley, at the edge of the large floodplain at Canton Point. The wood charcoal associated with the maize in Feature 1 has been dated to 260 ± 60 B.P. (cal 2σ 469-0 B.P., Beta-103494); additional dates on red oak group wood from Feature 1 are 390 ± 60 B.P. (cal 2σ 526-299 B.P., Beta-103493) and 220 ± 60 B.P.

(cal 2σ 430-0 B.P., Beta-103495) (Corey et al. 1997). The maize was associated with abundant seeds, including wild pea (*Lathyrus* cf. *palustris* L.), an unidentified legume, pin cherry, Solomon's seal, and other unidentified seeds. The Androscoggin Indian name for the Canton Point locale translates as "hoe-land," an obvious reference to the agricultural activities that took place there. At contact, this village was the center of Indian population in the Androscoggin River valley, and the planting fields covered 600 to 700 hundred acres. The village was occupied until the end of the French and Indian War in 1749 (Starbird 1928).

In the upper Kennebec River valley, we know from Father Rasles' letter of 1723 that the Norridgewock grew maize, beans, and squashes in their gardens (Thwaites 1959). The archaeological record shows that at Norridgewock Mission, 10 of 11 features contained cultivated plants; at Tracy Farm, it was 20 of 36 features; and at Sandy River site, 2 of 3 features.

Maize was found in 9 of the 11 features examined from the Norridgewock Mission site. In 8 of the features, the maize consisted of small, fragmentary pieces of kernels, cupules (cob fragments that hold the kernels), and glumes (normally attached to the edges of the cupule). In those 8 features, 43 percent of the maize represented edible parts of the plant, either kernels or embryos. Feature 63 at Norridgewock Mission was a concentration of entire burned maize cobs, minus the kernels. Based on the average weight of 28 cobs collected individually or in small groups from Feature 63, it is estimated that this feature contained the remains of at least 120 maize cobs. The maize appears similar to eight-rowed Northern Flint described by Wagner (1987) as having 8 (sometimes 10 or 12) rows of flour or flint kernels on a sturdy cob tapering toward the tip from an enlarged butt; the kernels are wide and relatively thick. Other inclusions in Feature 63 are seven types of wood charcoal, bark, pitch, maize stalk fragments, grass stems, butternuts, hazelnut, one pumpkin/squash rind, and 13 seeds (10 raspberry/blackberry/dewberry, 2 goosefoot, and 1 strawberry). The 1-mm and 1/8-in water-screened fractions have not been examined, but judging from the tiny seeds and nut

fragments accidentally caught in the 1/4-in screen, it is likely that many more types of plant remains will be identified from this pit at the Norridgewock Mission.

When maize is excluded, seeds of domesticated plants make up 5.4 percent of the seeds at Norridgewock Mission. Domesticated seeds include one pumpkin/squash (*Cucurbita* spp.); four beans (*Phaseolus vulgaris* L.) from two features; and two whole peas (*Pisum sativum* L.) plus one pea fragment from a post mold that was 25 cm x 25 cm in size and located 50-90 cm beneath the ground surface. The post mold contained calcined bone, glass beads, and one lead shot in addition to the carbonized peas and other charcoal consisting of wood (birch, beech, ash, butternut, pine, red oak group), bark, butternut shell, maize kernel and cob fragments, three unknown seeds, and a pin cherry pit.

The Indians of the Kennebec River valley may have been introduced to peas by European fishermen who worked the Maine coast in the sixteenth century. The first written reference to the introduction of peas is from Rosier's account of Captain George Waymouth's exploration in 1605. The Kennebec Indians came to trade and smoke tobacco daily at the English ship. Waymouth fed them "pork, fish, bread and pease" and gave them bread and peas to carry to their women and friends on shore. He used "a platter of pease, which meat they loved" to lure two reluctant Indians so that he could capture them (Rosier 1843).

Three features at Tracy Farm each contained one well-preserved grain of wheat (*Triticum aestivum* L.) as well as maize. Other features have yielded cucurbit rind and beans. None of the plant remains from the Norridgewock Village sites has been directly dated to determine the antiquity of cultivation in the upper Kennebec River valley.

It is not known if tobacco was grown at the Norridgewock Village sites, although Rasles remarked that Abnaki Indians dearly loved to smoke tobacco, with the women and girls smoking even more than the men (Calvert 1991, translation of Rasles' letter of August 26, 1690).

## CLIMATE IN RELATION TO PREHISTORIC AGRICULTURE

On the basis of early historic accounts, the Saco River in southwestern Maine was presumed to be the apparent boundary between subsistence systems, with foraging to the north and east and maize-based agriculture to the south and west (Demeritt 1991:183; Snow 1978).

Northern Flint maize is adapted to cool temperatures and short growing seasons. The critical factors limiting maize maturity are the amount of summer heat and the length of the growing season (Demeritt 1991:187). For prehistoric maize cultivation, Demeritt has suggested that 2,000 corn heat units or growing degree days (GDDs) provides an arbitrary estimate of agricultural potential. Figure 12.5 maps Maine archaeological sites with maize and cucurbit in relation to the modern distribution of GDDs. During the Little Ice Age beginning between 750 and 650 B.P. and lasting until between 90 and 70 B.P. (A.D. 1200-1300 to 1860-1880), generalized global cooling translated into increased climatic variability in New England. Long cold winters and short cool summers alternated with mild, nearly snowless winters and hot summers, especially during the latter third of the Little Ice Age (Baron and Smith 1996:14). Growing seasons fluctuated from one year to the next by as many as 40 to 50 days, with an average growing season length of 143 days in coastal Maine (measured between A.D. 1745-1947) and 125 days in southern interior Maine (from A.D. 1787-1947). Estimating mean July and mean annual temperatures to decline by 2°F (1.1°C), Demeritt hypothesizes that the 2,000 GDD isoline would not even have extended into Maine during the Little Ice Age.

Since six archaeological sites in Maine have produced evidence of maize being grown during the Little Ice Age, Demeritt's model seems to have little utility for predicting the practical limits of prehistoric maize horticulture. Evidently of more importance are the microclimatic factors of soil type and aspect, which can provide favorable areas for cultivation within generally unfavorable zones.

## CONCLUSION

Prior to the present study, discussions of subsistence strategies at Maine sites have focused on faunal remains (Sanger 1995; Spiess 1992). Any statements about plant use were based primarily on historic accounts or conjecture. Archaeobotanical analysis of flotation and water-screened samples has led to new and sometimes startling knowledge about the prehistoric use and distribution of plants in Maine. The abundant wood charcoal from all sites, along with carbonized nutshell and seed fragments, provides a basis for environmental reconstruction. The great variety of wood charcoal recovered from most contexts indicates that the nearest available deadwood was used for firewood, as expected. The mixture of many species of hardwoods and softwoods at most sites suggests that a forest with resources similar to those found today has been in place since at least Early Archaic times in most of southwestern Maine, with the exception of some species of nut trees (some oaks, shagbark hickory, and chestnut) that migrated more recently. Further analysis of wood at Paleoindian sites is needed to see if the open spruce/pine woodland documented at the Hedden site at 10,580-10,500 B.P. (cal 2σ 12,677-12,191 B.P.) was unique to this sandy outwash location or typical of Early Holocene landscapes in southern Maine.

During the Middle Archaic occupation of the Sharrow site, the most abundant plant food remains were acorn nutshell and hawthorn seeds, which were ubiquitous in the three features studied. One fragment of beechnut shell and three fragments of beech wood were also identified, indicating that beech had migrated to central Maine by 6,320 ± 110 B.P. (cal 2σ 7,392-6,941 B.P.).

Extensive flotation sampling at the three Late Archaic sites in this analysis revealed few nuts and seeds. Site 27.60 is thought to have been a winter habitation/workshop site on the basis of presence of bones of fur-bearing mammals, lack of fish and bird bones, paucity of nutshell and seeds, abundance of lithic reduction materials, and a linear arrangement of features suggesting longhouses were used (Cranmer and Spiess 1993). At the Hunter Farm and Fort Halifax sites, the

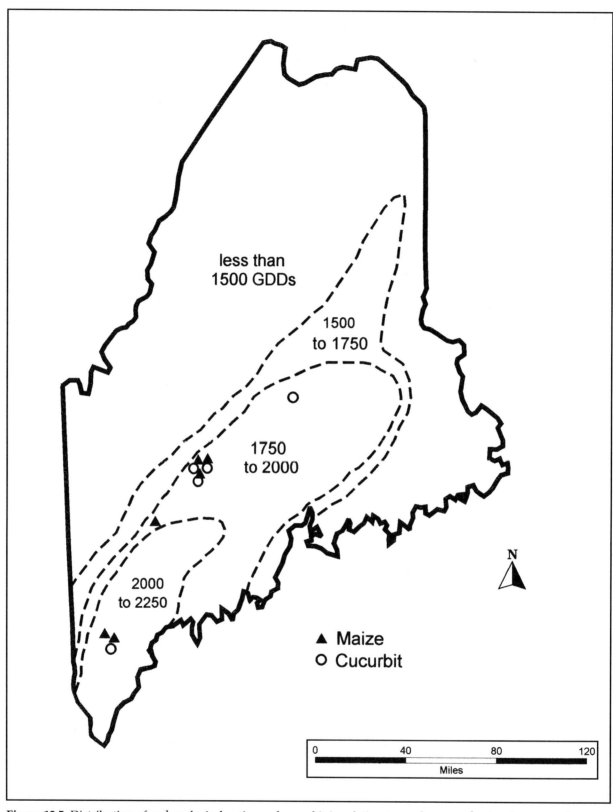

**Figure 12.5.** Distribution of archaeological maize and cucurbit in relation to modern corn heat units or growing degree days (GDDs) in Maine (after Demeritt 1991:188).

*Asch Sidell*

paucity of nutshell and seeds could likewise be an indicator of seasonality. Faunal analysis of Hunter Farm and Fort Halifax suggests a probable late spring or summer occupation on the basis of calcined sturgeon and striped bass bone at both sites (Arthur Spiess, personal communication). Occupation at that time of the year could account for the absence of nutshell, but there should be a record of fruit seeds unless the sites were occupied only in the spring or very early in the summer. It is also possible that the fruits and berries were consumed where found rather than being collected and brought back to the site.

Although the horticultural potential of Maine seems marginal, the present study shows that prehistoric peoples took advantage of new advances in technology in favorable locations with the introduction of pepo gourd (*Cucurbita pepo* L.) to central Maine at 5,695 B.P. (approximately 1,300 years after its hypothesized introduction to west-central Illinois as a cultivated plant) and the cultivation of maize starting by 570 B.P. in interior southwestern Maine in the Saco River valley. Maize cultivation extended to the Androscoggin and upper Kennebec River valleys, making use of easily tilled, well-drained sandy soils.

The Norridgewock Mission study, which compared archaeobotanical evidence with historic accounts of plant use, can serve as a baseline against which to measure prehistoric plant assemblages. Charred plant remains confirm that in early historic times the Norridgewock grew maize, beans, and squash or pumpkin as noted in the accounts of Father Sebastian Rasles. The importance of domesticated plants in the diet is highlighted by the fact that, at Norridgewock Mission, 10 of 11 features contained carbonized remains of cultivated plants. One of those features yielded a concentration of entire eight-rowed maize cobs. Unexpectedly, domesticated peas were also found in one context at the Norridgewock Mission, as well as wheat from three features at the Tracy Farm site across the river.

It is known that field peas, wheat, barley, and maize were among the first crops grown in the coastal Maine settlements (Day 1954). By the early 1640s, the farmers of Saco were growing and selling a substantial quantity of wheat (Churchill 1979:110). Although coastal settlers adopted the growing of native crops (e.g., maize, beans, pumpkins) in their gardens, the interior-dwelling Indians apparently continued their traditional gardening and did not adopt the grains and vegetables introduced by the settlers (Day 1954:24). Since the Norridgewock Mission gardens were said to be devoted chiefly to maize, beans, and squashes, it is likely that the Norridgewock Indians obtained the dried peas from the English at Cushnoc trading post (about 75 km downstream), which stocked maize, biscuits, peas, and prunes (Day 1954:23). Similarly, the wheat found at Tracy Farm might also have been obtained as a trade item.

Despite the reliance on domesticated plants perhaps as early as 570 B.P., this study has shown that collection of wild resources was not neglected. Rasles mentioned that acorns were a valued part of the diet at the Norridgewock Mission, and archaeobotanical analysis detected acorn nutshell fragments in three of the eleven features and acorn nutmeats in one feature. The fragments of nutshell recovered in nine of the eleven features were from all types of nuts that would have grown near the site: butternut, acorn, beechnut, and hazelnut. Seeds of at least twelve kinds of fleshy fruits were recovered in low frequency from the Norridgewock Village sites. The great variety represented indicates that fruits were an important part of the diet.

A greater quantity and variety of seeds have been recovered from sites after 1,000 B.P., perhaps coincident with the introduction of maize agriculture. Grass seeds appear for the first time, and seeds of "weedy" plants, including *Desmodium* spp. (tick-trefoil) and *Chenopodium berlandieri* Moq. (goosefoot), increase in abundance. *C. berlandieri* comprised 3.5 percent of the carbonized seeds at Tracy Farm and 5.5 percent at Norridgewock Mission. Although not recognized in the checklist of Maine vascular plants, its presence at these sites suggests that further study of the modern flora needs to be undertaken, using revised systematics based on seed characteristics (Gleason and Cronquist 1991).

In Southern New England, the Indians burned extensive areas of forest once or twice a year to keep them parklike for easier hunting of game. The frequent ground fires had the effect of thinning the canopy, thus increasing the growth of grasses, herbs, and shrubs, and increasing the populations of game animals and gatherable foods for human consumption (Cronon 1983). A corollary effect is that frequent burning leads to elimination of northern trees that are intolerant of fire, such as beech, hemlock, sugar maple, red maple, black birch, and even white pine. They are replaced by trees that can sprout from the roots, such as chestnuts, oaks, and hickories. Cronon (1983) suggested that northern New England Indians did not engage in such burning because they relied upon the canoe for transportation and because the northern tree species were not adapted to repeated burning. The wood analysis from Maine archaeological sites lends support to Cronon's assessment and shows that, if anything, the species that might be most favored by repeated burning (i.e., the oaks) are less abundant in Ceramic and Contact contexts (Table 12.3). Therefore, the increase in variety and density of seeds after 1,000 B.P. is probably not a side effect of more frequent widespread forest fires. Rather, it is more likely to be a fringe benefit of the adoption of agricultural practices. Agriculture would have opened up the landscape, making more edges available for growth of sunlight-loving brambles and fruit bushes, increasing the opportunity for growth of disturbance-loving weeds and grasses, and increasing the mast of nut trees and hazel bushes on the field edges.

This paper has also shown that the technique of fine water-screening using 1/8-in and 1-mm screens, which has been frequently used in Maine to recover subsistence remains, can recover a large amount of seeds, nutshell fragments, and cultivated plants. However, based on sampling at Little Ossipee North and Tracy Farm sites, using flotation can be expected to recover the tiniest seeds seldom represented in water-screened samples—strawberry, blueberry, certain grass seeds, and other types yet to be identified. If we are to recover evidence for use of the specialty plant, tobacco, flotation sampling rather than water-screening must be used in the future. Clearly, the collection and analysis of charred materials from

Maine and other New England archaeological sites should become a routine procedure that is adequately planned and budgeted for in the early stages of any project, so that a truly regional comprehensive synthesis can be accomplished in the near future.

## ACKNOWLEDGEMENTS

This study would not have been possible without the efforts of the many Maine archaeologists and volunteers who excavated and processed the soil samples. The data analysis for each site (and others not specifically mentioned in this summary) was funded through subcontracts with the University of Maine at Farmington, Archaeology Research Center; the Maine Historic Preservation Commission; the University of Maine at Orono, Robert G. MacKay Archaeology Laboratory; the University of Southern Maine; Archaeological Research Consultants, Inc. of Ellsworth, Maine; and The Abbe Museum. Much of the funding was provided by Central Maine Power Company as part of FERC dam relicensing requirements, and the Town of Kennebunk funded research at the Hedden site. The following persons contributed suggestions for improvement of this paper: Gayle Fritz, John Hart, Jim Petersen, Art Spiess, and Rick Will. Special thanks go to John Hart for providing the impetus for this summary paper as well as the calibrated calendric data for Table 12.1.

## END NOTES

1. Only sites subjected to extensive water flotation or fine water-screening are included in this summary. Sampling strategies varied among the sites. If numerous features had been excavated, at least one flotation/water-screened sample from each was analyzed (e.g., at Site 27.60, 44 samples were analyzed from 44 features). At sites with only a few features, several samples from each were analyzed to determine variation in feature contents (e.g., at Sharrow site, the 44 samples were from only 3 features). Often, all the charcoal from a feature was lumped to make one large sample that

was subsampled to economize on analysis time (e.g., at Little Ossipee North site, the 336 g of charcoal was from only 6 samples, whereas the 322 g of charcoal from the Fort Halifax site was from 75 samples).

The Hedden site is included in the summary because it yielded the earliest plant remains from a possible cultural context. Hedden site is undersampled in terms of weight of charcoal examined (only 5.5 g) as compared to the other sites, but the 16 samples were from various contexts. An additional 37 hand-picked (non-flotation) samples of Hedden charcoal weighing 3.4 g were quantified and are included only in the wood analysis to increase the accuracy of the percentage composition calculations. Ideally, the summary would also include several components from a multicomponent site such as Sharrow. However, at Sharrow the Middle Archaic level containing *Cucurbita pepo* L. rind was far more heavily sampled than other levels in an attempt to discover more rind. For this first approximation of a regional synthesis, it was decided to include only the well-sampled horizon from Sharrow.

2. The Early Archaic component of Little Ossipee North was not included in the summary tables because only one feature was sampled. Dates obtained from the feature are listed in Table 12.7.

3. This is a reference to *Apios americana* Medic., groundnut (i.e., Indian potato). Today, 275 years later, groundnuts can still be found growing along the sandy riverbank at Old Point, although the Norridgewock Mission site has long been grown over with pine forest.

4. Father Aubrey's French Abnaki dictionary (compiled between 1700 and 1755) lists September as the month to gather the corn (Laurent and Huntoon 1995).

## REFERENCES CITED

Aellen, P., and T. Just. 1943. Key and Synopsis of the American Species of the Genus *Chenopodium L. American Midland Naturalist* 30:4776.

Asch, D. L. 1994. Aboriginal Specialty-Plant Cultivation in Eastern North America: Illinois Prehistory and A Post-Contact Perspective. In *Agricultural Origins and Development in the Midcontinent*, edited by W. Green, pp. 25-86. Report 19, Office of the State Archaeologist, The University of Iowa, Iowa City.

Asch, D. L., and N. B. Asch. 1985. Archeobotany. In *Smiling Dan: Structure and Function at a Middle Woodland Settlement in the Illinois Valley*, edited by B. D. Stafford and M.B. Sant, pp. 327-401. Kampsville Archeological Center, Research Series, Vol. 2. Center for American Archeology, Kampsville, Illinois.

Asch, N. B., and D. L. Asch. 1985. Archaeobotany. In *The Hill Creek Homestead and the Late Mississippian Settlement in the Lower Illinois Valley*, edited by M. D. Conner, pp. 115-170. Research Series No. 1. Center for American Archaeology, Kampsville Archaeological Center, Kampsville, Illinois.

**Table 12.7. Radiocarbon dates from the Early Archaic at Little Ossipee North.**

| Lab No. | Age (B.P.± 1S.D.) | Calibrated Calendric Date 2s (cal date) B.P. | Carbonized Material Dated |
|---------|-------------------|-----------------------------------------------|---------------------------|
| Beta-29665 | 9,350 ± 90 | 10,793 (10,350, 10,312, 10,308) 10,044 | Hemlock, pine, ash, beech wood |
| Beta-75010 | 8,470 ± 110 | 9,646 (9,448) 9,216 | Pine wood |
| Beta-75513 | 7,970 ± 80 | 8,995(8,944, 8,904, 8,890, 8,875, 8,817, 8,792, 8,726) 8,517 | Red oak wood |
| Beta-89981 | 7,980 ± 100 | 9,190 (8,946, 8,869, 8,844, 8,789, 8,733) 8,500 | Spruce(?) wood |

Asch, N. B., R. I. Ford, and D. L. Asch. 1972. *Paleoethnobotany of the Koster Site: The Archaic Horizons*. Report of Investigations No. 24. Illinois State Museum, Springfield.

Asch Sidell, N. 1989. *Carbonized Plant Remains from the Late Archaic Components at the Hunter Farm Site, in Sagadahoc County, Maine*. Report submitted to the Maine Historic Preservation Commission.

————. 1990. Archaeobotany of Early Fall Site (ME 7-13), a Late Woodland Site in the Bonny Eagle Project Area: Results of Phase I and Phase II Investigations. In *Archaeological Phase II Survey and Testing of the Bonny Eagle Project (FERC No. 2529), Cumberland and York Counties, Maine, Volume II*, edited by E.R. Cowie, and J.B. Petersen, pp. AVI-i to AVI-30. University of Maine at Farmington, Farmington, Maine.

————. 1995. Archaeobotany of the Hedden Site. In *The Hedden Site 1994 Season: Progress on Environmental Reconstruction,* edited by A. Spiess and J. Mosher. Maine Historic Preservation Commission.

————. 1996. *Norridgewock Mission Floral Remains*. Report submitted to Archaeology Research Center, University of Maine at Farmington.

————. 1998. *Tracy Farm Floral Remains*. Report submitted to Archaeology Research Center, University of Maine at Farmington.

Baron, W. R., and D. C. Smith. 1996. *Growing Season Parameter Reconstructions for New England Using Killing Frost Records, 1697-1947*. Maine Agricultural and Forest Experiment Station, Bulletin 846. University of Maine, Orono, Maine.

Bartlein, P. J., and T. Webb, III. 1985. Mean July Temperature at 6000 Yr. B.P. in Eastern North America: Regression Equations for Estimates from Fossil Pollen Data. In *Climatic Change in Canada 5*, edited by C. Harington. Syllogeus 55, pp. 301-342. National Museums of Canada.

Bennett, M. 1955. The Food Economy of the New England Indians, 1605-75. *The Journal of Political Economy* LXIII:369-397.

Biggar, H. (editor). 1922-1936. *The Works of Samuel de Champlain* [1626]. The Champlain Society, Toronto.

Black, M. J. 1980. *Algonquin Ethnobotany: An Interpretation of Aboriginal Adaptation in Southwestern Quebec*. National Museum of Man Mercury Series. National Museums of Canada, Ottawa.

Calvert, M.R. 1991. *Black Robe on the Kennebec*. The Monmouth Press, Monmouth, Maine.

Churchill, E. A. 1979. *Too Great the Challenge: The Birth and Death of Falmouth, Maine, 1624-1676*. Unpublished Ph.D. dissertation, Department of History. University of Maine.

Corey, R. P., J. B. Petersen, E. R. Cowie, J. A. Wolford, and E. C. Kitson. 1997. *An Archaeological Phase I Survey and Phase II Testing of the Riley-Jay-Livermore (FERC No. 2375) and Otis (FERC No. 8277) Projects, Androscoggin, Franklin and Oxford Counties, Maine*. University of Maine at Farmington Archaeology Research Center. Submitted to International Paper Co., Jay, Maine.

Cowan, C. W. 1985. Understanding the Evolution of Plant Husbandry in Eastern North America: Lessons from Botany, Ethnography, and Archaeology. In *Prehistoric Food Production in North America*, edited by R. I. Ford, pp. 205-244. Anthropological Papers No. 75. Museum of Anthropology, University of Michigan, Ann Arbor.

Cowie, E. R., and J. B. Petersen. 1990. *Archaeological Phase II Testing of the Bonny Eagle Project (FERC No. 2529), Cumberland and York Counties, Maine*. Archaeology Research Center, University of Maine at Farmington, Farmington, Maine.

————. 1992. *Archaeological Phase II Testing of the Weston Project (FERC No. 2325), Somerset County, Maine*. Archaeology Research Center, University of Maine at Farmington, Farmington, Maine.

Cowie, E. R., J. B. Petersen, and N. Asch Sidell. 1992. The Contact Period in Central Maine: Archaeological Investigations at Ethnohistoric Norridgewock. Paper presented at the Annual Meeting of the Northeastern Anthropological Association. Bridgewater, Massachusetts.

Cranmer, L., and A. E. Spiess. 1993. Discussion of Site 27.60. Vol. II, Chapter 11 in *U.S. Route 1 Reconstruction Archaeology in Warren, Maine: Sites 27.59 and 27.60*, edited by A. E. Spiess, pp. 174-178. Unpublished report on file at Maine Historic Preservation Commission.

Crawford, G. W., D. G. Smith, and V. E. Bowyer. 1997. Dating the Entry of Corn (*Zea mays*) into the Lower Great Lakes. *American Antiquity* 62:112-119.

Cronon, W. 1983. *Changes in the Land: Indians, Colonists, and the Ecology of New England.* Hill and Wang, New York.

Davis, M. B. 1983. Holocene Vegetational History of the Eastern United States. In *Late Quaternary Environments of the United States*, Vol. 2, The Holocene, edited by H. E. Wright, Jr., pp. 166-181. University of Minnesota Press, Minneapolis.

Davis, R. B., and G. L. Jacobson, Jr. 1985. Late Glacial and Early Holocene Landscapes in Northern New England and Adjacent Areas of Canada. *Quaternary Research* 23:341-368.

Day, C. A. 1954. *A History of Maine Agriculture, 1604-1860.* University Press, Orono.

Demeritt, D. 1991. Agriculture, Climate, and Cultural Adaptation in the Prehistoric Northeast. *Archaeology of Eastern North America* 19:183-202.

Fernald, M. L. 1973 [1950]. *Gray's Manual of Botany.* 8th edition. Corrections supplied by R. C. Collins. Dioscorides Press, Portland, Oregon.

Fernald, M. L., and A. C. Kinsey. 1958. *Edible Plants of Eastern North America.* Harper and Row, New York.

Fritz, G. J. 1990. Multiple Pathways to Farming in Precontact Eastern North America. *Journal of World Prehistory* 4:387-435.

Gleason, H. A., and A. Cronquist. 1991. *Manual of Vascular Plants of Northeastern United States and Adjacent Canada.* 2nd edition. The New York Botanical Garden, Bronx, New York.

Hart, J. P., and N. Asch Sidell. 1997. Additional Evidence for Early Cucurbit Use in the Northern Eastern Woodlands East of the Allegheny Front. *American Antiquity* 62:523-537.

Heckenberger, M. J., J. B. Petersen, and N. Asch Sidell. 1992. Early Evidence of Maize Horticulture in the Connecticut River Valley of Vermont. *Archaeology of Eastern North America* 20:125-149.

Hill, R. A. 1989. *Maine Forever: A Guide to Nature Conservancy Preserves in Maine.* 2nd edition. J. S. McCarthy Company, Augusta.

Kavasch, E. B. 1981. *Guide to Northeastern Wild Edibles.* Hancock House Publishers Ltd., North Vancouver, British Columbia.

King, F. B. 1984. *Plants, People and Paleoecology.* Scientific Papers, Vol. 20. Illinois State Museum, Springfield.

Laurent, S., and C. R. Huntoon. 1995. *Father Aubrey's French Abnaki Dictionary.* Chisholm Brothers Publishers, Portland.

Little, E. L., Jr. 1971. *Atlas of United States Trees*, Vol. 1, Conifers and Important Hardwoods. U.S. Department of Agriculture Forest Service, Miscellaneous Publication Vol. 1146.

——————. 1977. *Atlas of United States Trees*, Vol. 4, Minor Eastern Hardwoods. U.S. Department of Agriculture Forest Service, Miscellaneous Publication Vol. 1342.

Mack, K., D. Sanger, C. Quinn, and A. Kelley. 1998. *Phase 3 Archaeological Investigations of the Bob Site, Pushaw Stream, Maine.* Manuscript on file with Maine Historic Preservation Commission.

Martin, A. C., and W. D. Barkley. 1961. *Seed Identification Manual.* University of California Press, Berkley.

Petersen, J. B. 1991. *Archaeological Testing at the Sharrow Site: A Deeply Stratified Early to Late Holocene Cultural Sequence in Central Maine.* Occasional Publications in Maine Archaeology, Vol. 8. Maine Historic Preservation Commission, Augusta, Maine.

Petersen, J. B., and N. Asch Sidell. 1996. Mid-Holocene Evidence of *Cucurbita* sp. from Central Maine. *American Antiquity* 61:685-698.

Peterson, L. 1978. *A Field Guide to Edible Wild Plants of Eastern and Central North America.* The Peterson Field Guide Series. Houghton Mifflin Company, Boston.

Prins, H. E. L., and B. J. Bourque. 1987. Norridgewock: Village Translocation on the New England-Acadian Frontier. *Man in the Northeast* 33:137-158.

Rasles, S. 1833. *A Dictionary of the Abnaki Language in North America.* Published from the original manuscript of the author. Excerpt from Memoirs of the American Academy of Arts and Sciences, New Series, Volume 1.

Richards, C. D., F. Hyland, and L. M. Eastman. 1983. Revised Check-List of the Vascular Plants of Maine. *Bulletin of the Josselyn Botanical Society* 11:173.

Richardson, J. 1981. *Wild Edible Plants of New England: A Field Guide Including Poisonous Plants Often Encountered.* DeLorme Publishing Company, Yarmouth, Maine.

Rosier, J. 1843. A True Relation of the Most Prosperous Voyage of Captain George Waymouth. *Massachusetts Historical Society Collections* (3rd series) 8.

Russell, H.S. 1980. *Indian New England Before the Mayflower.* University Press of New England, Hanover, New Hampshire.

Sanger, D. 1995. Mesolithic Maritime Adaptations: The View from North America. In *Man and Sea in the Mesolithic,* edited by Anders Fischer, pp. 335-349. Oxbow Monograph 53. Oxbow Books, Oxford.

——————. 1996. Testing the Models: Hunter-Gatherer Use of Space in the Gulf of Maine, USA. *World Archaeology* 27:512-526.

Snow, D. R. 1978. Eastern Abenaki. In *Northeast,* edited by Bruce G. Trigger, pp. 137-147. Handbook of North American Indians, Vol. 15, W. C. Sturtevant, general editor. Smithsonian Institution, Washington, D.C.

Spiess, A. E. 1992. Archaic Period Subsistence in New England and the Atlantic Provinces. In *Early Holocene Occupation in Northern New England,* edited by B. S. Robinson, J. B. Petersen, and A. K. Robinson, pp. 163-185. Occasional Publications in Maine Archaeology 9. Maine Historic Preservation Commission, Augusta.

——————. 1993. *U.S. Route 1 Reconstruction Archaeology in Warren, Maine: Sites 27.59 and 27.60.* Unpublished report on file at Maine Historic Preservation Commission, Augusta.

Spiess, A., and J. Mosher. 1994. Hedden: A Paleoindian Site on the Kennebunk Plains. *Maine Archaeological Society Bulletin* 34(2):25-54.

Spiess, A., J. Mosher, K. Callum, and N. Asch Sidell. 1995. Fire on the Plains: The Hedden Paleoindian Site in Kennebunk, Maine. *Maine Archaeological Society Bulletin* 35(1):13-52.

Starbird, C. M. 1928. *The Indians of the Androscoggin Valley: Tribal History, and Their Relations with the Early English Settlers of Maine.* Lewiston Journal Printshop.

Stuiver, M., and P.J. Reimer. 1993. Extended [14]C Data Base and Revised Calib 3.0 [14]C Calibration Program. *Radiocarbon* 35:215-230.

Thwaites, R. G. (editor). 1959. Relation of New France, of Its Lands, Nature of the Country, and of Its Inhabitants [in 1616]. In *The Jesuit Relations and Allied Documents: Travels and Explorations of the Jesuit Missionaries in New France 1610-1791,* Volume III, Acadia: 1611-1616, Vol. 67. Pageant Book Company, New York.

Wagner, G. E. 1987. *Uses of Plants by the Fort Ancient Indians.* Unpublished Ph.D. dissertation, Department of Anthropology, Washington University, St. Louis, Missouri.

Westveld, M., R. I. Ashman, H. I. Baldwin, R. P. Holdsworth, R. S. Johnson, J. H. Lamvert, H. J. Lutz, L. Swain, and M. Standish. 1956. Natural Forest Vegetation Zones of New England. *Journal of Forestry* 54:332-338.

Will, R., J. Clark, E. Moore, J. Cormier, K. Sobolik, N. Asch Sidell, and H. Mitchell III. 1996. *Phase III Archaeological Data Recovery at the Little Ossipee North Site (7.7), Bonny Eagle Project (FERC #2529), Cumberland, County, Maine.* Draft report on file with the Maine Historic Preservation Commission.

Woodman, C. 1855. *The Memoir and Journals of Rev. Paul Coffin,* D.D. B. Thurston, Steam Printer, Portland, Maine.

Young, J. A., and C. G. Young. 1992. *Seeds of Woody Plants in North America.* Dioscorides Press, Portland, Oregon.

# CHAPTER 13

# NORTHEASTERN PALEOETHNOBOTANY: HOW ARE WE DOING?

Gary W. Crawford

The potential for northeastern macrobotanical studies clearly is being realized with this collection of papers. No longer can we say, "all is potential" (Dincauze 1981). Some of the potential had been envisioned and realized as early as the 1960s, but until flotation caught on the following decade, many questions had yet to be formulated, let alone answered (Crawford and King 1978; Finlayson and Byrne 1975; King and Crawford 1979; Yarnell 1964). The contributors to this volume have articulated a series of questions and are engaged in important research and debate adding to the quickly developing field of northeastern palaeoethnobotany. Here, I explore the contributions to this volume from the vantage of having been involved with some of the first flotation in the Great Lakes region and from having access to a database from the Canadian side of the border (see Figure 13.1). As such, I more broadly define the Northeast than do the other papers and include eastern Canada as well as Michigan and northern Ohio.

The chapters sort into three general groups as I see them: (1) syntheses or flotation studies (Chapters 2, 5, 7, 8, 10, 12); (2) examinations of particular taxa (Chapters 3, 5, and 9); and (3) two miscellaneous contributions (Chapters 4 and 11). Among the themes common to many of the papers is the timing of maize's introduction to the Northeast and its role in local subsistence regimes. Wild plants are certainly not ignored but are somewhat secondary to the issue of cultigen presence, particularly in the later periods. Seasonality and settlement pattern figure prominently, and some consideration is given to the potential for the presence of cultigens other than maize. But cultigens and their context and meaning are high priorities to many of the contributors.

With the exception of Bodner, King, Asch Sidell, Largy and Almquist-Jacobson, the contributors are not specialist archaeobotanists. As Hart

(Chapter 1) points out, several other collected works on palaeoethnobotany in eastern North America have appeared in the last ten years, but the contributors to these volumes are, for the most part, specialists. Why the opposite should be the case here may partially be understood because few specialist archaeobotanists have been trained in the Northeast. Yet there are compelling reasons, such as those listed above, to carry out research on the relationship between plants and people in the Northeast. Those who need the information are creating the discipline in the Northeast.

Among the nine papers dealing with diverse collections of plant remains from specific sites, probably the most dramatic among these because of its time depth is Asch Sidell's (Chapter 12) that presents nearly 10,000 years of Maine prehistory. As further evidenced by Almquist-Jacobson and Sanger (Chapter 11), Maine is proving to have a rich body of information on the relationship between plants and people in prehistory. Asch Sidell has continued to pursue her botanical interests developed and first applied in the Illinois valley. Her depth of experience is welcome news to Maine archaeology. In the Great Lakes region, plant remains data from the Paleoindian period (11,000-10,000 B.P.) have not been collected systematically by flotation so the Early Holocene data from Maine is almost without precedent. The nearest Early Holocene archaeobotanical collection is from Meadowcroft Rockshelter in Pennsylvania (Cushman 1982; King, this volume).

The Archaic (10,000-3,000 B.P.) is better represented in the Northeast. Archaic flotation samples in the Great Lakes region include those from Weber I and Eidson in Michigan (Egan 1988; Parker 1984), and McIntyre (McAndrews 1984; Yarnell 1984), Bell, Innes and Peace Bridge in Ontario (Ellis et al. 1990; Monckton 1997). Based on these collections, we had begun to see a range of variation in the archaeobotanical record of the Early and Middle Holocene inhabitants of the Northeast. The nuts evident at Meadowcroft are

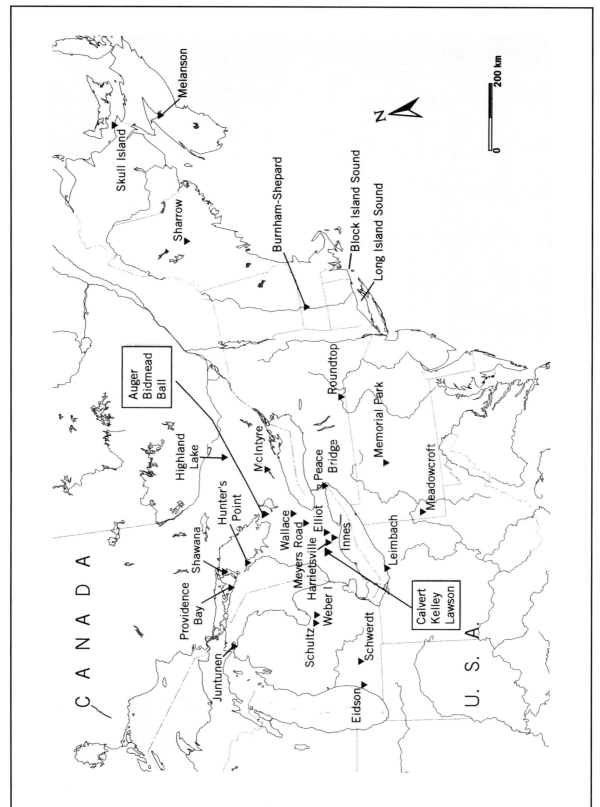

**Figure 13.1.** Location of sites mentioned in text.

not part of the Maine Paleoindian record, although the samples are small, and we ought not to attach much significance to negative evidence from small samples. The explanation for the lack of nuts in the Maine Paleoindian record is that nut trees had not yet migrated into the area (Chapter 11). Despite its northeastern location, the environment around Meadowcroft during Paleoindian times, unlike Maine, was similar to today's environment (Adovasio et al. 1982:264). Nevertheless, seeds of other plants are part of the record of the Early through Middle Holocene record at Meadowcroft, and the pattern is the same in Maine. Nuts are part of the Maine Archaic record as are fleshy fruits. Plants such as buttercup (Chapter 5), chenopod, lily family, a wild bean, and cleavers hint at a broader range of plants having been collected. This range may have included wetland plants, if Almquist-Jacobson and Sanger (Chapter 11) are correct in their interpretation that uplands provided a changing and less dependable resource base, while the more stable wetlands fostered a greater dependence on associated resources.

Beyond the presence of fleshy fruits and nuts in Archaic period samples, no consistent pattern is apparent. One oddity in the apparently idiosyncratic archaeobotanical record of many sites is a domination by a single and varying taxon of small-seeded plant. At the Weber I site, for example, a mustard (Brassicaceae) seed is most common (Egan 1988). In Middle Archaic Maine, the most common small seed is *Galium* (cleavers) (Asch Sidell). At McIntyre in Ontario (ca. 3,700 B.P.) a chenopod, *Chenopodium gigantospermum*, is the most common small seed (Yarnell 1984). We still have a long way to go and many more samples to collect before we can assess what was probably a complex relationship between plants and people in the Northeast during the Paleoindian and Archaic.

The cucurbit rind from the Sharrow site (6,700-6,300 cal B.C.) is an extraordinary find indicative of the kinds of discoveries that must still await us in the Northeast. Coupled with the Memorial Park site cucurbit remains dating to roughly the same time (Hart and Asch Sidell 1997), no doubt the plant was present in the

Northeast then. Until recently, the earliest cucurbit evidence in the region was an impression of a seed in an Early Woodland (2,400 B.P.) sherd from the Schultz site, Michigan, two seeds from the nearby Green Point site (Ozker 1982:40), rind from four features at the Leimbach site (Ozker 1982:198), and Cucurbita "remains" from Strata III and IV at Meadowcroft (ca. 3,000 B.P.) (Cushman 1982). Similar cucurbit is evidenced further west from a Late Archaic context in Minnesota (2,530±60 B.P.) (Perkl 1998), indicating that the plant was probably widely known in the Northeast well before other southern plants diffused north. Asch Sidell seems assured that the cucurbit was growing in Maine during the Middle Holocene, but I am less confident. It would be prudent to keep open the possibility that cucurbit was traded into New England and did not grow there. Although Asch Sidell points out that there is no long-distance trade evident in the New England archaeological record at this time, she may have just found it. Often plant remains provide a more fine-grained resolution for exploring such issues than other archaeological remains do.

To the south, Long Island and Block Island Sound also have significant depth to their archaeological assemblages (Bernstein, Chapter 7). Here, too, nuts are common in the Archaic record, as are fleshy fruit seeds. Diversification of plant use was ultimately an important adaptation, although Bernstein sees no major changes in plant use for millennia. The Long Island sites with no carbonized plant remains except wood charcoal are unusual. I wonder if they may be winter occupations? Apparently, the sites have an abundance of mollusk shell, so some direct evidence of seasonal harvesting of shellfish, at least, could be obtained. The only potential native cultigen they report is *Chenopodium*, but it is probably wild (Chapter 8). Corn is reported from a few sites but is rare.

The McIntyre site in Ontario has the most comprehensive Late Archaic archaeobotanical data set in the province (Yarnell 1984). A large quantity of seeds resulted from the excavation (7,500 from 5,400 liters of soil). To Yarnell, the assemblage contains clear evidence of anthropogenesis, a theme not taken up by any of the papers in this volume. The hemlock (*Tsuga canadensis)* crash (Almquist-Jacobson and Sanger, Chapter 11) in the Northeast during the Archaic might have compounded with anthropogenesis to provide even more productive open habitats (McAndrews 1984). In reality, however, we simply do not know what the local ecological impact of the short-term demise of hemlock was.

George and Dewar (Chapter 8) focus on *Chenopodium* whose record extends from the Late Archaic through Late Woodland. Although they can find no clear evidence of domesticated *Chenopodium* in Connecticut, they raise some interesting points. First, *Chenopodium* use extends beyond the Midcontinent, and second, processes that may have ultimately led to domestication of *Chenopodium* and other plants in the Midcontinent were impacting the Northeast. In the southeasternmost corner of the Northeast as defined in this volume (Pennsylvania), thin-testa *Chenopodium berlandieri* ssp. *jonesianum* and a potential pale-seeded type resembling the Mexican cultigen huazontle are reported from early Clemson's Island features at the Memorial Park site in Pennsylvania (Hart and Asch Sidell 1996:17). The most common seed at Memorial Park is little barley (*Hordeum pusillum*) that was likely grown at the site (Hart and Asch Sidell 1996:17). It may not be far-fetched to consider that chenopods were being grown in early Connecticut as well.

*Chenopodium* use in the Northeast extends beyond Pennsylvania and Connecticut. In Ontario, *Chenopodium* is documented in the Late Archaic (the McIntyre site). Chenopod is also common in Late Woodland sites (ca. 1,400-400 B.P.). Unlike in Connecticut, the species from the Late Archaic McIntyre site (*C. gigantospermum*) is not the same as the one from Late Woodland sites. Just as in New England, the later prehistoric Ontario chenopod is an intermediate, weedy form that appears to be quite similar to, if not, *Chenopodium berlandieri* that was domesticated further to the west. It seems that two other plants, little barley and a small- seeded form of *Iva annua*, had also made their way to Ontario by the Late Woodland. One specimen of *Iva* is reported from the Harrietsville site, and little barley is reported

from at least three other sites in addition to Harrietsville (Monckton, personal communication; Ounjian 1998). People may well have been spreading weedy/cultigen chenopods in addition to these other plants. This is speculative, but might be worth a look. At the least, chenopod will need continued serious attention in this region, and we should be scouring our samples for signs of other native cultigens.

The timing of the appearance of tropical cultigens, maize in particular, and their meaning in terms of the extent to which people were agricultural is a theme common to several papers. The lack of agreement between Chilton (Chapter 10) and the others intrigues me. All have access to roughly the same data, yet the major point of disagreement seems to be the extent to which interior groups relied upon maize. Chilton raises some pertinent questions. Unfortunately, the answer to the debate is not at hand. A methodological point of contention is how to interpret quantities of maize from various sites. This is exacerbated by the general lack of quantitative rigor in these papers. Without digressing to the large literature on the issue of cultigen representation and quantification at sites, I think that too often plant husbandry is presumed on the basis of small quantities of cultigens from sites all over the world, not just the Northeast. But dismissing the Burnham-Shepard case with its 1,500 fragments of maize from 16 features does not make sense either. Density or other ratios would help assess the quantitative significance, of course. In Ontario Iroquoian sites from 750 B.P. and later, there is a marked range of variation in maize densities within which the Burnham-Shepard numbers seem to fit. At three extensively sampled sites in Huronia (Auger, Ball, and Bidmead), kernel densities, on average, range from 2 per liter at Ball to 13 per liter at Bidmead (Monckton 1992). The Wallace site kernel density is higher at roughly 30 per liter (Crawford 1986). Kernel densities at Glen Meyer (ca. 850-650 B.P.) and prehistoric Neutral (ca. 500 B.P.) sites are generally less than 1 per liter except for Calvert, Kelly, Elliot, and Lawson, whose average kernel densities range from 1.3 to 33 per liter (Ounjian 1998). The Middle Iroquoian Myers Road site kernel density is also less than 1 per liter (Monckton 1998). Few would question that maize was grown at these sites, yet the densities of kernels ranges from low at some sites to quite high at others. Other information such as technology, settlement pattern, and indicators of anthropogenesis (e.g., weeds) must complement the quantity of maize reported from sites to help us understand what maize's presence means.

Other northeastern sites have cultigen remains that are in all likelihood in hunting and gathering contexts. They include Juntunen (Yarnell 1964), Providence Bay (Conway 1986), Shawana (Conway 1989; Crawford 1989), Hunter's Point (Goode 1991), and Highland Lake (von Gernet 1992). Coupled with ethnohistoric evidence of interaction between Algonquins and Iroquoians, I am not surprised to see some convergence in their archaeobotanical assemblages. No one seriously contends that crops were grown at these northern tier sites. The situation along the diffuse northern boundary between Iroquoians and Algonquins is reminiscent of the one in New England described by Chilton. Highland Lake, Ontario, for example, is interesting for a number of reasons including its small size, its rugged setting, its artifact assemblage, and the range of cultigens recovered (maize, sunflower, tobacco). Highland Lake is in Algonquin territory, but the artifact assemblage is very much Iroquoian if the pottery is traditionally interpreted (von Gernet 1992). Von Gernet eschews interpretations that make simplistic links between pottery styles and linguistic groupings. He feels that Highland Lake is an Algonquin site because of its locale (von Gernet 1992:109). However, Iroquoian groups traveled outside their territories, so if Highland Lake represents such a group, we have an example of people transporting crops outside their normal growing range. If the occupants were Algonquin, then here is a case where hunter-gatherers were consuming cultigens. In contrast, on the lower Kalamazoo River in southwestern Michigan is the Schwerdt site, an Upper Mississippian fishing camp, with a completely wild plant assemblage recovered from 46 features (Cremin 1980). Considering the dependence of Upper Mississippian peoples on food production, they might well have brought maize and other

crops to Schwerdt, but the evidence is to the contrary. So the presence or absence of crop remains on sites is not so simple to explain.

Setting aside the debate about the relative importance of agriculture at various sites in the Northeast, we need to better understand the middle ground between hunter-gatherers and agricultural people. In the Northeast, people were living in some areas with a mixed economy variably dependent on crops and wild resources. Continued work on the nature of this variation will be of comparative importance to modeling behavior elsewhere in the world when similar situations seem to have existed (Archaic and Formative Mexico, the North American Midcontinent, and Jomon Japan, to name a few).

At any rate, Cassedy and Webb (Chapter 4), Bendremer (Chapter 9), George and Dewar (Chapter 8), Largy et al. (Chapter 5), Asch Sidell (Chapter 12), and Chilton (Chapter 10) provide important data that, for the most part, are not available elsewhere. I would like to see more methodological clarity in the papers, though. Only one paper uses densities, while another (Largy, Chapter 5) includes a self-conscious discussion of methodology. The lack of consistent, standard reporting methods by the authors has drawbacks too. Although useful to explore various data-presentation formats, each author seems to devise their own system. I prefer to use a cascading tabular system that moves from general to specific categories with plant names across the top and samples/context down the left (see Monckton 1992). Finally, archaeobotanical reports should normally list sample volumes. Many of the reports in this volume do not.

The Late Woodland is better documented than nearly any other time throughout the Northeast. This appears to be the case in many of the papers in this volume as well. In Ontario, numerous sites have had systematic flotation conducted on them. Today, nearly all CRM work includes extensive flotation. My students and I have worked on over thirty comprehensive Late Woodland collections. Two excellent studies, one on a set of four contemporaneous populations in Huronia and another on a series of five Glen Meyer and eight prehistoric Neutral sites in southwestern Ontario, span the period from 750 B.P. to 300 B.P. (Monckton 1992; Ounjian 1998). Monckton has explored the relationship between the ethnohistoric record in Huronia (see, for example, (Heidenreich 1972) and the archaeobotanical record while researching dietary and ecological questions. Ounjian (1998) similarly has provided a detailed palaeoethnobotanical assessment of the thirteen sites in her study. Both have incorporated context as an important analytical variable; that is, their intersite comparisons try to control for context specific variation. Both studies provide exceptionally good insights into Late Woodland subsistence ecology in Ontario. Particularly relevant to the issue of whether the presence of maize indicates its local production is the extensive record of anthropogenic plants, many of which were field weeds.

We have good samples today from Princess Point, Clemson's Island, Owasco, Mahikan, Monongahela, Glen Meyer, Neutral, Huron, and St. Lawrence Iroquois sites, to name a few. All represent groups developing, or with, an intensive maize-based system. Although the record is becoming more comprehensive, when and how intensification occurred is far from being answered. Most of the papers acknowledge that it appears to have been time-transgressive, being earlier in the west than in the east. For the most part, no one has confirmed the notion that a form of horticulture similar to the system in the Midwestern Early and Middle Woodland existed before maize was introduced. George and Dewar (Chapter 8) raise the possibility of *Chenopodium* production before the introduction of maize in the Northeast. The early northeastern cucurbit suggests to Asch Sidell that gardening was going on in the Middle Holocene, but complementary lines of evidence are required to confirm this. Nevertheless, Hart and Asch Sidell's (1997) hypothesis that maize and other cultigens were adopted into an existing system of plant husbandry in some areas of the Northeast must be tested if we are to understand the late prehistoric shift to horticulture there. In northeastern Japan where I have been working on a similar problem, data indicate that a similar process actually took place there, and in a north temperate situation not

unlike that found in the Northeast (Crawford 1992, 1997). Finally, maize has been AMS-dated to as early as cal 1,500-1,400 B.P. in the Northeast (Crawford et al. 1997).

We are not yet in a position to explain the process of agricultural intensification. It may be linked to the evolution of northern tolerant maize, although Fritz has indicated that by 1,850 to 1,450 B.P., maize had already become adapted to temperate zones (Fritz 1990:490). King tries to link intensification to climatic amelioration and population growth. Yet such minimalist proximate causes are weak explanations for primary agricultural origins and likely for secondary origins too. I'd like to see how they might work in the Northeast. In Ontario, population pressure seems not to have stimulated the adoption of maize production; reduced crisis mortality apparently led to population growth after A.D. 900 (Warrick 1983:411). Population pressure as a cause for agricultural origins has not been a particularly useful explanatory device in general (Bronson 1975; Hassan 1975; Polgar 1975a, 1975b; Price and Gebauer 1995). Furthermore, climate as a determining factor has been criticized thoroughly over the years (Price and Gebauer 1995). In Ontario, the Medieval Warm Epoch has left no strong signature in the pollen record (Crawford et al. 1998), although elsewhere in the Northeast its impact may be visible in pollen records. The sociopolitical context of the process is an important consideration as well, and even this context is difficult to assess (Crawford and Smith 1997; Snow 1996). Given this complex situation, we are currently exploring other conditions in which intensification occurred. Just one set of conditions is the floodplain setting and how people interacted with floodplain dynamics. This is particularly interesting in view of Midcontinent processes that led to plant domestication and the rise of plant husbandry (Crawford et al. 1998; Smith 1992).

Crops do not seem to have become important in the Late Woodland in Maritime Canada. However, the ethnohistoric record indicates that although only tobacco was grown in the Maritime region at the time of European contact, maize husbandry may have briefly appeared only to be abandoned (Leonard 1996). Plant remains have been reported from at least 15 sites in Nova Scotia and New Brunswick, and none include cultigens (Lackowicz 1991). The Melanson site in Nova Scotia, a prehistoric Mi'kmaq occupation, has been explored periodically for 50 years (Nash et al. 1991). Among the 514 identified seeds from 9 flotation samples are 4 types of fleshy fruits as well as sumac, knotweed, wood sorrel, 2 grasses, and a sedge (Deal 1990). The Skull Island burial site on a small island in coastal New Brunswick is the subject of a doctoral dissertation (Leonard 1996). From this small site, 26 taxa of plant remains have been identified in the 384 liters of floated soil. These include small seeds of fleshy fruits and herbaceous plants as well as nuts and 75 g of carbonized groundnut (*Apios americana*) tubers. In addition, some charred bread-like material was recovered. Rather than being made from plant material, isotopic analysis indicates that the constituents of the bread-like material have a marine origin, possibly quahogs (*Mercenaria mercenaria*) (Leonard 1996:142). Leonard has argued that the plum pits from Skull Island are evidence that the range of Canada plum (*Prunus nigra*), not indigenous to the area, was being extended by the ancestors of the Mi'kmaq (Leonard 1996). Leonard has also reviewed evidence for potential Mi'kmaq management of groundnut. So despite the lack of maize and other well-known crops, the palaeoethnobotany of the Canadian Maritime region has considerable potential for research on a number of plant-people interrelationship issues.

Bodner's paper (Chapter 3) on sunflower in western New York is a welcome assessment. Until now, we have not had a synthetic treatment of northeastern sunflower. Bodner notes a general expansion of its range north to Ohio and Indiana bordering the Northeast by 1050 B.P.. The possibility that sunflower was in Michigan by 3,000 B.P. at the Eidson site needs to be evaluated though (Parker 1984). For now, this early report is anomalous. No sunflower earlier than Glen Meyer is known in Ontario (Ounjian 1998). The collection of sunflower achenes, nearly all uncarbonized, from New York is mainly from burials. In contrast, the entire archaeological sunflower collection in Ontario is from occupation sites. They are recovered regularly from nearly every Late Woodland

site in the province. As Bodner points out, sunflower is not common in any single context. There is one exception, however. A mass of achenes that appeared to be still attached to the sunflower head was recovered from a pit at the Lawson site (Crawford and Smith in prep.; Ounjian 1998). The size ranges for 140 measured achenes from New York is narrower than the range for 1,079 measured specimens from Ontario. The achenes from Late Woodland Ontario sites are similar in size (mean length of about 8 mm) to Early and Middle Woodland achenes in the Midcontinent (Crawford and Smith in prep.). Without mean achene sizes for the New York samples, it's hard to tell if they, too, are smaller than are their contemporaries in the Midcontinent. At any rate, the Ontario Late Woodland sunflower population does not fit the model of increasing size through time. This is an issue that needs to be examined. It may relate to the shorter growing season in the north, other growing conditions, or a unique variety of sunflower growing in the area, perhaps for its oil rather than for its grain potential (Crawford and Smith in prep.). With the extraordinary resource of uncarbonized archaeological achenes from New York, DNA analysis could help resolve the problem.

Finally, Hart (Chapter 4) challenges several generally accepted notions about the age of the maize, beans, and squash triad recovered from the Roundtop site, New York. He returns to the original field notes for part of his reassessment. More importantly, he reports AMS dates on Roundtop cultigens for the first time. The earliest maize at Roundtop is about 830 B.P., not too far off what we had thought. The 660 and 320 B.P. AMS dates on beans will disappoint some, but the case to eliminate the 950-850 B.P. dates for the maize, beans, and squash triad at Roundtop is strong. This study, along with Conard et al. (1984), is an example of how important it is to reevaluate cultigen remains and their associated dates, particularly if the remains have not been AMS-dated. For the moment, we do not know how early the triad of maize, beans, and squash came together in the Northeast. In Ontario, the earliest association of the triad appears during the Glen Meyer period (c. 800-650 B.P.) but just how early the three crops were grown together in this period we do not know. Hart may get into trouble examining Ritchie's motives for pushing early dates for the triad of maize, beans, and squash at Roundtop, but given the historical importance of the site, he provides some insight as to how we came to understand the Roundtop site as we did.

Palaeoethnobotany in the Northeast is fast becoming a challenging research area. Many issues are finally being examined because of the more regular application of flotation, but much more work remains to be done. The spread of cultigens and the development of agriculture are issues common to the region and the Midcontinent, although evidence of indigenous domestication in the former is, as yet, absent. However, we should not lose sight of the relationship between wild and weedy plants on the one hand, and people on the other. This relationship has a long, rich history in the Northeast. Yarnell (1964) raised a series of questions regarding plants and people in the region that are important to reflect upon today. Unfortunately, some of these questions seem to have been lost in the pages of an older and, at times, forgotten literature. Yarnell (1964) saw value in exploring anthropogenesis and the use of disclimax vegetation, plant range modification, small seeds as food, and exploring the extent to which archaeological plant remains correspond with the ethnohistoric record in addition to the cultigen and agriculture issues. Other productive areas of inquiry that interest me include forager-farmer interaction, subsistence ecology, site-formation processes, and the extensive medicinal aspects of plants, to name a few. Despite the many contributions made to date, the discipline in the Northeast is still young, so I anticipate considerable progress in the future.

## REFERENCES CITED

Adovasio, J. M., R. Stuckenrath, J. Herbstritt, and W. C. Johnson. 198.2 The Meadowcroft Rockshelter/Cross Creek Archaeological Project: Retrospect 1982. In *Meadowcroft: Collected Papers on the Archaeology of Meadowcroft Rockshelter and the Cross Creek Drainage*, edited by R. C. Carlisle and J. M. Adovasio, pp. 257-270. Prepared for the Symposium "The Meadowcroft Rockshelter Rolling Thunder Review: Last Act." Forty-seventh Annual Meeting of the Society for American Archaeology, Minneapolis, April 14-17, 1982.

Bronson, B. 1975. The Earliest Farming: Demography as Cause and Consequence. In *Population, Evolution, and Theoretical Paradigms*, edited by S. Polgar, pp. 53-78. Mouton Publishers, The Hague .

Conard, N., David L. Asch, N. B. Asch, D.Elmore, H. Gove, M. Rubin, J. A. Brown, M. D. W. K. B. Farnsworth, and T. G. Cook. 1984. Accelerator Radiocarbon Dating of Evidence for Prehistoric Horticulture in Illinois. *Nature* 308:443-446.

Conway, T. 1986. *The Providence Bay Site - An Early Historic Ottawa Village on Manitoulin Island.* Heritage Branch, Ontario Ministry of Culture and Communications, Toronto.

Crawford, G. W. 1986. The Wallace Site. University of Toronto. Unpublished Licence and Grant Report.

—————. 1989. Shawana Site Plant Remains. University of Toronto. Unpublished report.

—————. 1992. The Transitions to Agriculture in Japan. In *Transitions to Agriculture in Prehistory*, edited by A. B. Gebauer and T. D. Price, pp. 117-132. Monographs in World Archaeology No. 4, Prehistory Press, Madison.

—————. 1997. Anthropogenesis in Prehistoric Northeastern Japan. In *People, Plants, and Landscapes: Studies in Paleoethnobotany*, edited by K. Gremillion, pp. 86-103. University of Alabama Press, Tuscaloosa.

Crawford, G. W., and L. King. 1978. Floral Analysis. In *The Armstrong Site*, edited by W. M. Hurley, pp. 108-117. *Wisconsin Archaeologist* 59(1).

Crawford, G. W., and D. G. Smith. in prep. Paleoethnobotany in the Northeast. In *People and Plants in Ancient North America*, edited by P. Minnis. Smithsonian Institution Press, Washington, D.C.

Crawford, G. W., D. G. Smith, and V. Bowyer. 1997. AMS Dated Early Late Woodland Corn (*Zea mays*) from the Grand Banks Site, Ontario, Canada. *American Antiquity* 62:112-119.

Crawford, G. W., D. G. Smith, J. R. Desloges, and A. M. Davis. 1998. Floodplains and Agricultural Origins: A Case Study in South-Central Ontario, Canada. *Journal of Field Archaeology* 25: 123-137.

Cremin, W. M. 1980. The Schwerdt Site: A Fifteenth Century Fishing Station on the Lower Kalamazoo River, Southwest Michigan. *Wisconsin Archaeologist* 61:280-291.

Cushman, K. A. 1982. Floral Remains from Meadowcroft Rockshelter, Washington County, Southwestern Pennsylvania. In *Meadowcroft: Collected Papers on the Archaeology of Meadowcroft Rockshelter and the Cross Creek Drainage*, edited by R. C. Carlisle and J. M. Adovasio, pp. 207-220. Prepared for the Symposium "The Meadowcroft Rockshelter Rolling Thunder Review: Last Act." Forty-seventh Annual Meeting of the Society for American Archaeology, Minneapolis, April 14-17, 1982.

Deal, M. 1990. Preliminary Report on Macroplant Remains from the Melanson Site; Kings County, Nova Scotia. In *Melanson: A Large Micmac Village in Kings County, Nova Scotia*, edited by R.J. Nash and F. Stewart, pp 177-186. Nova Scotia Museum, Halifax.

Dincauze, D. F. 1981. Paleoenvironmental Reconstruction in the Northeast: The Art of Multidisciplinary Science. In *Foundations of Northeast Archaeology*, edited by D. R. Snow, pp. 51-96. Academic Press, New York.

Egan, K. C. 1988. Middle and Late Archaic Phytogeography and Floral Exploitation in the Upper Great Lakes. *Midcontinental Journal of Archaeology* 13:83-89.

Ellis, C. J., I. Kenyon, and M. Spence. 1990. The Archaic. In *The Archaeology of Southern Ontario to A.D. 1650*, edited by C. J. Ellis and N. Ferris, pp. 65-124. Occasional Publication of the London Chapter, Ontario Archaeological Society.

Finlayson, W., and R. Byrne. 1975. Investigations of Iroquoian Settlement and Subsistence Patterns at Crawford Lake, Ontario–A Preliminary Report. *Ontario Archaeology* 25:31-36.

Fritz, G. J. 1990. Multiple Pathways to Farming in Precontact Eastern North America. *Journal of World Prehistory* 4:387-435.

Goode, D. 1991. Plant Remains from Hunter's Point. University of Toronto. Unpublished Manuscript.

Hart, J. P., and N. Asch Sidell. 1996. Prehistoric Agricultural Systems in the West Branch of the Susquehanna River Basin, A.D. 800 to A.D. 1350. *Northeast Anthropology* 52:1-30.

—————. 1997. Additional Evidence for Early Cucurbit Use in the Northern Eastern Woodlands East of the Allegheny Front. *American Antiquity* 62:523-537.

Hassan, F. A. 1975. Determination of the Size, Density, and Growth Rate of Hunting-Gathering Populations. In *Population, Evolution, and Theoretical Paradigms*, edited by S. Polgar, pp. 27-52. Mouton Publishers, The Hague.

Heidenreich, C. 1972. *Huronia: A History and Geography of the Huron Indians*. McClelland and Stewart Limited, Toronto.

King, L., and G. W. Crawford. 1979. Paleoethnobotany of the Draper and White Sites. In *Settlement Patterns of the Draper and White Sites*, edited by B. Hayden, pp. 169-173. Department of Archaeology, Simon Fraser University, Burnaby.

Lackowicz, R. 1991. *Plant Use amongst the Recent and Prehistoric Populations of Acadia: A General Overview, Synthesis and Critique.* B.A. Honours thesis, Memorial University of Newfoundland.

Leonard, K. 1996. *Mi'kmaq Culture During the Late Woodland and Early Historic Period.* Unpublished Ph.D. dissertation, Department of Anthropology, University of Toronto.

McAndrews, J. H. 1984. Late Quaternary Vegetation History of Rice Lake, Ontario, and the McIntyre Archaeological Site. In *The McIntyre Site: Archaeology, Subsistence and Environment*, edited by R. B. Johnston, pp. 159-189. National Museum of Man Mercury Series, Paper No. 126, Ottawa.

Monckton, S. G. 1992. *Huron Palaeoethnobotany.* Ontario Archaeological Reports 1, Ontario Heritage Foundation, Toronto.

————. 1997. Plant Remains. In *In the Shadow of the Bridge: The Archaeology of the Peace Bridge Site (AfGr-9), 1994-1996 Investigations*, edited by R. F. Williamson and R. I. MacDonald, pp. 427-440. Vol. 1. Occasional Papers of Archaeological Services Inc., Toronto.

Nash, R. J., F. L. Stewart, and M. Deal. 1991. Melanson: A Central Place in Southwestern Nova Scotia. In *Prehistory of the Maritime Provinces: Past and Present*, edited by M. Deal and S. Blair, pp. 221-228. Council of Maritime Premiers, Fredericton.

Ounjian, G. 1998. *Glen Meyer and Neutral Palaeoethnobotany.* Unpublished Ph.D. dissertation, Department of Anthropology, University of Toronto.

Ozker, D. 1982. *An Early Woodland Community at the Schultz Site 20SA2 in the Saginaw Valley and the Nature of the Early Woodland Adaptation in the Great Lakes Region.* Anthropological Papers No. 70. Museum of Anthropology, University of Michigan, Ann Arbor.

Parker, K. E. 1984. Botanical Remains. In *Late Archaic and Early Woodland Adaptation in the Lower St. Joseph River Valley Berrier County, Michigan*, edited by E. B. Garland, pp. 396-411. State of Michigan Department of Transportation and Department of State, United States Department of Transportation and Federal Highway Administration.

Perkl, B. E. 1998. *Cucurbita pepo* from King Coulee, Southeastern Minnesota. *American Antiquity* 63:279-288.

Polgar, S. 1975a. Population, Evolution, and Theoretical Paradigms. In *Population, Evolution, and Theoretical Paradigms*, edited by S. Polgar, pp. 1-25. Mouton Publishers, The Hague.

————. 1975b. *Population, Evolution, and Theoretical Paradigms.* Mouton Publishers, The Hague.

Price, T. D. and A. B. Gebauer. 1995. New Perspectives on the Transition to Agriculture. In *Last Hunters-First Farmers*, edited by T. D. Price and A. B. Gebauer, pp. 3-19. School of American Research Press, Santa Fe.

Smith, B. D. 1992. *Rivers of Change: Essays on Early Agriculture in Eastern North America.* Smithsonian Institution Press, Washington, D.C.

Snow, D. R. 1996. More on Migration in Prehistory: Accommodating New Evidence in the Northern Iroquoian Case. *American Antiquity* 61:791-796.

von Gernet, A. 1992. *1990-1991 Excavations at the Highland Lake Site.* Ontario Heritage Foundation Research Grant Report.

Warrick, G. A. 1983. *A Population History of the Huron-Petun, A.D. 900-1850.* Unpublished Ph.D. dissertation, Department of Anthropology, McGill University.

Yarnell, R. A. 1964. *Aboriginal Relationships Between Culture and Plant Life in the Upper Great Lakes Region.* Anthropological Papers No. 23. Museum of Anthropology, University of Michigan, Ann Arbor.

————. 1984. The McIntyre Site: Late Archaic Plant Remains from Southern Ontario. In *The McIntyre Site: Archaeology, Subsistence and Environment*, edited by R. B. Johnston, pp. 87-111. National Museum of Man Mercury Series, Paper No. 126, Ottawa.

# CONTRIBUTORS

Heather Almquist-Jacobson, Institute for Quaternary Studies, and Departments of Geological Sciences and Plant Biology, University of Maine, Orono, Maine 04469

Nancy Asch Sidell, 46 Heath Street, Oakland, Maine 04963

Jeffrey C. Bendremer, Department of Anthropology, Indiana University-Purdue University Indianapolis, Indiana 46202

David J. Bernstein, Department of Anthropology, State University of New York at Stony Brook, Stony Brook, New York 11794

Connie Cox Bodner, Department of Collections and Research, Rochester Museum & Science Center, Rochester, New York 14607

Daniel Cassedy, 1903 Alexander Road, Raleigh, North Carolina 27608

Elizabeth S. Chilton, Department of Anthropology, Harvard University, Cambridge, Massachusetts 02138

Gary W. Crawford, Department of Anthropology, University of Toronto at Mississauga, Mississauga, Ontario L5L 1C6

Robert E. Dewar, Department of Anthropology, University of Connecticut, Storrs, Connecticut 06520

Kathleen Furgerson, Greenhorne & O"Mara, Inc., 9001 Edmonston Road, Greenbelt, MD 20770

David R. George, Department of Anthropology, University of Connecticut, Storrs, Connecticut 06269

John P. Hart, Anthropological Survey, New York State Museum, Albany, New York 12230

Frances B. King, Department of Archaeology, Cleveland Museum of Natural History, Cleveland, Ohio 44106

Tonya B. Largy, Department of Anthropology, Yale University, New Haven, Connecticut 06520

Lucianne Lavin, American Cultural Specialists, LLD, 437 Broad Street, Meriden, Connecticut 06450

Elizabeth A. Little, Nantucket Historical Association, Lincoln, Massachusetts 01773

Marina E. Mozzi, Environment & Archaeology, LLC., 6948 Oakwood Dr., Suite 202, Florence, KY 41014

David Sanger, Institute for Quaternary Studies, and Department of Anthropology, University of Maine, Orono, Maine 04469

Paul Webb, TRC Garrow Associates, Inc., 6340 Quadrangle Drive, Suite 200, Chapel Hill, North Carolina 27514